RAILW
RESTORED 1998

THE BEST-SELLING GUIDE TO HERITAGE RAILWAYS

Edited by Alan C. Butcher

IAN ALLAN Publishing

Contents

Front cover: LNER Class A4 Pacific No 60007 *Sir Nigel Gresley* at Grosmont on the North Yorkshire Moors Railway. *Alan P. Barnes*

Back cover: Industrial power at Andrews House station on the Tanfield Railway. *John East*

Previous page:* Locomotive exchanges have become popular over recent years. Here GWR No 9466, usually resident at the Buckinghamshire Railway Centre, basks in attention at Shackerstone station on the Battlefield Line. *John East

Late News: As the final pages of this edition of *Railways Restored* were being printed, members at the AIRPS agm voted to change the name to the Heritage Railway Association, or HRA for short.

First published 1998

ISBN 0 7110 2559 2

Published by Ian Allan Publishing

an imprint of Ian Allan Ltd, Terminal House, Station Approach, Shepperton, Surrey TW17 8AS
Printed by Ian Allan Printing Ltd at its works at Coombelands in Runnymede, England

Code: 9803/D

The publishers, the railway operators and the Heritage Railway Association accept no liability for any loss, damage or injury caused by error or inaccuracy in the information published in *Railways Restored* 1998. Train services may be altered or cancelled without prior notice, and at some locations diesel traction may be substituted for scheduled steam workings.

Foreword

I do not think that a year has passed since the first issue of *Railways Restored* was published without yet another railway or steam centre being added to the galaxy of entries described in this indispensable guide. While I worry that this growth cannot continue unchecked, last year saw another increase in visitor figures, unlike many other rival attractions.

Part of the reason for this is, I believe, due to the fact that our heritage railways do not stand still, and are developing all the time. There is always a new project in hand and therefore heritage railways continually present a changing scene, all testimony to the resilience and commitment of the volunteers who run and fund our steam railways.

One of the most encouraging aspects of all this is that the standards continue to rise, as a visit to Swanage Railway, winner of the 1997 AIRPS Award, or to the West Somerset Railway, winner of the Ian Allan National Railway Heritage Award will show. Of course, it is not enough to provide an enjoyable ride between two beautifully restored stations. The visiting public have rightful expectations of wholesome refreshments, clean loos and reasonably priced souvenirs. As Ian Allan pointed out in his foreword to last year's *Railways Restored*, we are not so much competing with each other as with alternative attractions such as zoos and theme parks.

I am confident that our tourist railways offer good value for money. Apart from anything else, the visitor is being subsidised (if that is the right word) by the fact that a large part of the workforce are volunteers who are giving their labour for free. This commitment has other spin-offs. Because the train crews and station staff so obviously enjoy what they are doing, they find it easy to strike a rapport with members of the public who take an interest in their activities.

This is also true of the *Heritage Railway Association* (under the name of which AIRPS now trades). The Association, which is the umbrella organisation for all those involved in the restoration, conservation and operation of our Heritage Railways, Museums, Steam Centres, locomotive and rolling stock groups is run by a team of dedicated volunteers, most of whom have been themselves (and often still are) involved in such activities 'at the coal face'.

It is fair to say that most of us prefer to paddle our own canoe, but quite apart from the friendly co-operation that exists between members of the different railway organisations, we often combine to lobby Government, the European Commission or other Government agencies. We have developed a Policy on Lottery Funding for Heritage Railways. The Association is also adopting a Passenger Charter which recognises the service which has already been offered to our customers as follows:

Members of the Association will always endeavour to:

1. Provide a reliable and punctual service
2. Provide a clean and safe environment on trains and in stations, museums and steam centres
3. Provide a professional and courteous service
4. Undertake to deal with complaints in an efficient and courteous manner
5. In so far as is reasonably practical, give advance notice of any change to advertised train services, connectional facilities and opening hours.

In the event of any disruption to advertised train services each railway will:

6. Do its utmost to restore normal arrangements as soon as possible
7. Ensure that any inconvenience to passengers is kept to a minimum
8. Keep both passengers and prospective passengers as fully advised of the situation as circumstances permit
9. Help to make alternative transport arrangements and facilities whenever necessary and practicable.

Note: Paragraphs 1 to 5 shall apply to all member organisations which provide any service or facilities which is open to the public (eg operating railways, museums and steam centres).

David Morgan
Chairman, AIRPS

From the Editor

Whilst 1998 has seen a further increase in visitor numbers to Heritage Railways, whether it will go down in history as a good year remains to be seen.

For various reasons several locations included in previous issues of *Railways Restored* are no more. Birmingham Museum of Science and Industry closed pending the opening of a Discovery Park, which as yet is only a set of plans, with the exhibits remaining entombed for the next three years. Steamtown at Carnforth closed its doors to the public having decided to concentrate on its engineering activities, a number of exhibits moving elsewhere. The delightful station at County School remained closed during the year, although there is hope that it will be connected to the revived Mid-Norfolk Railway based at Dereham. The Mid-Norfolk Railway has plans to extend north from Dereham following the re-opening, and consolidation, of the southern section to Wymondham. Ultimately the Mid-Norfolk hopes to run from Wymondham to Fakenham. On a more disturbing note the Southall Railway Centre's lease on the former depot at Southall was re-assigned from under its wheels with the result of virtual instant closure and orders to remove all items from the site. Despite promises from Railtrack Property to find an alternative site the Great Western Railway Preservation Group Ltd is having to restructure its organisation. Details can be obtained from: R. A. Gorringe, GWR Preservation Group Ltd, 16 Grange Close, Heston, Middx TW5 0HW.

The Museum of Army Transport at Beverley survived closure, following the loss of a grant, re-opening in the late summer; whilst the future of Transperience is under a cloud with it allegedly being 'for sale' at the time of writing. Glasgow Museum may be closed from April to September for budgetary reasons — the local council, like so many others, has to reduce expenditure; but during the main tourist season?

Steamport Railway Centre closed at the end of 1997 with plans to re-open at Preston Docks in the spring of 1998 but, despite several requests for information, failed to respond with even basic information so regretfully is not included. Moseley Railway Museum will also be on the move during 1998.

Despite this year's editorial list of departures, there is much to look forward to with a number of fledgling preservation centres and plans for new lines appearing all the time. Hopefully the next edition of *Railways Restored* will include a few of these.

Amongst the new entries in this year's edition is the Spa Valley Railway which finally responded with information so that it could be included. Kew Bridge Steam Museum also features for the first time, the Hampshire Narrow Gauge Railway Society operate the short 2ft gauge line, and *Cloister* will return to steam for the first time in 22 years during early 1998. As some readers will be aware, the HNGRS used to operate from a private site at Durley, and are currently developing an ambitious railway system at the Centre for the Conservation of the Built Environment at Bursledon Brickworks at Swanwick, near Southampton.

For those wishing to take a ride on a preserved line, there is now no excuse. This year's *Railways Restored* includes 32 pages of timetables in the *Heritage Railways 1998 National Timetable of Scheduled Services.*

Editor's Notes

On the following pages will be found a guide to the major preserved railways, railway museums and preservation centres in the British Isles. Information for visitors has been set out in tabular form for easy reference, together with a locomotive stocklist for most centres.

Many preservation centres and operating lines provide facilities for other groups and organisations to restore locomotives and equipment on their premises. It has not been possible to include full details of these groups, but organisations which own locomotives are shown under the centres at which they operate. In addition, a full list of member societies of the AIRPS is given elsewhere. In the case of most operating lines their length is given, but there is no guarantee that services are operated over the entire length.

Within the heading to each entry a heading block has been incorporated for easy reference as to what each site offers in the way of passenger service to visitors. These are as follows:

Timetable Service: Railways providing a passenger service between two or more stations with public access; eg Mid-Hants Railway.

Steam Centre: A railway or preservation site offering a passenger service on a short length of line, on a regular basis, with public access at only one point; eg Lavender Line.

Museum: A museum or site that does not offer a passenger service on a regular basis, if at all; eg Science Museum, London. Some sites may however offer rides on miniature railways.

As well as a guide as to what to expect on each site, this year's *Railways Restored* shows what, if any, particular professional body the Companies or Societies belong to. These are:

AIRPS: Indicates that the organisation is a member of

the Association of Independent Railways & Preservation Societies (AIRPS).

TT: Indicates that the organisation is a member of the Transport Trust (TT)

Membership of the AIRPS and TT is open to both organisations and private individuals. Private members are able to take advantage of concessions offered to them by the organisations that subscribe to these two bodies.

The concessions range from a discount on the admission price to free entry. The TT's Travel Back leaflet provides details.

Details given under **Access by public transport** should be checked beforehand to ensure services shown are operating. Unless the Heritage Railway, Steam Centre or Museum has identified the privatised train company operating the service, the phrase 'by rail', or 'main line', has been used to identify access by train.

Visitors wishing to see specific items of rolling stock or locomotives are advised to check before their visit that the exhibit is available for inspection. It should be stressed that not all items are usually available for inspection due to restoration, operating or other restrictions.

Ian Allan National Railway Heritage Awards

The Awards have been made annually since 1979 with the object of encouraging high standards of structural restoration and environmental care, thereby promoting public recognition and awareness of historic railway structures and their place in the environment. The aim is to promote careful design and quality workmanship in restoration, modernisation and maintenance, after taking full account of all relevant factors, particularly, of course, manpower and finance.

In this way, we encourage both public and private railways to present their operational premises as an attractive 'shop window', while occupiers of former railway buildings now used for other purposes are similarly encouraged to retain as much as possible of the original character.

A number of awards are made: The *Premier Award* for the most mentions award in the volunteer section; the *Ian Allan Award* for the commercial sector; the *Railtrack Award*; the *London Underground Award* is made to the urban station showing the greatest improvement in Heritage features; the *Railway Heritage Trust Award* for the best restored listed structure or structure of historic interest in which there has been involvement by the Trust; the *Westinghouse Signalling Award*; the *National Railway Museum Award* is awarded by the NRM for the best interpretation of a heritage building or other feature. There is also a *Keighley & Worth Valley Railway Award* and Certificates of Excellence.

WHAT IS ELIGIBLE?

1 Any present or former railway structure such as a station, warehouse, bridge, viaduct, tunnel or signalling installation, that has been sympathetically restored for whatever purpose.

2 A replica structure intended to re-create or augment some aspect of the railway heritage.

3 A new structure designed in traditional style in order to blend with or complement the local environment.

WHO CAN ENTER?

Any group in Great Britain and Ireland involved in railway preservation, whether as a private railway company or as a less formal organisation. Railtrack, Irish Rail, Northern Ireland Railways (NIR). Other public or commercial organisation. Private individuals.

The scheme is divided into:

(a) The Volunteer Sector for organisations run wholly or largely by volunteers.

(b) The Public & Commercial Sector. In cases of doubt, the awards committee decides which sector is appropriate.

For application forms apply to:

Arthur Harding,
6 Ullswater Grove
Alresford, Hants
SO24 9NP
Tel: 01926 733327.

The AIRPS Annual Award

This, the premier award made by AIRPS, for a group or organisation making an outstanding contribution to railway preservation during the year of the Award.

The Award takes the form of a Royal Train Headboard from the London, Brighton & South Coast Railway, which is on loan to AIRPS from the National Railway Museum. The Award is held for one year and the winning group also receives a commemorative plaque. The Award is announced and presented at the Association's Annual General Meeting which is held on the last weekend of January each year.

Standard Abbreviations

AEC	Associated Equipment Co
AEG	Allgemeine Eletricitaets Gesellschaft
A/Barclay	Andrew Barclay
A/Porter	Aveling & Porter Ltd
A/Whitworth	Armstrong Whitworth
B/Drewry	Baguley/Drewry
B/Peacock	Beyer Peacock & Co
B/Hawthorn	Black, Hawthorn & Co
BRCW	Birmingham Railway, Carriage & Wagon
BTH	British Thomson Houston
Buch	23 August Locomotive Works
D/Metcalfe	Davies & Metcalfe
E/Electric	English Electric Ltd
F/Jennings	Fletcher Jennings & Co
F/Walker	Fox Walker
G/England	George England & Co
GRCW	Gloucester Railway, Carriage & Wagon
H/Leslie	Hawthorn Leslie & Co
H/Hunslet	Hudson Hunslet
H/Clarke	Hudswell Clarke & Co Ltd
K/Stuart	Kerr Stuart & Co Ltd
M/Cam	Metropolitan Cammel
M/Rail	Motor Rail Ltd
M/Vick	Metrovick (Metropolitan-Vickers)
M/Wardle	Manning Wardle & Co Ltd
N/British	North British Locomotive Co Ltd
N/Wilson	Nasmyth Wilson & Co Ltd
O&K	Orenstein & Koppel
P/Steel	Pressed Steel Co Ltd
RSH	Robert Stephenson & Hawthorn Ltd
R/Hornsby	Ruston Hornsby
R/Proctor	Ruston Proctor
S. F. Belge	Société Franco Belge
YEC	Yorkshire Engine Co

Company abbreviations

BR	British Railways
DB	German Federal Railway
DSB	Danish State Railways
GWR	Great Western Railway
JZ	Jugoslave Railways
LMS	London Midland & Scottish Railway
LNER	London & North Eastern Railway
MoS	Ministry of Supply
NSB	Norwegian State Railways
RR	Rhodesian Railways
SJ	Swedish Railways
SAR	South African Railways
SNCF	French National Railways
SR	Southern Railway
USA TC	United States Army Transportation Corps
WD	War Department

Other abbreviations

BE	Battery-electric
DE	Diesel-electric
DH	Diesel-hydraulic
DM	Diesel-mechanical
DMU	Diesel Multiple-Unit
E	Overhead electric
EMU	Electric multiple-unit
F	Fireless
G	Geared
GH	Gas-hydraulic
LRO	Light Railway Order
PM	Petrol-mechanical
PH	Petrol-hydraulic
ParM	Paraffin-mechanical
PT	Pannier tank
R	Railcar
ST	Saddle tank
T	Side tank
VB	Vertical boiler
WT	Well tank
4w	Four-wheel

The Welshpool & Llanfair Railway's diminutive tank engine *Dougal* was used at Glasgow's Provan gas works prior to preservation. ***Alan C. Butcher***

INVERNESS
Alford
Strathspey
Caledonian Rly (Brechin)
Kerr's
Mull Rail
NORTH SEA
Summerlee
Bo'ness
Prestongrange
EDINBURGH
GLASGOW Museum
Scottish Ind. Rly Museum Dalmellington
Leadhills
North Tyneside (North Shields)
Foyle
South Donegal
CARLISLE
Bowes
Tanfield
Beamish
South Tynedale
Rly Pres. Society of Ireland
Ulster Folk & Transport Museum
BELFAST
Downpatrick
Darlington
North Yorkshire
Snaefell Mountain
Ravenglass & Eskdale
Lakeside & Haverthwaite
Lightwater Valley (Ripon)
Groudle Glen
Manx Electric
DOUGLAS
I.O.M Railway
Embsay
Keighley & Worth Valley
National Rly Mus. YORK
Mus. of Army Transport (Beverley)
LEEDS
Middleton Leeds Industrial
Blackpool
West Lancs
East Lancs (Bury)
IRISH SEA
Kirklees
Cleethorpes Light Rly
Liverpool Mus
MANCHESTER Museum
South Yorkshire
DUBLIN
Great Orme
Penrhyn Castle
Llanberis
Conwy Valley
Snowdon Mountain
Crich (Nat. Tramway)
Peak Rail
Midland Rly
Churnet Valley
Railway Age
Foxfield
Nottingham
Wells & Walsingham
North Norfolk Rly
Bure Valley
Irish Steam Pres. Society
Ffestiniog
Welsh Highland
Llangollen
Cambrian Rlys (Oswestry)
Bala
Chasewater
Great Central
Abbey
Rutland Rly Mus.
PETERBOROUGH
Mid-Norfolk
East Anglia Transport
Corris
Fairbourne
Talyllyn
Welshpool & Llanfair
Telford
Ironbridge
Battlefield (Shackerstone)
Nene Valley Rly
BIRMINGHAM
Cadeby
Bressingham
Severn Valley
Railway Museum
Kidderminster
Northampton Steam
Colne Valley
Vale of Rheidol
Airfield Line
Northampton Ironstone
Irchester
Mid-Suffolk
East Anglian Rly
Audley End
Leighton Buzzard
Buckinghamshire
Tuam - Westrail 20m NE of Galway
Teifi
Glouc. & Warks Rly
Winchcombe
National Waterways
Gwili
Brecon
Dean Forest
Swindon & Cricklade
Didcot
Princes Risborough
Ruislip Lido
Mangapps Farm
N. Woolwich
Pontypool
Cholsey
LONDON
Kew Bridge
London Transport
Science Museum
Vale of Glamorgan
Bristol Ind.
Avon Valley
Swindon GWR Mus.
Great Cockcrow
Sittingbourne
Swansea Vale + Maritime & Ind
East Somerset
Spa
East Kent
Mid-Hants
Bluebell Rly
K&ESR
Hollycombe
Romney
West Somerset
Lavender Line
Gartell
Amberley
Bideford
Tiverton
Moors Valley (Ringwood)
Bicton
Launceston
Seaton
Swanage
Isle of Wight
South Devon
Bodmin
Dobwalls
Plymouth
Plym Valley
Paignton & Dartmouth
Alderney
ENGLISH CHANNEL

England

Museum — Abbey Pumping Station — Leicester

Members: TT
Narrow gauge site railway (2ft gauge) formerly part of a sewage pumping station that now forms museum site. Railway relaid in concrete by MSC scheme during early 1980s to original track layout. New track layout as an extension to original laid with 35lb rail on wooden sleepers. All the railway system is now run by volunteers. Original Simplex locomotive kept on site in operational condition. A Planet petrol locomotive and a Ruston diesel are used to demonstrate the railway with typical tipper wagons and mine tubs. Line originally used for transferring solid material from screens to tip (about 100yd).

Industrial locomotives
Narrow gauge:

Name	*No*	*Builder*	*Type*	*Built*
—	—	Motor Rail (5260)	4wPM	1931
—	—	Hibberd (1776)	4wPM	1931
—	—	R/Hornsby (223700)	4wDM	1944

Stock
10 skip wagons, 6 mine tubs, 2 flats, various miscellaneous

Location: Abbey Pumping Station, Corporation Road, off Abbey Lane, Leicester LE4 5XP
Operating group: Leicester City Council Museum, Arts & Records Service and Leicestershire Museums Technology Association
Telephone: 0116 299 5111
Fax: 0116 299 5125
Car park: Free on site
Access by public transport: Main line Leicester (London Road). Leicester City Bus route 54 or 54K from city centre (alight at Beaumont Leys Lane)
Length of line/gauge: About 300yd, 2ft gauge. No public riding on line
Period of public opening: Daily from 9 April, 10.00 to 17.30 Monday to Saturday and 14.00 to 17.30 Sunday (until 1 April 1997)
On site facilities: Museum/shop/toilets/car park. Refreshments only on Special Event Days
Facilities for disabled: Access to museum lower floor and grounds. Steps to Engine House and refreshments on event days
Volunteer contact: Mr N. Pell, c/o Abbey Pumping Station
Museum contact: Mr C. Stevens, c/o Abbey Pumping Station (Tel: 0116 299 5111)
Other attractions: Museum holds various transport, steam navvy, beam engines. Some items only viewable by appointment or on Special Event Days
Special events: Please contact for details
Important note: From 1 April 1997 Abbey Pumping Station became the responsibility of Leicester City Council Arts & Leisure Services Dept. At the time of writing no details were available of LCC's plans for the Museum. Visitors are requested to contact before planning a visit

Steam Centre — Airfield Line — Warwickshire

Member: AIRPS
The railway is the only standard gauge line in Warwickshire and has been constructed on a 'greenfield' site by members of The 1857 Society, work beginning in 1983. Originally known as the Coventry Steam Railway Centre, the public were first admitted in 1988, after which time the marketing name — Airfield Line — was adopted. Development continues and the site now houses ex-MR Little Bowden Junction signalbox, and the rebuilt 118-year old LNWR North Kilworth station building, to be renamed Thistledown Halt on completion. Work is on-going to convert the six acre site to an authentic railway setting. The site also contains a collection of vintage road vehicles
Location: Within the boundary of Coventry Airport, south of the city. Easily reached via Rowley Road, junction with A45/A46, Coventry eastern bypass — M6/M69/M1 link road. Follow Coventry Airport direction signs — entrance is adjacent to Emergency Exit Gate 2
OS reference: SP 349750
Access by public transport: BR Coventry, West Midlands bus route 20/21 from City Centre to Toll Bar end
Operating society/organisation: Coventry Steam Railway Centre Ltd, 18 Lochmore Close, Hinckley, Leics LE10 0TY in conjunction

with Carrick Wardale Steam Crane Group, The 1857 Society and MATEP Co Ltd
Telephone: Hinckley (01455) 634373/635440 evenings only and/or answerphone
On site facilities: Buffet car, souvenir sales shop and picnic area
Catering facilities: Buffet
Length of line: Third of a mile (under construction)
Public opening: Every Sunday and bank holiday from Easter to October, 11.00-17.00, static display. See press for operating days and special events. Other times and party visits by prior arrangement. (No access at other times.)
Car park: On site, access off Rowley Road
Facilities for disabled: Site relatively flat. Members willing to assist if prior notice given. No access to buffet coach, no toilets

Multiple units

Name	*No*	*Origin*	*Class*	*Type*	*Built*
—	29720	LMS	503	TSO	1938
—	28690	LMS	503	DMBSO	1938

Industrial locomotives

Name	*No*	*Builder*	*Type*	*Built*
—	N2	H/Clarke (1857)	0-6-0T	1952
—	1	A/Barclay (1772)	0-4-0F	1922
Southam	—	H/Clarke (D604)	0-4-0DM	1936
Mazda	—	R/Hornsby (268881)	0-4-0DE	1950
—	L7	R/Hornsby (349038)	4wDM	1954
C. P. May	—	Hibberd (2895)	4wPM	1944
Crabtree	—	R/Hornsby (338416)	4wDM	1953

Rolling stock
1 BR Mk 1 Res/buffet (TSO conversion), 2 cranes, 2 fitted vans, 1 LNER brake van, 1 SR brake van, Gresley corridor third 320946*

Owners
Class 503 vehicles the Merseyside & Tyneside Electric Traction Preservation Co Ltd
*LNER Coach Association

Steam Centre | Amberley Museum | West Sussex

Member: AIRPS, TT

Narrow Gauge and Industrial Railway Collection (incorporating the Brockham Museum of Narrow Gauge Railways)
The NG&IR Collection is part of an open air industrial museum set in 36 acres of the former Pepper & Co chalk pits. A 2ft gauge line has been constructed and this is used for carrying passengers in genuine workmen's vehicles
Museum Director: Robert Taylor
Location: Houghton Bridge, Amberley, West Sussex (3 miles north of Arundel) on B2139. Adjacent to Amberley main line station
OS reference: TQ 030122
Operating society/organisation: Amberley Museum Trust, Amberley Museum, Houghton Bridge, Amberley, Arundel, West Sussex BN18 9LT
Telephone: Bury (01798) 831370 (Museum office)
Car park: Adjacent to Amberley station
On site facilities: Shop, cafe, audio-visual show

Locomotives
(2ft or 60cm unless otherwise indicated)

Name	*No*	*Builder*	*Type*	*Built*
Polar Bear	—	Bagnall (1781)	2-4-0T	1905
Peter	—	Bagnall (2067)	0-4-0ST	1918
Townsend Hook	4	F/Jennings (172L)	0-4-0T (3ft 2.25in gauge)	1880
Scaldwell	—	Peckett (1316)	0-6-0ST (3ft 0in gauge)	1913
—	23†	Spence	0-4-0T (1ft 10in gauge)	1921
—		Decauville (1126)	0-4-0T	1950
—**	—	Baldwin (778)	4-6-0T	1917
Monty	(6)	O&K (7269)	4wDM (3ft 2.25in gauge)	1936
The Major	(7)	O&K (7741)	4wDM	1937
—	2	Ransomes & Rapier (80)	4wDM	1937
—	—	Hudson-Hunslet (3097)	4wDM	1944
—	2	R/Hornsby (166024)	4wDM	1933
—		(3041)		
—	3101	M/Rail (Simplex) (1381) Armoured	4wPM	1918
Peldon	—	John Fowler (21295)	4wDM	1936
Redland	—	O&K (6193)	4wDM	1937
—	—	Lister (35421)	4wPM	1949
—		(LR 2593)		
—	—	M/Rail (Simplex) (872)	4wPM	1918
—	27	M/Rail (Simplex) (5863)	4wDM	1934

Public opening: Wednesday to Sunday (inclusive) each week, and Bank Holiday Mondays, (open all week in school holidays) 10.00-last entry 17.00, 14 March-1 November 1998
Special events: Railway Gala Weekend — 11/12 July. Please see press for details of further activities
Special Notes: Displays include working potter, blacksmith, boatbuilder and printer, stationary engines, historic radio collection and vintage Southdown garage and buses. A 2ft 0in gauge industrial railway system is demonstrated when possible, and a 3ft 2.25in gauge line is under construction. In addition, a 2ft 0in gauge 'main line' has been constructed. The 500yd line, was officially opened by HRH Prince Michael of Kent on 5 June 1984. The railway is operated every day the museum is open (subject to mechanical availability), with steam locomotive haulage on certain days — for details contact the museum office. Wheelchairs can normally be accommodated on the train. A Narrow Gauge & Industrial Railway Introductory Exhibition sets the scene for these and other set-piece display areas. New steam running shed opening for 1998
Membership details: Friends of Amberley Museum, c/o above address
Membership journal: *Wheelbarrow* — bi-monthly

Name	*No*	*Builder*	*Type*	*Built*
—	—	M/Rail (Simplex) (10161)	4wDM	1949 (2ft 11in gauge)
Ibstock	—	M/Rail (Simplex) (11001)	4wDM	1951
*Burt**	—	Simplex 9019))	4wDM	1959
CCSW	—	Hibberd (1980)	4wDM	1936
Thakeham Tiles	No 3	Hudson-Hunslet (2208)	4wDM	1941
Thakeham Tiles	No 4	Hudson-Hunslet 4wDM (3653)		1948
—	—	H/Clarke (DM686)	0-4-0DM	1948
Star Construction	—	Hudson-Hunslet 4wDm		c1941
—	18	R/Hornsby (187081)	4wDM	1937
—	—	Lister (33937)	4wDM	1949
—	—	R/Hornsby (172892)	4wDm	1934
— WD 904		Wickham (3403)	2w 2PMR	1943
—	2	Wingrove & Rogers (5031)	4wBE	1953
—	—	Wingrove & Rogers (5034)	4wBE	1953
—	—	Wingrove & Rogers (4998)	4wBE	1953
—	—	Wingrove & Rogers (T8033)	0-4-0BE	1979

** on loan to Leighton Buzzard Railway for restoration
* standard gauge
†Includes hoist and 'haulage truck' for conversion to 5ft 3in gauge

Stock
2 Penrhyn Quarry Railway 4-wheel coaches (2ft gauge, ex-1ft 10.75in gauge); RAF Fauld bogie coach (1940) (2ft gauge); Rye & Camber Tramway bogie (incomplete) (1895) (3ft gauge); Post Office Railway unit No 808 of 1930; 4 Groudle Glen Railway 4-wheel coaches (1896 and 1905) (2ft gauge); 60 other varied pieces of rolling stock of 12 different gauges ranging from 1ft 6in to 3ft 2.25in plus numerous miscellaneous exhibits including track, signals, etc

Now preserved at Amberley, *Polar Bear* originally saw service on the original Groudle Glen Railway in the Isle of Man before being acquired for preservation. Replica/rebuilt GGR coaches form the train. *Alan C. Butcher*

Steam Centre | Amerton Railway | Staffordshire

Construction of the Amerton Railway started in June 1990. Over the following two years volunteers of the Staffordshire Narrow Gauge Railway Society Ltd constructed a new 2ft gauge railway on a greenfield site. Work undertaken in this period consisted of building a trackbed, laying a quarter mile of track and building a stock shed and station facilities. The railway opened to the public on 14 July 1992. There are plans to extend the railway and construct a museum dedicated to Staffordshire narrow gauge railway history

Location: Amerton Railway, Amerton Working Farm, Stowe-by-Chartley, Stafford ST18 0LA (situated between Stafford and Uttoxeter, signposted off A51 at Weston)

Operating company: Staffordshire Narrow Gauge Railway Society Ltd, c/o above address

Telephone: (Railway only) (01785) 284388. Working Farm (01889) 270294

OS reference: SJ 993278

On site facilities: Car park at Working Farm. Museum under construction; licensed tea room and bakery (not operated by railway). Souvenir shop in railway booking hall. The railway is one of the main attractions at the Working Farm, admission to most attractions is free

Access by public transport: By rail to Stafford, then Stevenson's of Uttoxeter Ltd bus to Weston, then a mile walk to Amerton (no Sunday service)

Period of public operation: Sundays from mid-March to beginning of October. Saturdays from Easter until August Bank Holiday. Bank Holiday Mondays. Trains run 12.00 until 17.00. Subject to availability *Isabel* will be in steam Sundays and Bank Holidays. Diesel haulage on Saturdays

Special events: *Isabel* will be celebrating its 100th birthday on 17/18 May, visiting locomotives will be in attendance. Santa Specials in December. Footplate experience courses (contact for details)

Membership details: Membership Secretary, c/o above address

Membership journal: *Isabel Gazette,* quarterly

Industrial locomotives

Name	*No*	*Builder*	*Type*	*Built*
Isabel	—	Bagnall (1491)	0-4-0ST	1897
—	746	M/Rail (40SD501)	4wDM	1975
Dreadnought	—	Baguley (3024)	0-4-0DM/SO	1939
—	Yard No 70	R/Hornsby (221623)	4wDM	1943
—	—	Hunslet (8561)	4wDH	1978

Rolling stock

3 Baguley toastrack coaches (2 converted to semi-enclosed, 1 being rebuilt into balcony-ended coach). Various wagons and SNGRS built brake van

Timetable Service | Avon Valley Railway | Glos

Member: AIRPS

Progress on the AVR's southern extension towards Bath continues, and the section to Barrow Hill is expected to be open from Easter. This three-quarter-mile extension will give the AVR an operating line of nearly two miles. A new five-coach platform at the northern terminus of Oldland Common has been completed.

Headquarters: Bitton Railway Company Limited, Bitton Station, Willsbridge, Bristol BS15 6ED

Telephone: (0117) 329 7296 for timetable information. (0117) 329 5538 weekends

Main station: Bitton

OS reference: ST 670705

Car park: Bitton

Locomotives

Name	*No*	*Origin*	*Class*	*Type*	*Built*
Sir Frederick Pile	34058	SR	BB	4-6-2	1947
—	44123	LMS	4F	0-6-0	1925
—	48173	LMS	8F	2-8-0	1943
—	D2994	BR	07	0-6-0DE	1962
—	51909	BR	108	DMBS	1958
—	54271	BR	108	DTC	1958

Locomotive notes: All steam locomotives undergoing restoration.

Industrial locomotives

Name	*No*	*Builder*	*Type*	*Built*
Edwin Hulse	2	Avonside (1798)	0-6-0ST	1918
Littleton No 5	—	M/Wardle (2018)	0-6-0ST	1922
—	—	RSH (7151)	0-6-0T	1944
—	—	R/Hornsby (235519)	4wDM	1945
—	—	Baguley/Drewry (2153)	0-4-0	1941
—	2*	Bagnall (2842)	0-4-0ST	1946
General Lord Robertson	610	Sentinel (10143)	0-8-0DH	1961

Access by public transport: Badgerline service No 332 (Bristol-Bath), No 558 (Bristol-North Common).
Catering facilities: Buffet is able to provide hot and cold snacks, confectionery, hot and cold drinks and ice creams
On site facilities: Toilets, picnic area, children's play area close-by
Public opening: Open every weekend for static viewing. Please contact for operating dates
Special events: Please contact for details
Facilities for disabled: Coach converted for disabled use (no toilet facilities)
Membership details: Membership Secretary, c/o Bitton station
Membership journal: *Semaphore* — quarterly

Name	*No*	*Builder*	*Type*	*Built*
Kingswood	—	Barclay (446)	0-4-0DM	1959
—	D1171	H/Clarke (D1171)	0-6-0DM	1959

*On display at Warmley station, Bristol

Locomotive notes: R/Hornsby (235519) and Bagnall (2842) undergoing restoration. D1171 undergoing overhaul off-site.

Stock
16 ex-BR Mk1 coaches (9 stored off-site); 1 ex-BR Mk 1 Restaurant Coach; 1 ex-BR Mk 1 sleeper; 1 ex-LMS brake composite corridor; 2 cranes; 2 Wickham trolleys; numerous assorted wagons

Owners
44123 the London Midland Society
48173 the Bitton 8F Locomotive Group

Timetable Service

The Battlefield Steam Railway

Leicestershire

Members: AIRPS, TT
A quiet country railway operated by the Shackerstone Railway Society Ltd. 1998 is the 125th anniversary of the opening of the Ashby & Nuneaton Joint Railway, weekends earmarked for celebrations are 1/2, 15/16, 29-31 August
Headquarters: Shackerstone station (3 miles north of Market Bosworth in Leicestershire)
Address: Shackerstone Station, Shackerstone, Nuneaton CV13 6NW
Telephone: Timetable enquiries: (01827) 880754, other enquiries (0116) 291 7460
Operating Manager: D. Weightman
Main station: Shackerstone
Other public station: Shenton
OS reference: SK 379066
Car park: Shackerstone (free), Shenton (council car park)
Access by public transport: No services to either Skackerstone or Shenton
Refreshment facilities: Tea rooms on Shackerstone station. Buffet/bar on most trains
Souvenir shop: Shackerstone
Museum: Shackerstone
Depot: Shackerstone

Locomotives and multiple-units

Name	*No*	*Origin*	*Class*	*Type*	*Built*
—	20048	BR	20	BO-BO	1959
—	D5217	BR	25	BO-BO	1963
Harlech Castle	25265	BR	25	BO-BO	1963
—	D5518	BR	31	A1A-A1A	1958
—	11215	BR	04	0-6-0DM	1956
—	D3236	BR	08	0-6-0DE	1956
—	D3429	BR	08	0-6-0DE	1958
—	51131	BR	116	DMBS	1958
—	51321	BRCW	116	DMS	1959
—	54289	P/Steel	121	DTS	1960
—	55005	GRCW	122	DMBS	1958
—	59496	P/Steel	117	TCL	1959
—	59508	P/Steel	117	TCL	1959
—	59522	P/Steel	117	TSL	1959
—	59791†	P/Steel	107	TSL	1960

†Converted to locomotive-hauled vehicle
Ex-BR locomotives are expected to pay a visit during 1998

Industrial locomotives

Name	*No*	*Builder*	*Type*	*Built*
Linda	—	Bagnall (2648)	0-4-0ST	1941
Waleswood	—	H/Clarke (750)	0-4-0ST	1906
—	11	Hunslet (1493)	0-4-0ST	1925
Dunlop No 7	—	Peckett (2130)	0-4-0ST	1951
—	3	RSH (7537)	0-6-0T	1949
Lamport No 3	—	Bagnall (2670)	0-6-0ST	1942
Florence	2	Bagnall (3059)	0-6-0ST	1953
—	—	R/Hornsby (235513)	4wDM	1945
—	—	R/Hornsby (263001)	4wDM	1949
—	—	R/Hornsby (347747)	0-6-0DM	1957
—	—	R/Hornsby (393304)	4wDM	1956
—	—	R/Hornsby (423657)	0-4-0DE	1958

Length of line: 4.5 miles (8km)
Passenger trains: Shackerstone-Market Bosworth-Shenton
Period of public operation: Steam service: weekends and bank holiday Mondays 14 March-1 November (diesel service: Saturdays 4 April, 9 May, 4 July, 8 August, 12 September, 3 October. Midweek diesel railcar: 14-17 April, 26-29 May, Wednesdays in June, July and August, 1-4 September)
Special events: Diesel Galas — 7/8 March, 5-7 June, 7/8 November, 27 December; Fish & Chip evening specials — 4 April, 9 May, 4 July, 8 August; Easter Eggstras — 12/13 April; Teddy Bear's Picnic — 3/4 May; Spring Bank Holiday (intensive service)— 24/25 May; Friends of Thomas the Tank Engine — 20/21, 27/28 June, 26/27 September; Industrial/Model/ Miniatures — 25 July; 125th Anniversary celebrations — 1/2, 16/16, 29-31 August; August Bank Holiday (intensive service) — 22-24 August; Steam & Canal Weekend — August or September (contact for details); Postman Pat — 1 November; Santa Specials — 5/6, 12/13, 19/20, 24 December See press for details of Bank Holiday weekend and Diesel Gala
Special notes: Family tickets available. 'Tudor Rose' dining train. School Special Days Wednesdays in June. Must book for dining and schools. Scenic countryside views including Ashby Canal. Shenton station is adjacent to Bosworth Battlefield (1485) Country Park. 20 minute walk along 'Battlefield Trail' to visitor centre, return by later train
Operating company/ preservation society contact: The Secretary, Shackerstone Railway Society, Shackerstone Station, Shackerstone, Nuneaton CV13 6NW
Membership journal: *Shackerstone News* — 3/4 times/year
Marketing name: The Battlefield Line

Name	*No*	*Builder*	*Type*	*Built*
—	—	R/Hornsby (420142)	0-4-0DE	1958
—	—	S/Crossley (7697)	0-6-0DM	1953
—	RS/140	Planet (3892)	4wDM	1958

Stock
7 ex-BR Mk 1 coaches (including Griddle Car); 5 passenger-rated vans; 2 rail mounted steam cranes; 2 rail mounted diesel cranes; 35 wagons (inc 3 goods brake vans SR, MR, BR); 2 LNER ballast brakes

Museum — Beamish — County Durham

The railway station, signalbox and goods shed have been completely recreated along with the other exhibits to show a way of life long past. There are some very old locomotives in the collection.
Museum Director: Peter Lewis
Location: The North of England Open Air Museum, Beamish, County Durham DH9 0RG.
OS reference: NZ 214548
Telephone: Stanley (01207) 231811
Fax: (01207) 290933
Car park: At museum
Access by public transport: Bus service from Eldon Square, Newcastle upon Tyne; bus service Nos 775 and 778 from Sunderland via Chester-le-Street; bus service 720 from Milburngate, Durham City
On site facilities: This 200-acre open air museum vividly recreates life in the North of England in the early 1800s and 1900s. The Town has dentist's surgery, solicitor's office, Co-op shops, garage, sweet shop and sweet factory. The

Locomotives

Name	*No*	*Origin*	*Class*	*Type*	*Built*
—††	876	NER	C1	0-6-0	1889
Locomotion	1*	—	—	0-4-0	1975

Replica, and may be out on loan

Industrial locomotives

Name	*No*	*Builder*	*Type*	*Built*
Twizell†	3	Stephenson (2730)	0-6-0T	1891
—††	14	H/Leslie (3056)	0-4-0ST	1914
South Durham Malleable††	No 5	Grange Ironworks	0-4-0ST	c1880
Coffee Pot†††	—	Head Wrightson	0-4-0VB	1871
—*	E1	Black, Hawthorn (897)	2-4-0CT	1883
Hetton Loco	—	G. Stephenson	0-4-0	1822
—	—	R/Hornsby (476140)	0-4-0DM	1963
Jacob†††	680	McEwan Pratt	0-4-0P	1916
—**	18	Lewin (693)	0-4-0WT	1877

†Currently running in at Tanfield
*In store for long-term restoration
††On static display
** Undergoing major rebuild
†††Under repair

Locomotive notes: No 3 in working order. R/Hornsby not usually on display. Others usually on display

Owner
Hetton Loco on loan from National Railway Museum
Locomotion the Locomotion Trust

Note
Not all exhibits on display

Colliery Village has pit cottages, village school and chapel, 'drift' mine and pithead. Home Farm with farm house, livestock and exhibitions. Railway station complete with goods yard and signalbox, locomotives and rolling stock on static display. Pockerley Manor and Horse Yard illustrates the lifestyle of a yeoman farming family in the early 1800s
Public opening: Summer (April-October) daily 10.00-17.00, last admission 15.00. Extended summer opening (18 July-6 September) – daily 10.00-18.00, last admission 16.00. Winter (November-March) 10.00-16.00, last admission 15.00, closed Mondays and Fridays. Please check for Christmas opening times
NB: A winter visit to Beamish is centred on the Town and Tramway, other areas of the museum are closed and admission charges are, consequently, reduced
Special events: A full programme of events is planned for 1998
Length of line: Rebuilt NER station, colliery sidings
Facilities for disabled: Not ideal for wheelchairs. Rolling stock not converted. Advanced notice for parties to Bookings Officer preferred

Steam Centre

Bicton Woodland Railway

Devon

A passenger-carrying line of 18in gauge with stock mainly from the Woolwich Arsenal Railway and of World War 1 vintage
Location: Bicton Park, near Budleigh Salterton
OS reference: SY 074862
Operating society/organisation: Bicton Woodland Railway, Bicton Gardens, East Budleigh, Budleigh Salterton, Devon
Telephone: Colaton Raleigh (01395) 568465
Car park: On site
Access by public transport: Buses pass half-hourly from Exeter, Exmouth, Sidmouth in season
On site facilities: Refreshments, shop, one museum, toilets, 18in gauge railway, Grade 1 gardens
Length of line: 3,250yd
Public opening: Open March to October, 10.00-18.00. Please enquire for winter opening
Facilities for disabled: Toilets, wheelchairs available. Special carriage for wheelchairs

Locomotives

Name	*No*	*Builder*	*Type*	*Built*
Woolwich	1	Avonside (1748)	0-4-0T	1916
Bicton	2	R/Hornsby (213839)	4wDM	1942
Carnegie	3	Hunslet (4524)	0-4-4-0DM	1954
Clinton	4	H/Hunslet (2290)	0-4-0	1941
*Budley**	—	R/Hornsby (235624)	4wDM	1945

*Static exhibit

Stock

4 open bogie coaches; 5 closed bogie coaches

Museum

Bideford Railway Museum

Devon

Based at the former LSWR/SR station on the now closed Barnstaple-Torrington line, the site is undergoing restoration. The former signalbox has been rebuilt, double track laid throughout and signals erected. A growing collection of rolling stock is being gathered. Funds are being raised for an ex-BR shunter to give brake van rides in the near future
Headquarters: Bideford Station, Railway Terrace, East-the-Water, Bideford, Devon EX39 4BB
OS reference: SS 456263
Operating society: Bideford & Instow Railway Group
Access by public transport: By train — Barnstaple 9 miles. Station is within walking distance from the town of Bideford and its bus stops
On site facilities: Museum, souvenir shop, book shop, refreshments, visitor centre, rolling stock under restoration
Period of public opening: Easter to end October — Sundays, Tuesdays and bank holidays 14.00-17.00; November to Easter - Sundays & bank holidays only
Special events: Annual open day — Sunday 9 August
Membership details: Mr Taylor, 7 Myrtle Gardens, Bideford, Devon EX39 3HU
Membership journal: *Atlantic Coast Express* (quarterly)

Rolling stock

BR Mk 1 TSO No 4489, ex-SR Parcels Van No S2142, ex-BR brake van, ex-LMS closed box van, platelayer's trolley

Steam Centre

Birmingham Railway Museum

Birmingham

Member: AIRPS
Location: 670 Warwick Road (A41), Tyseley, Birmingham B11 2HL
OS reference: SP 105841
Operating society/organisation: Birmingham Railway Museum Trust
Telephone: (0121) 707 4696
Car park: Site
Access by public transport: West Midlands Travel bus routes No 37 from city centre. Main line rail service to Tyseley station
On site facilities: The Museum is on the site of a former GWR/BR steam shed and has been equipped with specialised railway engineering machinery. Souvenir shop, restaurant, passenger demonstration line and station, viewing gallery, schools' education service
Refreshment facilities: Available in 'Chuffs' restaurant
Length of line: Third of a mile
Public opening: Static display daily 10.00-17.00 except Christmas and New Year. Steam days most Saturdays, Sundays, Bank Holidays and some weekdays
Special events: Santa and Thomas (see press for details)
Special notes: Tyseley is a centre for 'Steam on the Main Line' railtours over former BR lines to Stratford-upon-Avon and Didcot (via Oxford). Full education service providing guided tours, worksheets and live presentation. The Museum is noted for its driving experience courses where members of the public can actually drive and fire a steam locomotive. These courses mainly feature *Clun Castle* and range from four hours to all day. Please contact for prices
Membership details: Membership is available to the public, providing free entry to site events, newsletters, members' evenings, etc; details from the museum office
Note: All attractions and facilities are advertised subject to availability

Locomotives

Name	*No*	*Origin*	*Class*	*Type*	*Built*
*Albert Hall**	4983	GWR	'Hall'	4-6-0	1931
Earl of Mount Edgcumbe	5043	GWR	'Castle	4-6-0	1936
Defiant	5080	GWR	'Castle'	4-6-0	1939
Clun Castle	7029	GWR	'Castle'	4-6-0	1950
—	7752	GWR	5700	0-6-0PT	1930
—	7760	GWR	5700	0-6-0PT	1930
—	9600	GWR	5700	0-6-0PT	1945
Kolhapur	5593	LMS	'Jubilee'	4-6-0	1934
Galatea	5699	LMS	'Jubilee'	4-6-0	1936
Scots Guardsman	6115	LMS	'Royal Scot'	4-6-0	1927
—	13029	BR	08	0-6-0DE	1953
—	08631	BR	08	0-6-0DE	1959
—	33103	BR	33	Co-Co	1960
—	40118	BR	40	1Co-Co1	1961
Davies the Ocean	47488	BR	47	Co-Co	1964
Waverley	47701	BR	47	Co-Co	1966
The Queen Mother	47703	BR	47	Co-Co	1967
The Lord Provost	47709	BR	47	Co-Co	1966
Quasimodo	47710	BR	47	Co-Co	1966
Dick Whittington	47712	BR	47	Co-Co	1966

Note: Not all locomotives are on site, and some are undergoing restoration may carry the alternative identity of 4965 *Rood Aston Hall*

Industrial locomotives

Name	*No*	*Builder*	*Type*	*Built*
Cadbury No 1	—	Avonside (1977)	0-4-0T	1925
—	1	Peckett (2004)	0-4-0ST	1942
—	—	Baguley (800)	0-4-0PE	1920
Henry	—	H/Leslie (2491)	0-4-0ST	1901
Victor	—	Bagnall(2996)	0-6-0ST	1950

Stock

Various passenger, goods and departmental vehicles, including buffet car, engineer's saloon and steam crane

Owners

Class 47s and 08631 — Fragonset Railways (on hire to various Train Operating Cos, here for maintenance/storage)

Blackpool & Fleetwood Tramway

Timetable Service

Lancashire

The Blackpool & Fleetwood Tramway is the sole surviving traditional street tramway system in the United Kingdom and attracts visitors from all over the country. During the autumn the streets are illuminated and several specially decorated trams are used. 1998 is the centenary of the Blackpool & Fleetwood Electric Tramroad.

Details from the Commercial Manager

Operating organisation: Blackpool Transport Services Ltd, Rigby Road, Blackpool, Lancashire FY1 5DD

Telephone: (01253) 473001

Managing Director: Anthony Depledge

Commercial Director: David Eaves

Commercial Manager: Michael Morton

Length of line: 11.5 miles, standard gauge

Period of public operation: Daily throughout the year

Number of trams: 86 double and single-deck trams.

Bluebell Railway

Timetable Service

East Sussex

Member: AIRPS, TT

This famous steam railway was the first standard gauge passenger line to be taken over by enthusiasts. It derives its name from the bluebells which proliferate in the woodlands adjoining the line. A strong Victorian atmosphere pervades this branch line which has a large collection of Southern and pre-Grouping locomotives and coaches.

Contact: Mr John Potter

Headquarters: Bluebell Railway Preservation Society, Sheffield Park Station, Uckfield, East Sussex TN22 3QL

Telephone: Newick (01825) 722370 for travel information (24hr talking timetable); (01825) 723777 for general enquiries etc during office hours. (01825) 722008 – Golden Arrow Pullman (reservations and Catering Department)

Main station: Sheffield Park

Other public stations: Horsted Keynes and Kingscote

Car parks: Sheffield Park, Horsted Keynes

OS reference: Sheffield Park TQ 403238, Horsted Keynes TQ 372293

Access by public transport: Bus service 473 between main line East Grinstead and Kingscote (2 miles) connects with all Bluebell trains

Refreshment facilities: Sheffield Park restaurant/bar/self-service; Horsted Keynes – Victorian bar/buffet. The line's 'Golden Arrow'

Locomotives

Name	*No*	*Origin*	*Class*	*Type*	*Built*
Stepney	55	LBSCR	A1X	0-6-0T	1875
Fenchurch	72	LBSCR	A1X	0-6-0T	1872
Birch Grove	473	LBSCR	E4	0-6-2T	1898
—	27	SECR	P	0-6-0T	1910
—	65	SECR	O1	0-6-0	1896
—	263	SECR	H	0-4-4T	1905
Bluebell	323	SECR	P	0-6-0T	1910
—	592	SECR	C	0-6-0	1902
—	1178	SECR	P	0-6-0T	1910
—	96	LSWR	B4	0-4-0T	1893
—	120	LSWR	T9	4-4-0	1898
—	488	LSWR	0415	4-4-2T	1885
—	58850	NLR	2F	0-6-0T	1880
Earl of Berkeley	3217	GWR	9000	4-4-0	1938
—	541	SR	Q	0-6-0	1939
—	830*	SR	S15	4-6-0	1927
—	847	SR	S15	4-6-0	1937
Stowe	928	SR	V	4-4-0	1934
—	1618	SR	U	2-6-0	1928
—	1638	SR	U	2-6-0	1931
—	30064	SR	USA	0-6-0T	1943
—	C1	SR	Q1	0-6-0	1942
Blackmore Vale	21C123	SR	WC	4-6-2	1946
Sir Archibald Sinclair	34059	SR	BB	4-6-2	1947
Port Line	35027	SR	MN	4-6-2	1948
Camelot	73082	BR	5MT	4-6-0	1955
—	75027	BR	4MT	4-6-0	1954
—	78059†	BR	2MT	2-6-0	1956
—	80064	BR	4MT	2-6-4T	1953
—	80100	BR	4MT	2-6-4T	1954
—	92240	BR	9F	2-10-0	1958

Industrial locomotives

Name	*No*	*Builder*	*Type*	*Built*
¶*Blue Circle*	—	A/Porter (9449)	2-2-0TG	1926
Baxter	3	F/Jennings (158)	0-4-0T	1877
Stamford	4	Avonside (1972)	0-6-0ST	1927
Sharpthorn	24	M/Wardle (641)	0-6-0ST	1877

Pullman operates a dinner service most Saturday evenings and Pullman luncheon service most Sundays.

Telephone (01825) 722008 during normal office hours for details.
Souvenir shops: Sheffield Park, Horsted Keynes
Museum: Sheffield Park
Depots: Sheffield Park (locomotives), Horsted Keynes (stock)
Length of line: 9 miles
Passenger trains: Sheffield Park-Horsted Keynes-Kingscote
Period of public operation: Weekends all year round; daily May-September; additional trains run in school half-term weeks and in the lead up to Christmas. Museum, locomotive sheds, buffet and shop at Sheffield Park open daily except Christmas Day
Special events: Children's Fun Weekend — 28/29 March; Vintage Bus Day — 26 April; *Birch Grove* Centenary — 13/14 June; Friends of Thomas the Tank Weekend — 27/28 June; Toy & Collector's Fair — 18/19 July; Steam Fair — 25/26 July; Summer Steam Gala — 22/23 August; Starlight Special — 24 October; Giants of Steam — 25 October. Further details of events available on request
Facilities for disabled: All station facilities are on the level and ramps available for placing wheelchair visitors into trains. Special toilets in buffet at Sheffield Park and at Kingscote
Membership details: Membership Secretary, c/o above address
Membership journal: *Bluebell News* — quarterly

*Purchased without tender, in store
†Purchased without tender, for conversion to tank engine, work in hand
¶On long-term loan to the Buckinghamshire Railway Centre

Stock
Substantial collection of pre-Nationalisation coaches including SECR, LSWR, Bulleid, Maunsell and Chesham vehicles. Also freight stock and engineers' vehicles plus 45ton steam crane

Owners
592 the Wainwright C Class Preservation Society
541, 830, 847 and 1618 the Maunsell Locomotive Society Ltd
96 and 21C123 the Bulleid Society Ltd
263 the H Class Trust
73082 the Camelot Locomotive Society
C1, T9 on loan from the National Railway Museum
928 on loan from Montagu Venturers Ltd
35027, 1178 the Southern Locomotives Ltd
80064 the 80064 Group

Timetable Service

Bodmin & Wenford Railway

Cornwall

Member: AIRPS
The Bodmin & Wenford Railway typifies the bygone branch railways of Cornwall. The terminus, close to Bodmin town centre, has an interesting collection of small standard gauge locomotives and rolling stock, and the operating line winds down to a junction with Wales & West rail services at Bodmin Parkway. Passengers can alight at the intermediate Colesloggett Halt from where a footpath (not suitable for wheelchairs or the infirm) leads to Cardinham Woods (FC) with waymarked trails, picnic areas, a café and cycle hire facilities. From the train there are scenic views across the beautiful valley of the River Fowey. A second line circles Bodmin to Boscarne junction where it meets the Camel Trail, a recreational path for cyclists and walkers. The Borough Arms public house is about 10 min walk from Boscarne and a visit can be made to the nearby Camel Valley Vineyard.

Locomotives and multiple-units

Name	*No*	*Origin*	*Class*	*Type*	*Built*
—	3802	GWR	2884	2-8-0	1938
—	5552	GWR	4575	2-6-2T	1928
Wadebridge	34007	SR	WC	4-6-2	1945
Triumph	50042	BR	50	Co-Co	1968
River Fowey	20166	BR	20	Bo-Bo	1966
—	20197	BR	20	Bo-Bo	1967
—	33110	BR	33	Bo-Bo	1960
—	D3452	BR	10	0-6-0DE	1957
—	D3559	BR	08	0-6-0DE	1958
—	51947	BR	108	DMBS	1960
—	52054	BR	108	DMCL	1960
—	53980	BR	108	DMBS	1960

Industrial locomotives

Name	*No*	*Builder*	*Type*	*Built*
—	—	Bagnall (2766)	0-6-0ST	1944
—	19	Bagnall (2962)	0-4-0ST	1950
Alfred	—	Bagnall (3058)	0-4-0ST	1953
—	—	Bagnall (3121)	0-4-0F	1957
Peter	—	Fowler (22928)	0-4-0DM	1940
Progress	—	Fowler (4000001)	0-4-0DM	1945
Swiftsure	—	Hunslet (2857)	0-6-0ST	1943
Progress	—	Peckett (1611)	0-4-0ST	1923
Lec	—	R/Hornsby (443642)	4wDM	1960
—	—	RSH (7597)	0-6-0ST	1949
Ugly	62	RSH (7673)	0-6-0ST	1950

Most trains are steam-hauled except Saturday
Location: Bodmin General station, on B3268
General Manager: Mr R. Webster
Operating society/organisation: Bodmin & Wenford Railway, Bodmin General Station, Bodmin, Cornwall PL31 1AQ
Telephone: All enquiries (01208) 73666
Car park: Bodmin General only, no parking permitted at Wales & West station at Bodmin Parkway
Access by public transport: Interchange with Wales & West services at Bodmin Parkway (arrivals by main line train only), through tickets available from stations in Devon and Cornwall. Local bus services to Bodmin
Refreshment facilities: Light refreshments at Bodmin General and on most trains
On site facilities: Railway shop, limited display of historic artefacts, toilets
Length of lines: 3.5 miles General-Parkway; 3 miles General-Boscarne
Passenger trains: 5-19, 22, 26, 29 April; 3-6, 10, 13, 17, 20, 25-31 May; daily June to 27 September; 30 September; 4, 7, 11, 14, 17/18, 21, 25-30 October; 5/6, 12/13, 19-24, 26, 27, 31 December; 1 January 1999
Special events: Friends of Thomas the Tank — 10-13 April, 7-10 August; Steam & Diesel Gala — 23/24 May; Steam Gala — 5/6 September; Diesel Weekend — 17/18 October
Driving experience courses: Courses held in spring and autumn. Please apply for details
Facilities for disabled: Yes
Membership details: Mr J. Tizzard, Bodmin Railway Preservation Society, c/o above address
Special notes: Reduced fares for family groups and for passengers arriving at Bodmin Parkway in possession of a valid main line ticket
Membership journal: *Bodmin & Wenford News* — 3 issues/year

Stock
9 BR Mk 1 coaches; 3 BR Mk 2 coaches; 1 Mk 3 Sleeper, 6-wheel 10-ton steam crane, 4 GWR coaches; 2 GWR Siphon G; Various freight wagons

Owners
34007 the Wadebridge 34007 Ltd)
3802 GW 3802 Ltd)
7597 Railway Vehicle Preservations Ltd)

Ugly* has run round its train at Bodmin in preparation for a run up to Boscarne Junction in June 1997.** ***Alan C. Butcher

Steam Centre

Bowes Railway

County Durham

Members: AIRPS
The railway includes the only preserved rope-hauled standard gauge inclines, whose operation requires considerable skill and dexterity. You should not miss the opportunity of inspecting the inclines and cable house and haulage engine when you can
Chairman: Phillip Dawe
Location: Bowes Railway, Springwell Village, near Gateshead, (on B1288)
OS reference: NZ 285589
Operating society/organisation: Bowes Railway Co Ltd

Industrial locomotives

Name	*No*	*Builder*	*Type*	*Built*
WST	—	Barclay (2361)	0-4-0ST	1954
—	22	Barclay (2274)	0-4-0ST	1949
—	20/110/709	Barclay (613)	0-6-0DH	1977
—	—	Hunslet (6263)	0-4-0DH	1964
-	503	Hunslet (6614)	0-6-0DH	1965
Norwood	77	RSH (7412)	0-6-0ST	1948
—	101	Planet (3922)	4wDM	1959
—	2207/456†	E/Electric (2476)	4wBE	1958
Victoria	2216/286†	H/Clarke (DM842)	0-6-0DMF	1954
BO3	20/122/514*	Hunslet (8515)	Bo-BoDMF	1981
—	—*	EIMCO (LD2163)	Rockershovel	1959
—	DB965071	Wickham (7586)	2w-2PMR	1957

†2ft gauge
*2ft 6in gauge

Above: WST **on the Pelaw branch of the Bowes Railway during the course of a photographic charter.** *John East*

Below: **The Severn Valley Railway's '3F' No 47383 at Consall Forge, Cheddleton, on the Churnet Valley Railway.**
John East

Telephone: Tyneside (0191) 416 1847
Car park: Springwell
Access by public transport: Northern Buses services Nos 184 Washington/Birtley, 187/188 Gateshead Metro/Sunderland, 189 Washington (Brady Sq)-Gateshead 638 Ryton/Sunderland
On site facilities: Exhibition of Railway's history, wagon exhibition, workshop displays. On operating days — shop, refreshments and guided tours. Steam-hauled brake van rides. Rope haulage demonstration trains
Public opening: Bank Holidays, also second and fourth Sunday in each month, Easter-September. Santa specials week prior to Christmas. Disabled Children's Day — mid July. Guided tours midweek/out of season can be accommodated with prior notice (not trains)
Length of line: 1.25 miles total length; 1.25 miles of rope haulage; three-quarter-mile used for passenger trains (extension in hand)
Special notes: Preserved section of the Pontop & Jarrow Railway; designed G. Stephenson; opened 1826; largest collection of colliery wagons in country, the only standard gauge rope-hauled incline railway in the world; Railway's own historic workshops preserved, with examples of all of the Railway's wagon types
Facilities for disabled: Toilet and refreshment room
Membership details: Dr Peter Norman, Railway Secretary, c/o above address or telephone (0191) 4877548
Membership journal: *The Incline* — quarterly
Disclaimer: The Bowes Railway Co Ltd wish to point out that all advertised facilities are subject to alteration without prior notice. The company can therefore not be held responsible for any loss or expense incurred

Owners
WST on loan from British Gypsum Ltd
Barclay 0-6-0DH on loan from Mr P. Dawe
DB965071 on loan from Mr M. Smith & Mr N. Whaler

Stock
20 Ordinary 10-ton wooden hopper wagons (Springwell built); 16 other wooden hopper wagons (of various pedigrees); 3 steel 14-ton hopper, 2 steel 16ton hopper wagons; 7 wagons; 7 steel 21-ton hopper wagons; 1 reel bogie (for rope replacement); 1 drift bogie (for shunting by rope); 1 loco coal wagon; 7 material wagons; 2 tool vans; 4 brake vans; 4 flat wagons; 1 17-ton wooden hopper (ex-NER); 1 18-ton wooden hopper (ex-Ashington); 1 21-ton wooden hopper (ex-Seaham); 2 steel ballast Hopper Wagons; 1 tank wagon; 1 wooden side door coal wagon; Londonderry Chaldron wagons, 1 Wickham trailer, 2ft gauge 4-wheel manrider, 2ft 6in gauge R. B. Bolton-type bogie manrider, Easington Colliery weights wagon

Stationary haulage
Met-Vick/Wild, 300bhp electric (Blackham's Hill) 1950
BTH/Robey, 500bhp electric (Black Fell) 1950
Clarke Chapman, 22hp electric (Springwell Yard)
14ft Diam, Gravity Dilly Wheel (Springwell)

Steam Centre — Bressingham Steam Museum — Norfolk

Five miles of various gauges of railway running through extensive gardens and a collection of well-maintained and impressive main line locomotives. All the fun of the fair, with something for everyone, a great day out for all the family
Location: Two miles west of Diss on the A1066
OS reference: TM 080806
Operating society/organisation: Bressingham Steam Preservation Co Ltd, Bressingham Hall, Diss, Norfolk IP22 2AB
Telephone: Bressingham (01379) 687386. 24hr hotline (01379) 687382
Car park: Steam Centre (free)
Access by public transport: Diss Main line station (3 miles)
On site facilities: 10.25/15/24in and standard gauge lines, totalling

Locomotives

Name	No	Origin	Class	Type	Built
Martello	662	LBSCR	A1X	0-6-0T	1875
Thundersley	80	LTSR	3P	4-4-2T	1909
Granville	102	LSWR	B4	0-4-0T	1893
—	490	GER	E4	2-4-0	1894
Henry Oakley	990	GNR	C2	4-4-2	1898
Royal Scot	6100	LMS	7P	4-6-0	1927
Oliver Cromwell	70013	BR	7MT	4-6-2	1951
Peer Gynt	5865	NSB	52	2-10-0	1944
King Haakon VII	377	NSB	21c	2-6-0	1919

Industrial locomotives

Name	No	Builder	Type	Built
Beckton	1	Neilson (4444)	0-4-0ST	1892
Beckton	25	Neilson (5087)	0-4-0ST	1896
William Francis	6841	B/Peacock (6841)	0-4-0+0-4-0T	1937
Millfield	—	RSH (7070)	0-4-0CT	1942
Bluebottle	—	Barclay (1472)	0-4-0F	1916

nearly 5 miles. Museum, steam roundabout, fire museum, souvenir shop and restaurant, extensive gardens and plant centre
Public opening: Open daily from April to October. Full steam days every Sunday and Thursday, August, and Bank Holiday Mondays, 10.30-17.30 on all open days. Christmas events in December (dates to be confirmed).
Education services for schools are available with pre-booking in March-October period
Special events: Please contact for details
Facilities for disabled: Toilets, wheelchairs available. Able to take wheelchairs on Nursery Line Railway
Special notes: Reduced rates for coach parties. Prices on application

2ft gauge locomotives

Name	No	Builder	Type	Built
Gwynedd	—	Hunslet (316)	0-4-0ST	1883
George Sholto	—	Hunslet (994)	0-4-0ST	1909
Bronllwyd	—	H/Clarke (1643)	0-6-0WT	1930
Toby	—	M/Rail (22120)	4wDM	1964

15in gauge locomotives

Name	No	Builder	Type	Built
Rosenkavalier	—	Krupp (1662)	4-6-2	1937
Mannertreu	—	Krupp (1663)	4-6-2	1937
Flying Scotsman	4472	W. Stewart (4472)	4-6-2	1976
Works Loco	—	Diss	0-4-0DM	1992

10.25in gauge locomotives

Name	No	Builder	Type	Built
Alan Bloom	1	BSM	0-4-0ST	1995

Owners
80, 490, 990, 70013 on loan from the National Railway Museum

Steam Centre — Bristol Industrial Museum — Bristol

The Museum houses machinery and vehicles associated with Bristol's industrial past, from horse-drawn vehicles to aircraft
Location: Princes Wharf, Bristol
OS reference: ST 585722
Operating society/organisation: Bristol Industrial Museum, Princes Wharf, Bristol BS1 4RN
Telephone: (0117) 925 1470
Fax: (0117) 929 7318
Car parks: Available nearby
Access by public transport: Buses to centre of city, 1km from Temple Meads station
On site facilities: Shop

Industrial locomotives

Name	No	Builder	Type	Built
Portbury	—	Avonside (1764)	0-6-0ST	1917
Henbury	—	Peckett (1940)	0-6-0ST	1937
—	3	F/Walker (242)	0-6-0ST	1874
—	—	R/Hornsby (418792)	0-4-0DM	1958

Length of line: Half-mile, extension of one-mile open on special occasions only
Public opening: November-March — Saturdays & Sundays only 10.00-17.00; April-October — Saturday to Wednesday 10.00-17.00
Facilities for disabled: Reasonable access
Special notes: Operation of railway on advertised weekends only, 12.00-17.30
Membership details: Officer in charge — D. Martin, Bristol Harbour Railway c/o above address

Steam Centre — Buckinghamshire Railway Centre — Bucks

Member: AIRPS
The Buckinghamshire Railway Centre is situated at Quainton Road on the freight-only Aylesbury-Calvert line, once part of the Metropolitan and Great Central line from London to Verney junction.

Locomotives and multiple-units

Name	No	Origin	Class	Type	Built
—	1	Met Rly	E	0-4-4T	1898
—	0314	LSWR	0298	2-4-0WT	1874
Wightwick Hall	6989	GWR	'Hall'	4-6-0	1948
—	7200	GWR	7200	2-8-2T	1934
—	7715	GWR	5700	0-6-0PT	1930

Quainton Road station is also the old junction for the Brill Tramway closed in 1935
Location: Adjacent to Railtrack goods-only line to Aylesbury. Turn off A41 at Waddesdon 6 miles NW of Aylesbury, Bucks
OS reference: SP 738190
Operating society/organisation: Quainton Railway Society Ltd, The Railway Station, Quainton, near Aylesbury, Bucks HP22 4BY
Telephone: Quainton (01296) 655450
Car park: Quainton Road — Free parking
Access by public transport: Main line Aylesbury station. Local bus Monday-Saturday only
On site facilities: Souvenir bookshop, light refreshments, toilets, steam-hauled train rides. Museum of small relics, secondhand bookshop, miniature railway
Catering facilities: Hot snacks and light refreshments available
Length of line: Two half-mile demonstration lines
Public opening: Sundays and Bank Holidays: Easter-end October. Wednesdays in June, July and August. Limited opening (no engines in steam) daily
Special events: A series of special events is held throughout the year including Thomas the Tank Engine weekends
Facilities for disabled: Access to most of site including special toilets
Special notes: One of the largest collection of standard gauge locomotives, together with a most interesting collection of vintage coaching stock, much of which was built in the last century
General: The public area of the centre covers some 25 acres of land with views across the Buckinghamshire countryside. A picnic area is available at the miniature railway

Owners
41298, 41313, 46447 and *Juno* the Ivatt Locomotive Trust
9466 the 9466 Group
Blue Circle on long term loan from the Bluebell Railway

Name	*No*	*Origin*	*Class*	*Type*	*Built*
—	9466	GWR	9400	0-6-0PT	1952
—	41298†	LMS	2MT	2-6-2T	1951
—	41313†	LMS	2MT	2-6-2T	1952
—	46447	LMS	2MT	2-6-0	1950
—	D2298	BR	04	0-6-0DM	1960
—	3405*	SAR	25NC	4-8-4	1958
—	51886	BR	115	DMBS	1960
—	51899	BR	115	DMBS	1960
—	59761	BR	115	TCL	1960

*3ft 6in gauge
†due to move on loan to the Isle of Wight Steam Railway at end of 1998

Industrial locomotives

Name	*No*	*Builder*	*Type*	*Built*
Blue Circle	—	A/Porter (9449)	2-2-0TG	1926
Scott	—	Bagnall (2469)	0-4-0ST	1932
—	—	Baguley (2161)	0-4-0DM	1941
Swanscombe	—	Barclay (699)	0-4-0ST	1891
—	—	GF3 Barclay (1477)	0-4-0F	1916
—	—	Barclay (2243)	0-4-0F	1948
Osram	—	Fowler (20067)	0-4-0DM	1933
—	3	H/Leslie (3717)	0-4-0ST	1928
Sir Thomas	—	H/Clarke (1334)	0-6-0T	1918
—	—	H/Clarke (1742)	0-4-0ST	1946
—	—	Hunslet (2067)	0-4-0DM	1940
Arthur	—	Hunslet (3782)	0-6-0ST	1953
Juno	—	Hunslet (3850)	0-6-0ST	1958
—	65	Hunslet (3889)	0-6-0ST	1964
—	66	Hunslet (3890)	0-6-0ST	1964
—	26	Hunslet (7016)	0-6-0DH	1971
Redland	—	K/Stuart (K4428)	0-4-0DM	1929
Coventry No 1	—	NBL (24564)	0-6-0ST	1939
—	—	Peckett (1900)	0-4-0T	1936
Gibraltar	—	Peckett (2087)	0-4-0ST	1948
—	—	Peckett (2104)	0-4-0ST	1948
—	—	Peckett (2105)	0-4-0ST	1948
—	T1	Hibberd (2102)	4wD	1937
Tarmac	—	Hibberd (3765)	0-4-0DM	1955
—	—	Sentinel (6515)	4wVBTG	1926
—	11	Sentinel (9366)	4wVBTG	1945
—	7	Sentinel (9376)	4wVBTG	1947
—	—	Sentinel (9537)	4wVBTG	1947
Chislet	9	Yorkshire (2498)	0-6-0ST	1951

Stock: *Coaches —*
1 LCDR 1st Class 4 wheeler; 1 MSLR 3rd Class 6 wheeler; 4 LNWR coach bodies; 2 GNR 6 wheelers; 3 LNWR; 3 LMSR; 1 BR(W) Hawksworth brake 3rd; 2 BR Mk 1; 1 BR Mk 2; 1 BR Suburban brake; 3 LNER; 1 LNWR full brake 6 wheeler; 1 LMSR passenger brake van; 1 GWR passenger brake van; 1 GCR Robinson brake third; 1 LNWR tri-compo lavatory coach
Wagons —
A large and varied collection including 1 LNWR combination truck; 1 LSWR ventilated fruit van; 1 SR PMV; 1 BR(W) 'Siphon G'; 1 BR horse box; 1 BR CCT

3 ex-London Underground coaches
1 2ft gauge post office mailbag car 803
Sentinel/Cammell 3-car steam railcar unit 5208 (ex-Egyptian National)
Numerous goods vehicles/wagons/vans

Bure Valley Railway

Member: AIRPS, TT
Opened in 1990 the BVR runs over the old Great Eastern Wroxham-Aylsham line. It is paralleled throughout the entire 9 miles by the Bure Valley Walk which offers excellent photographic opportunities
Headquarters: Bure Valley Railway (1991) Ltd, Aylsham Station, Norwich Road, Aylsham, Norfolk NR11 6BW
Managing Director: Paul Conibeare
Telephone: (01263) 733858
Fax: (01263) 733814
Main public station: Aylsham (Norwich Road); Wroxham (Coltishall Road)
Other public stations: Coltishall, Brampton and Buxton
Car and coach parks: Aylsham and Wroxham
OS reference:
Aylsham — TG 195264;
Wroxham — TG 303186
Access by public transport: By rail – Wroxham station is adjacent to main line Hoveton & Wroxham station (Norwich-Cromer/ Sheringham line). By bus – Eastern Counties buses run between Norwich and Aylsham
Refreshment facilities: Restaurant at Aylsham, with picnic area and light refreshments at Wroxham
Souvenir shops: Aylsham and Wroxham
Journey time: Approximately 45min each way plus turnround time
Length of line: 9 miles; 15in gauge
Passenger trains: Frequency depends on time of year, maximum frequency one per hour
Period of public operation: Open from Easter to end of October – trains run most days, telephone for details
Facilities for disabled: Toilets at Aylsham and Wroxham, special rolling stock to carry wheelchairs, advance notice would be appreciated
Special events: Please contact for details, Friends of Thomas the Tank 24/25 May & 26/27 September

Locomotives

Name	*No*	*Builder*	*Type*	*Built*
Wroxham Broad	1	G&S/Winson	2-6-4T	1992
Volunteer†	2	H/Hunslet	0-4-0DH	1996
Buxton Mill	3	BVR	4w-4wDH	1989
—	5	Lister	4wDM	
Blickling Hall	6	Winson*	2-6-2	1994
Spitfire	7	Winson*	2-6-2	1994
—	8	BVR/Winson*	2-6-2T	1997
Little Titan	9	Cheeseman	Steam crane	1975

*Based on Indian Railways 2ft 6in gauge 'ZB' class
†Rebuilt by EAGIT

Stock
21 fully enclosed saloons, 1 fully enclosed brake saloon, 2 guards vans, generator car, miscellaneous wagons

***Little Titan,* a quarter-scale steam crane being demonstrated at Aylsham.** *Alan C. Butcher*

Special notes: Steam locomotive driving courses. Party discounts available. Private charters by arrangement. Special combined train and Broads boat excursions run most days during the summer
Membership details: Friends of the Bure Valley Railway, Membership Secretary, c/o above address

Steam Centre | Cadeby Light Railway | Leicestershire

Members: AIRPS, TT
A new museum was opened in 1990, the 'Boston Collection', encompassing the lifetime collection of Teddy Boston and his family. The narrow gauge railway running in the grounds of the old rectory has been saved by Teddy Boston's enterprising widow and a small band of dedicated supporters in the face of considerable odds. Echoes of the *Titfield Thunderbolt* and Ancient and Modern. Their endeavours deserve your support
Location: 5.75 miles north of Hinckley on A447
OS reference: SK 426024
Operating society/organisation: Mrs J. A. Boston, The Old Rectory, Cadeby, Nuneaton CV13 0AS
Telephone: Market Bosworth (01455) 290462
Car park: Available
Access by public transport: Midland Fox/Stevenson 178 from Hinckley. 153 Midland Fox from Leicester to Market Bosworth (1.25 miles away)
On site facilities: 2ft gauge railway, also traction engine and steam rollers, model railway, and a museum housing the 'Boston Collection'. Brass rubbing centre in church with over 70 replica brasses
Refreshment facilities: Light refreshments available

Narrow gauge locomotives

Name	*No*	*Builder*	*Type*	*Built*
Pixie	—	Bagnall (2090)	0-4-0ST	1919
—	—	Baguley (1695)	0-4-0PM	1928
—	—	Deutz (10050)	0-4-0DM	1931
—	—	H/Clarke (D558)	4wDM	1930
—	—	Lister (4088)	4wPM	1931
—	—	M/Rail (1320)	4wDM	1918
—	87004	M/Rail (2197)	4wDM	1922
—	87009	M/Rail (4572)	4wDM	1929
—	—	M/Rail (5038)	4wPH	1930
—	—	M/Rail (5853)	4wDM	1934
—	—	M/Rail (7512)	4wDM	1938
—	42	M/Rail (7710)	4wDM	1939
—	20	M/Rail (8748)	4wDM	1942
—	—	O&K (4588)	4wPM	c1931
—	87008	R/Hornsby (179870)	4wDM	1936
—	87051	R/Hornsby (404967)	4wDM	1957
—	—	SMH(104063G)	4wDM	1976
—	—	Thakeham (4th)	4wDM	c1946

Standard gauge

Name	*No*	*Builder*	*Type*	*Built*
—	V47	Peckett (2012)	0-4-0ST	1942

Stock
Penrhyn Quarryman's coach; 2 flat trucks; 7 open trucks; 2 platelayers' trolleys

Public opening: 2nd Saturday of every month, plus 1st Saturday in November (Steam & Bonfire Party), Father Christmas Specials in December and Boxing Day. From 13.00 or by arrangement. Admission free (donations requested)
Special events: Please contact for details
Special notes: Party bookings by prior arrangement

Steam Centre | Cambrian Railways Society | Shropshire

Member: AIRPS
Location: Oswestry station yard, Oswald Road, Oswestry, Shropshire
OS reference: SJ 294297
Operating society/organisation: Cambrian Railways Society Ltd, C. W. Mottram, 'Delamere', Old Chirk Road, Gobowen, Oswestry, Shropshire SY11 3LH
Telephone: (01691) 671749
Car park: In Society's depot
Length of line: 400yd, opened 7 December 1996, the Light

Diesel Multiple-Units

Name	*No*	*Origin*	*Class*	*Type*	*Built*
—	53531	BRCW	104	DMC	1957
—	53479	BRCW	104	DMBS	1957

Industrial locomotives

Name	*No*	*Builder*	*Type*	*Built*
—	1	H/Clarke (D843)	0-4-0DM	1954
Adam	1	Peckett (1430)	0-4-0ST	1916
—	3	Hunslet (D3526)	0-6-0DM	1954
Oliver Velton	6	Peckett (2131)	0-4-0ST	1951
—	8	Barclay (885)	0-6-0ST	1900
—	322	Planet (3541)	4wDM	1952
Norma	3770	Hunslet (3770)	0-6-0ST	1952

Railway Order having been granted
Public opening: Daily 10.00-16.00
On site facilities: Refreshment room — the 'Whistle Stop' (open on special days in former Llansantffraid signalbox) and picnic area
Special notes: Railwayana, artefacts and 20 bicycles, 17 motor cycles and 7 auto-cycles/mopeds on display. Normally Peckett 2131 and Hunslet 3770 are on display inside the building. Group discount available. Also known as Oswestry Transport Museum

Name	*No*	*Builder*	*Type*	*Built*
—	—	Sentinel (9374)	4wVBT	1947
—*	—	Hibberd (3057)	4wDM	1946
—	—	Planet	4wDM	1960

*Mobile compressor

Locomotive notes
Barclay (885) is now on static display by the old Cambrian Railways locomotive works

Stock
1 GWR auto-trailer; 1 GWR brake van; 1 LMS brakevan; 2 tank wagons; 1 open wagon, 1 box van, 1 tank wagon (No 5), 2 tank wagon 4-wheel chassis (tanks removed) ex-Machynlleth Refuelling Depot.

Steam Centre

Chasewater Railway

West Midlands

Member: AIRPS, TT
Founded in 1959 as the Railway Preservation Society (West Midlands District), the Chasewater Railway was reformed in 1985 as a Registered Charity. The railway operates as 'The Colliery Line' to reflect its origins and location in the heart of the Cannock Chase coalfield. The railway extended its running line in October 1995 and now runs a regular timetabled service between Brownhills West station and the newly-opened Norton Lakeside station (which adjoins Chasewater's Wildfowl Reserve)
Location: Chasewater Park, Brownhills (off A5 southbound, nr jct A452 Chester Road)
OS Reference: SK 034070
Operating society/organisation: Chasewater Light Railway & Museum Co
Telephone: (01543) 452623
Car park: Within Chasewater Park
Access by public transport: By rail – Walsall (no Sunday service) and Birmingham New Street. Bus (Sunday services) – Midland Red North 156A from Birmingham (Dale End); 362 from Walsall (Bridge Street). For timetable information and details of midweek/Saturday services, contact Centro Hotline (0121) 200 2700
On site facilities: Refreshments, shop, lakeside walks and large grassed areas
Catering facilities: Hot and cold buffet

Diesel Multiple-Units

Name	*No*	*Builder*	*Class*	*Type*	*Built*
—	W51370	Pressed Steel	117	DMBS	1960
—	W51372	Pressed Steel	117	DMBS	1960
—	W51412	Pressed Steel	117	DMS	1960
—	W59444	BR Derby	116	TS	1958
—	W59603	Pressed Steel	127	TSL	1959

Industrial Locomotives

Name	*No*	*Builder*	*Type*	*Built*
Alfred Paget	11	Neilson (2937)	0-4-0ST	1882
Sheepbridge No.15	—	H/Clarke (431)	0-6-0T	1885
—	6	Peckett (917)	0-4-0ST	1902
Asbestos	4	H/Leslie (2780)	0-4-0ST	1909
Colin McAndrew	3	Barclay (1223)	0-4-0ST	1911
Little Lady	—	Peckett (1903)	0-4-0ST	1936
Invicta	8	Barclay (2220)	0-4-0ST	1946
Whit No.4		H/Clarke (1822)	0-6-0T	1949
Sentinel	5	Sentinel (9632)	4wVBT	1957
—	1	M/Rail (1947)	4wPM	1919
—	21	Kent Constr (1612)	4wDM	1929
—	—	Fowler (4100013)	0-4-0DM	1948
—	—	R/Hornsby (305306)	0-4-0DM	1952
Toad	37	Fowler (4220015)	0-4-0DH	1962
Fleet	7	R/Hornsby (458641)	0-4-0DE	1963

Rolling Stock
A variety of passenger and freight vehicles are housed on site, including a number of considerable historical importance

Length of line: 1.25 miles
Public opening: Sundays and Bank Holiday Mondays from Easter to end of October. Trains run at 45 min. intervals from 12.00 until 17.15pm
Special events: 21 June (Transport Festival); 10/11 October (Vintage Vehicle Rally). Santa Specials 13, 20 December
Facilities for disabled: Disabled access to stations, trains and buffet
Membership details: Membership Secretary, Brownhills West Station, Hednesford Road, Brownhills West, Walsall WS8 7LT

Chinnor & Princes Risborough Railway — 'The Icknield Line'

Steam Centre — Oxfordshire

Member: AIRPS
The Chinnor & Princes Risborough Railway Association was formed in 1989 with the aim of restoring the disused line from Princes Risborough to Chinnor, part of the former Watlington branch
Location: Chinnor, Oxon, 10 miles SW of Aylesbury. J6 on M40, station signposted from B4009, which passes through village
OS reference: TL 774362
Operating society/organisation: Chinnor & Princes Risborough Railway Co, Chinnor Station, Station Road, Chinnor, Oxon OX9 4ER
Access by public transport: Main line Princes Risborough then Wycombe Bus Nos 232/331/332 to Chinnor (Sats only)
Length of line: 4 miles. First 3.5 miles opened for 1995 season
Passenger trains: Chinnor-Thame Junction-Chinnor
Public opening: Weekends from Easter-end October. Thomas visiting in May and August. Santa & Mince Pie Specials in December. Up-to-date information on Talking Timetable (01844) 353535
On site facilities: Souvenir shop, buffet plus on train buffet. Toilets, free car park, picnic area
Special note: Visiting locomotives during the season, please phone for details or see railway press
Membership details: Mr Peter Harris, 12 Ann's Close, Aylesbury, Bucks
Membership journal: *The Watlington Flyer* — bi-monthly

Locomotives

Name	*No*	*Origin*	*Class*	*Type*	*Built*
Haversham	D3018	BR	08	0-6-0DE	1953
—	D8568	BR	17	Bo-Bo	1963
—	55023	BR	121	DMBS	1958
—	4247	GWR	4200	2-8-0T	1916

Industrial locomotives

Name	*No*	*Builder*	*Type*	*Built*
Sir Robert Peel	8	Hunslet (3776)	0-6-0ST	1952
Iris	459515	R/Hornsby (459515)	0-6-0DH	1952

Stock - coaches
1 ex-LNWR Mess coach, 1 ex-BR Mk 1 NDV, 1 ex-BR Mk 1 RMB, 1 ex-BR Mk 1 CK, 1 ex-BR Mk 1 BSK, 1 ex-BR Mk 2 FK, 12 various wagons, 1 Coles self-propelled crane

Cholsey & Wallingford Railway

Timetable Service — Oxfordshire

Member: AIRPS
Location: Hithercroft Industrial Estate, St Johns Road, Wallingford, Oxfordshire
Traffic Manager: Richard Hall
Operating Society: Cholsey & Wallingford Railway Preservation Society, PO Box 16, Wallingford, Oxon OX10 0NF
Telephone: (01491) 835067 (24hr information line)
Access by public transport: Thames Transit (390) from Oxford-London, BR Cholsey (2 miles)
Public opening: 11.00-17.00. 12/13 April; 3/4, 24/25 May; 7, 21 June; 5, 19 July; 9, 30/31 August; 13, 27 September; 17/18 October and Santa Specials
Length of line: 2.5 miles from Wallingford
Journey time: Approximately 20min (one way), 45min (return)
On site facilities: Souvenir and coffee shop, museum, model railway
Special events: Friends of Thomas the Tank Engine — 12/13 April; Santa Specials — 6, 13, 19/20 December
Special notes: Light Railway Order now granted. Railway crosses new bypass (A4130) at a level crossing. The Society has completed track into Cholsey bay platform.
Membership details: Ian Bowyer, at above address
Membership journal: *The Bunk* — 3 issues/year

Locomotives

Name	*No*	*Origin*	*Class*	*Type*	*Built*
Unicorn	(08022)	BR	08	0-6-0	1953
Lion	(08060)	BR	08	0-6-0	1953
George Mason	08123	BR	08	0-6-0	1955

Industrial locomotives

Name	*No*	*Builder*	*Type*	*Built*
Carpenter	3271	Planet (3271)	0-4-0	1949
—*	68006	Hunslet (3192)	0-6-0ST	1944

*Scheduled to visit during 1998

Rolling stock — coaches: 4 BR Mk 1 coaches, 1 BR Mk 2 brake coach

Churnet Valley Railway

Member: AIRPS
Easter 1996 saw the re-opening of the first mile of the Churnet Valley Railway from Cheddleton to Leekbrook. Cheddleton is a Victorian country station set in the attractive Staffordshire moorlands, situated adjacent to the River Churnet. Pleasant walks can be taken alongside the Caldon Canal, and the Flint Mill Museum is only 1,200yd away. Please ring to confirm timetable and events
Location: Cheddleton station, near Leek, Staffordshire
OS reference: SJ 983519
Operating society/organisation: Churnet Valley Railway (1992) plc
Telephone: Churnetside (01538) 360522
Car park: Riverside car park and picnic area opposite the station
Access by public transport: Main line Stoke-on-Trent (10 miles). A regular bus service operated by Proctors, PMT and Stevensons runs from Hanley, Longton and Leek to Cheddleton village
On site facilities: The station contains a refreshment room, souvenir shop and small relics museum. On open days visitors are allowed to visit the yard, signalbox and new locomotive display hall. Modern toilets and picnic area on site
Length of line: 1-mile, Cheddleton-Leekbrook
Public opening: Easter-September inclusive — Sundays and Bank Holiday Mondays, 11.00-17.30. Sundays October-March 12.00-17.00.
Refreshment room only April-September, 13.00-17.00 daily excluding Thursdays
Special events: Please contact for details
Facilities for disabled: Access to most of the site is possible by wheelchair. Train rides by arrangement
Membership details: North Staffordshire Railway Co, Membership Secretary, c/o above address
Special notes: Coach parties catered for by prior arrangement. Guided tours available for parties on request. The sale of track and trackbed between Leekbrook Junction and Oakamoor sand sidings (7 miles) has been agreed. A share issue of £400,000 is the target and the public are invited to buy shares in the Churnet Valley Railway (1992) plc to help develop the railway. The first stage of the CVR opened at Easter 1996 and then progressed over the next few years. Please phone to confirm the timetable

Locomotives and Multiple-units

Name	*No*	*Origin*	*Class*	*Type*	*Built*
—	2	NSR	New L	0-6-2T	1923
—	4422	LMS	4F	0-6-0	1927
Castell Dinas Bran	76079	BR	4MT	2-6-0	1957
—	80136	BR	4MT	2-6-4T	1956
—	D2070	BR	03	0-6-0DM	1959
—	D2334	BR	04	0-6-0DM	1961
—	D3420	BR	08	0-6-0DE	1957
Tamworth Castle	D7672	BR	25	Bo-Bo	1967
—	33102	BR	33	Bo-Bo	1960
Burma Star	33056	BR	33	Bo-Bo	1961
—	53455	BRCW	104	DMBS	1957
—	53517	BRCW	104	DMCL	1957

Industrial locomotives

Name	*No*	*Builder*	*Type*	*Built*
Josiah Wedgwood	52	Hunslet (3777)	0-6-0ST	1952

Locomotive notes: Locos expected to be in service: 4422, 76079 (due to arrive in May), D2070, D2334, D3420, D7672, 33102 and Class 104 DMU.

Owners
4422 the 4422 Locomotive Fund
D3420, 33056, 33102 and D7672 the NSR Diesel Group
NSR 2 the National Railway Museum

Stock
2 ex-BR Mk 1 CK coaches; 2 ex- BR Mk 1 BSK coaches; 1 ex-BR Mk 1 SO coach; 2 ex-BR Mk 1 TSO coaches; 2 ex-BR Mk 1 FK coaches; 1 ex-BR Mk 1 RMB coach; 2 ex-BR brake suburban coaches; 1 ex-NSR coach body; 1 ex-LMS 6-wheel full brake; 1 ex-LMS goods brake van; 1 ex-LMS 6-wheel CCT; 2 ex-LMS box vans; 3 ex-BR box vans; 2 ex-LMS 5-plank wagons; 1 ex-LMS hopper wagon; 1 Esso tank wagon; 1 7ton diesel rail-mounted crane; 1 ex-BR standard 20ton brake van

Timetable Service

Cleethorpes Coast Light Railway

North East Lincolnshire

Member: AIRPS, Britain's Great Little Railways

One of the country's latest 15in gauge recruits. Previously a 14.25in gauge railway it was converted to 15in in time for the 1994 Steam Gala. The railway is gaining a reputation for good events and galas, as well as now being the chosen site for a Museum of Seaside Miniature Railways. Planning for this major new project is well underway with the completion planned over the next four years.

1998 will again feature steam haulage on the line, with visiting locomotives planned for the main season to assist the resident stock. The railway operating company is lucky to be able to call upon the Cleethorpes Coast Light Railway Supporters' Association to provide the majority of operating staff. This small group are always looking for new helpers, and membership is free. Details are available from the company

Operating society/organisation: Cleethorpes Coast Light Railway Ltd, Lakeside Station, Kings Road, Cleethorpes, Lincolnshire DN35 0AG

Telephone/Fax: (01472) 604657

Access by public transport: By rail to Cleethorpes, Stagecoach service 17 from Sea Road passes the line. By car, Kings Road is the main resort road. Follow Lakeside brown tourist signs

On site facilities: Large 500 space car park (pay & display). Station gift shop at Kingsway station. Teapot tearoom for refreshments at Lakeside station. Lakeside picnic area

Period of public opening: Daily 1 April-14 September. Railway open from 10.00. *Winter weekends* — November-Good Friday. Winter daily running schools half term weeks (except 25/26 December)

Special events: Easter Egg Specials — 12/13 April; Spring Steam & Diesel Gala — 16/17 May; Festival of Transport — 30/31 May; 50 Golden Years Birthday Gala — 17-19 July; Friends of Thomas the Tank Engine — 28-31 August; 'Little Unusual Steam Weekend' — 26/27 September; Santa Trains — 13, 19/20 December

Locomotives

Name	*No*	*Built/rebuilt*	*Type*	*Date*
Konigswinter	1	CCLR	2-8-0GH	1992
Arnold J Rimmer	2	Lister	4wDH Tram	—
The Cub	3	CCLR	4w4DM	1993
*Siân**	4	Guest	2-4-2	1963
Haigh Hall/Katie†	5	Guest	2-4-2	1954
—	6	Stanhope/CCLR	0-4-0VBT	1995
—	24	Fairbourne	2-6-2	1989
—	—	Eclipse	4wDM	1956
Seabreeze	—	CCLR	4-6-2	Under construction

Also on site

Royal Scot	6100	Carland	4-6-0	—

Rolling stock

4 Severn Lamb semi-open saloons (one converted to brake coach by CCLR); 5 Alan Keef toastracks (one includes guard's compartment); 1 JMA open coach; 2 4-wheel tub wagons; 14-wheel box van; 14-wheel five plank wagon; 1 4-wheel ballast hopper, 1 bogie passenger brake van;

Owners/notes

24 — the Sandy River Consortium
*On loan from *Siân* Project Group
†On loan from Wigan Council

***Siân* and *Katie* (right) stand at Lakeside station during a gala weekend.**
John East

Steam Centre

Colne Valley Railway

Essex

Member: AIRPS, TT
A completely reconstructed country station and railway within sight of the 12th century castle and specialising in entertainment and education
Location: Castle Hedingham Station, Yeldham Road, Castle Hedingham, Halstead, Essex CO9 3DZ
OS reference: TL 774362
Operating society/organisation: Colne Valley Railway Preservation Society Ltd
Telephone: Hedingham (01787) 461174
Internet address: http://www.ourworld.com/homepages/paul-lemon.htm
Car park: At the site (access from A604 road) between Castle Hedingham and Great Yeldham
Access by public transport: Eastern National bus services 88 Colchester-Halstead, 89 Halstead-Hedingham and Hedingham Omnibuses 4 Braintree-Hedingham, 5 Sudbury-Hedingham. Nearest station — Braintree (7 miles)
On site facilities: Depot, museum, souvenir shop, buffet, 4-acre riverside wooded picnic area (suitable for nature studies by visiting school children), toilets, video carriage, information centre
Catering facilities: Buffet carriage when trains operating. Pullman on-train service on selected days for Sunday lunch, private hire and evening wine and dine (pre-booking essential for all Pullman services)
Length of line: Approx 1-mile
Public opening: Daily for static displays except 24 December to 31 January. Steam trains operate every Sunday from 22 March to 25 October, also Tuesdays Wednesdays and Thursdays during school summer holidays, and every Bank Holiday (except Christmas & New Year), Wednesdays during other school holidays (except February). Heritage diesel trains operate Saturdays 4 July to 29 August, Fridays during school holidays, Sundays 1, 8, 15 March and every Sunday in November
Special events: Gala Day — 19 July; Friends of Thomas the Tank — 20/21, 27/28 June; Santa Specials — 6, 12/13, 17, 19/20, 23 December
Educational events: Diesel trains available every day for school visits. Learning with Thomas in June, Victorian Special in October. All educational events must be pre-booked
Family tickets: Available — 2 Adults + 4 Children, giving unlimited train rides except on special events
Facilities for disabled: Access to most areas. Ramps to trains, staff will help. No toilets suitable for disabled

Locomotives and Multiple-units

Name	*No*	*Origin*	*Class*	*Type*	*Built*
Blue Star	35010	SR	MN	4-6-2	1942
—	45163	LMS	5	4-6-0	1935
—	45293	LMS	5	4-6-0	1936
—	D2041	BR	03	0-6-0DM	1959
—	D2184	BR	03	0-6-0DM	1962
—	D5634	BR	31	A1A-A1A	1960
—	51138	BR	116	DMBS	1958
—*	51151	BR	116	DMS	1958
—*	51669	BR	115	DMBS	1960
—	51894	BR	115	DMBS	1960
—	55033	P/Steel	121	DTC	1960
—	59664	BR	115	TCL	1960
—	W79976	AC Cars	—	Railbus	1958
—	E79978	AC Cars	—	Railbus	1958

*May be on loan to other railways

Industrial locomotives

Name	*No*	*Builder*	*Type*	*Built*
Victory	8	Barclay (2199)	0-4-0ST	1945
—	190	Hunslet (3790)	0-6-0ST	1952
—	68072	Vulcan (5309)	0-6-0ST	1945
Jupiter	60	RSH (7671)	0-6-0ST	1950
—	40	RSH (7765)	0-6-0T	1954
Barrington	—	Avonside (1875)	0-4-0ST	1921
—	1	H/Leslie (3715)	0-4-0ST	1928
—	—	Barclay (349)	0-4-0DM	1941
—	YD43	R/Hornsby (221639)	4wDM	1943
—	—	Hibbard (3147)	4wDM	1947
—	—	Unilok (2109)	4wDM R/R	1982
—	—	Lake & Elliot (1)	4wPM	1924

Locomotive notes: *Victory, Barrington* and 190 expected to be operational during 1998

Stock
10 ex-BR Mk 1 coaches (2xTSO, SO, 3xCK, SK, 2xBSK); 1 ex-Norwegian State Railway 18803 Balcony; Open Second; 2 ex-Pullman cars, *Aquila* and *Hermione;* 1 ex-BR Mk 3 SLEP; 9 BR NPCCS, 2 ex-LNER — 1xBTO (16551) 1xTK (42240); Travelling Post Office (BR 80318); Sundry items of freight stock

Owners
35010 and 45293 the British Enginemans Steam Preservation Society
51138, 51151, 51669, 51894, 55033 & 59664 Pressed Steel Heritage Ltd

Special notes: The railway has been completely rebuilt on part of the original Colne Valley & Halstead Railway trackbed. The railway offers much of educational value specialising in school party visits by appointment at any time of the year

Membership details: Membership Secretary, c/o Castle Hedingham Station

Museum

Darlington Railway Centre & Museum

County Durham

Located on the original 1825 route of the Stockton & Darlington Railway, the restored North Road station, dating from 1842, is now a museum which forms the centrepiece of an area devoted to railway history and preservation.

The Museum is administered by Darlington Borough Council. The collection includes locomotives, rolling stock and many small exhibits. A special display on the theme of holiday travel by train will be on view during 1998. The site also includes two other historic buildings of the S&DR — the former Goods Shed and the Hopetown Carriage Works. Steam train rides over a short length of line are available on selected dates, and there are plans for future extension of the line.

The Ken Hoole Study Centre houses a collection of reference material on the railways of north-east England including the library of the North Eastern Railway Association (access by appointment).

Regional Railways North East provides a link to Darlington's main line station and to Shildon, for the Timothy Hackworth Museum

Museum Curator: Steven Dyke

Location: North Road Station, Darlington, County Durham DL3 6ST. Approximately three-quarters of a mile north of town centre, off North Road (A167)

OS reference: NZ 289157

Telephone: (01325) 460532

Car park: At museum site

Access by public transport: Rail services to Darlington North Road station. Local bus services along North Road

Catering facilities: Refreshment area open Spring Bank Holiday to mid-September. Confectionery and drinks at other times

On site facilities: Souvenir and book shop, toilets, meeting room

Public opening: Daily February to

Locomotives

Name	*No*	*Origin*	*Class*	*Type*	*Built*
Locomotion	1	S&DR	—	0-4-0	1825
Derwent	25	S&DR	—	0-6-0	1845
—	1463	NER	1463	2-4-0	1885
—	910	NER	901	2-4-0	1875

Industrial locomotives

Name	*No*	*Builder*	*Type*	*Built*
Met	—	H/Leslie (2800)	0-4-0ST	1909
—	17	Head Wrightson (33)	0-4-0VB	1873
—	—	Bagnall (2898)	0-4-0F	1948
—	39	RSH (6947)	0-6-0T	1938

Stock

1 Stockton & Darlington Rly passenger coach (1846)
1 North Eastern Railway Coach body (c1860)
1 NER 20-ton mineral wagon
1 Chaldron wagon

Owners

Locomotion, Derwent, 1463 and 910 are all on loan from the National Railway Museum
Met is on loan from Messrs D. & R. Branch

Darlington Railway Preservation Society

Member: AIRPS

Locomotives

Name	*No*	*Origin*	*Class*	*Type*	*Built*
—	78018	BR	2MT	2-6-0	1954

Industrial locomotives

Name	*No*	*Builder*	*Type*	*Built*
—	2	RSH (7925)	0-4-0DM	1959
—	1	Peckett (2142)	0-4-0ST	1953
David Payne	185	Fowler (4110006)	0-4-0DM	1950
Smiths Dock Co Ltd	—	Fowler (4200018)	0-4-0DM	1947
—	—	GEC	4wE	1928
—	—	R/Hornsby (279591)	0-4-0DM	1949
—	—	R/Hornsby*	4wDM	—
—	—	R/Hornsby*	4wDM	—
—	—	R/Hornsby*	4wDM	—

*1ft 6in gauge

Stock

Various wagons, steam and diesel cranes

A1 Steam Locomotive Trust

Locomotives

Name	*No*	*Origin*	*Class*	*Type*	*Built*
Tornado	60163	A1SLT	8P6F	4-6-2	Under construction

December 10.00-17.00 (except Christmas holidays). Days and times may be subject to amendment
Special events: Railway Carnival — September; steam days; Santa Specials — December (contact for details)
Facilities for disabled: Access to main museum building for wheelchairs. Disabled persons toilet. Guide tape for visually handicapped
Membership details: Friends of Darlington Railway Museum, Darlington Railway Preservation Society, A1 Steam Locomotive Trust and North Eastern Railway Association all c/o above address
Note: Some locomotives are located in the former goods shed, where restoration work is being undertaken by the Darlington Railway Preservation Society (limited opening to visitors — times vary; groups by arrangement). Part of the former carriage works has been renovated and is now used by the A1 Steam Locomotive Trust for assembly of the new Peppercorn Pacific *Tornado* (visitor access at certain times, please enquire)

Timetable Service

Dean Forest Railway

Glos

Member: AIRPS, TT
Passenger services operate between Norchard and Lydney Junction (Severn & Wye Joint), with extension to Parkend planned to open in late 1998/early 1999. The current line boasts five level crossings, three of which are manually-operated
Location: Norchard Railway Centre on the B4234, 0.75-mile off A48 at Lydney, Glos
OS reference: SO 629044
Operations Manager: Keith Johnson
Operating society/organisation: Dean Forest Railway Society in conjunction with owning company, Forest of Dean Railway Ltd
Telephone: (01594) 843423 information line; (01594) 845840 (daytime); (01452) 840625 (general info and evenings)
Car park: Adequate for cars and coaches — no charge
Access by public transport: Main line station at Lydney
On site facilities: Shop available at Norchard along with a museum, riverside walk, forest trail and picnic area (cafeteria at Norchard on operating days)
Catering facilities: Hot and cold snacks on steam days. Parties catered for by appointment
Length of line: 2 miles
Public opening: Daily for static display — shop and museum, open every Saturday and Sunday 11.00-17.00 and weekdays April to December. Train rides: Good Friday, Easter Saturday and all Bank Holiday Sundays and Mondays (Christmas/New Year excepted). All Sundays April-September. Wednesdays in June and July. Tuesdays, Wednesdays, Thursdays and Saturdays in August
Special events: Friends of Thomas the Tank Engine — 26-31 May, 4-6 September; Western Branchline Festival — 26/27 September; Lydney Road & Rail Show — 18 October; Santa Specials in December; Mince Pie Specials — 27/28 December, 1 January 1999
Facilities for disabled: Access to museum, shop, toilets and train rides
Membership details: Mr R. Bramwell, 4 Poole Ground, Highnam, Gloucester GL2 8DJ
Membership journal: *Forest Venturer* — half yearly
Marketing name: The Friendly Forest Line

Locomotives and mutliple-units

Name	*No*	*Origin*	*Class*	*Type*	*Built*
—	28	TVR	O1	0-6-2T	1897
—	5541	GWR	4575	2-6-2T	1928
—	9681	GWR	5700	0-6-0PT	1949
—	08238	BR	08	0-6-0DE	1956
—	50619	BR	108	DMBS	1958
—	51914	BR	108	DMS	1960
—	56492	BR	108	DMC	1960

Industrial locomotives

Name	*No*	*Builder*	*Type*	*Built*
—	—	Barclay (2221)	0-4-0ST	1946
Jessie	—	Hunslet (1873)	0-6-0ST	1937
Uskmouth No 1	—	Peckett (2147)	0-4-0ST	1952
Wilbert	—	Hunslet (3806)	0-6-0ST	1953
Warrior	—	Hunslet (3823)	0-6-0ST	1954
—	—	Hunslet (2145)	0-4-0DM	1940
—	—	Fowler (4210127)	0-4-0DM	1957
—	—	Hibberd (3947)	4wPM	1960
Cabot	39	R/Royce (10218)	0-6-0DH	1965

Owners
28 the National Railway Museum, on loan from the Museum of Wales

Stock
4 ex-GWR coaches; 12 ex-BR coaches; 1 DFR constructed Cafeteria coach (static at Norchard), 3 Wickham trolleys; 1 steam crane Thos Smith (Rodley) TS 5027 (10ton); 100+ wagons

Museum

Derby Industrial Museum

Derbyshire

Member: TT
As would be expected of a railway town, the museum has an extensive collection of railway material including locomotives and rolling stock (most on display at the Midland Railway Centre). The railway gallery relates the stories of railway industries in Derby, especially as they relate to the Midland Railway and its successors. Replica Midland Railway signalbox and model railway (under construction). The story is brought up to date by the Railway Research Gallery which looks at the role of the Railway Technical Centre
Location: Silk Mill Lane, Derby

Industrial locomotives

Name	*No*	*Builder*	*Type*	*Built*
Victory	—	Peckett (1547)	0-4-0ST	1919
—	—	Motor Rail (6155)	4wPM	1919

Operating society/organisation: Derby Industrial Museum, Silk Mill Lane, off Full Street, Derby DE1 3AR
Telephone: (01332) 255308
Fax: (01332) 255804
Car park: Local car parks around city
Access by public transport: Bus station quarter mile, railway station three-quarter mile.
On site facilities: Shop, baby changing facilities

Opening times: Admission free. Mondays 11.00-17.00, Tuesdays to Saturdays 10.00-17.00, Sundays 14.00-17.00, Bank Holidays 14.00-17.00
Facilities for disabled: Parking by arrangement. Level access to building, lifts and ramps to all gallery areas, toilets, sign language and sub-titles in Rolls-Royce gallery

Steam Centre

Derwent Valley Light Railway

North Yorkshire

Location: Murton Park, Murton Lane, Murton, Nr York YO1 3UF
Operating society/organisation: Great Yorkshire Railway Preservation Society
Telephone: (01904) 489966
OS reference: SE 651537
On site facilities: Refreshments, souvenir shop (Yorkshire Museum of Farming)
Car park: Free, on site
Length of line: Half-mile
Access by public transport: York-Stamford Bridge bus service from main line York station
Facilities for disabled: Toilets, ramped ways etc
Public opening: Open daily mid-February-end October, for the Yorkshire Museum of Farming, Houlgate (Viking) Village and the Derwent Valley Light Railway. Trains operate Sundays and Bank Holidays Easter-end September and for Santa Specials
Membership details: Andy Bell, 45 Maryland Avenue, Willerby Road, Hull HU5 5JA
Society journal: *DVLR News* (quarterly)

Industrial locomotives

Name	*No*	*Builder*	*Type*	*Built*
—	—	A/Barclay (2369)	0-4-0ST	1955
—*	—	Peckett (2103)	0-4-0ST	1948
—	—	Fowler (22077)	0-4-0DM	1937
—	ED6	Fowler (4200022)	0-4-0DM	1948
Churchill	—	Fowler (410005)	0-4-0DM	1947
Jim	—	R/Hornsby (417892)	4wDM	1959
Octavius Atkinson	—	R/Hornsby (466630)	4wDM	1962
—	—	R/Hornsby (327964)	4wDM	1953

*May not be on site for all of 1998

Rolling stock
1 ex-LNER coach, 1 NER coach, 1 NER coach body, 10 various freight wagons, and 1 rail crane

Steam Centre

Didcot Railway Centre

Oxfordshire

Member: AIRPS, TT
Based around the GWR engine shed and depot, the Centre now has a typical GWR small country station with signalboxes (from Radstock and Frome), re-creation of Brunel's broad gauge railway, two demonstration lines, and a small relics museum

General Manager: Michael Dean
Location: Adjacent to BR station, Didcot, Oxfordshire. Access via station subway
OS reference: SU 525907
Operating society/organisation: Great Western Society Ltd, Didcot Railway Centre, Didcot, Oxon OX11 7NJ
Telephone: Didcot (01235) 817200
Car park: Didcot station
Access by public transport: Didcot Parkway BR station
Refreshment facilities: Refreshment room open all days centre is open (lunches, snacks). Picnic area
On site facilities: GWR locomotive depot, replica GWR station, museum and broad gauge demonstration. Souvenir sales. Rides are available on the demonstration lines on Steamdays. Admission price on Steamdays includes train rides
Length of line: 1,000yd
Public opening: Saturdays and Sundays all year. Daily 4 April-27 September, 24 October to 1 November, 27 December to 3 January. Steamdays first and last Sunday each month from March, Bank Holidays, all Sundays June-August, all Wednesdays in July and August, all Saturdays in August. Open 10.00-17.00 (November/December 11.00-16.00)
Train rides: On Steamdays there is normally continuous operation of the passenger train, interrupted by Travelling Post Office demonstrations and turning of the locomotives on some days
Special events: Friends of Thomas the Tank Engine — 13-15 March, 2-4 October; Photographers' Evening (to 9pm) — 30/31 October/; Santa Steamings — 11-13, 19/20 December; New Year Steamings — 1-3 January 1999
Facilities for disabled: Steps at access from station subway may cause problems, but assistance can normally be provided (advance notification is useful)
Membership details: Richard Bullock, at above address
Membership journals: *Great Western Echo* — quarterly; *National Newsletter* — seven times annually

Locomotives

Name	*No*	*Origin*	*Class/builder*	*Type*	*Built*
—	22	GWR	Diesel Railcar	1A-A1	1940
—	1338	GWR (Cardiff Rly)	Kitson (3799)	0-4-0ST	1898
Trojan	1340	GWR	Avonside (1380)	0-4-0ST	1897
—	1363	GWR	1361	0-6-0ST	1910
—	1466	GWR	1400	0-4-2T	1936
—	3650	GWR	5700	0-6-0PT	1939
—	3738	GWR	5700	0-6-0PT	1937
—	3822	GWR	2884	2-8-0	1940
—	4144	GWR	5101	2-6-2T	1946
Maindy Hall	4942	GWR	'Hall'	4-6-0	1929
Caerphilly Castle	4073	GWR	'Castle'	4-6-0	1923
Earl Bathurst	5051	GWR	'Castle'	4-6-0	1936
—	5322	GWR	4300	2-6-0	1917
—	5572	GWR	4575	2-6-2T	1927
Hinderton Hall	5900	GWR	'Hall'	4-6-0	1931
King Edward II	6023	GWR	'King'	4-6-0	1930
—	6106	GWR	6100	2-6-2T	1931
—	6697	GWR	5600	0-6-2T	1928
Burton Agnes Hall	6998	GWR	'Hall'	4-6-0	1949
—	7202	GWR	7200	2-8-2T	1934
Cookham Manor	7808	GWR	'Manor'	4-6-0	1938
—	D3771	BR	08	0-6-0DE	1959
Pontyberem	2	Burry Port & Gwendraeth Valley Rly		0-6-0ST	1900
Shannon	5	Wantage Tramway		0-4-0WT	1857

Industrial locomotives

Name	*No*	*Builder*	*Type*	*Built*
Bonnie Prince Charlie	1	RSH (7544)	0-4-0ST	1949
—	26	Hunslet (5238)	0-6-0DH	1962

Locomotive notes: Locomotives available in 1998 should be: 22, 1466, 3738, 4144, 5051. Locomotives under restoration include: 1340, 3650, 3822, 5322, 6023, 7202. Construction of the Firefly Trust's reproduction broad gauge locomotive *Firefly* is being undertaken

Stock
Over 40 ex-GWR coaches are preserved along with numerous ex-GWR freight wagons

Owners
5 and 4073 on loan from the National Railway and Science Museum

Operating Museum

East Anglia Transport Museum

Suffolk

Member: AIRPS, TT
The East Suffolk Light Railway is the title given to the 2ft gauge railway, which winds its way some 300yd or so along the northern perimeter of the museum site, between the stations of Chapel Road and Woodside. The railway commenced operation in 1973 and aims to re-create a typical passenger-carrying light railway of years gone by. Many aspects of railway interest can be found along its length. The track came from Leziate sand quarry and Canvey

Island, as well as from the Southwold Railway. There is also a signalbox from the Lowestoft-Great Yarmouth line, and signals from various local locations; all of which help to set the overall scene
Location: Carlton Colville, three miles south-west of Lowestoft in Suffolk
OS reference: TM 505903
Operating society/organisation: East Anglia Transport Museum Society Ltd, Chapel Road, Carlton Colville, Lowestoft, Suffolk NR33 8BL
Telephone: (01502) 518459
Car park: Adjacent
Access by public transport: Eastern Counties L11, L12 & 171 (Monday-Saturday); Blue Bus 171 and Eastern Counties L18 & L19 (Sundays and Bank Holidays) from Lowestoft. Main line rail, Oulton Broad South (1.5 miles)
On site facilities: Refreshments, picnic area, souvenir and bookshop, toilets, working transport museum, including trams, narrow gauge railway, trolleybuses, steamrollers and other commercial and public transport vehicles. Unlimited free rides
Public opening: Easter, and Sundays from beginning of May to end of September, also other Bank Holidays in this period; open from 11.00. Wednesdays and Saturdays from the beginning of June to the end of September, and every weekday from 20 July-4 September; open from 14.00
Special notes: Limited facilities for the disabled. Pre-booked party rates
Membership details: From the above address

Industrial locomotives

Name	*No*	*Builder*	*Type*	*Built*
—	2	M/Rail (5912)	4wDM	1934
—	4	R/Hornsby (177604)	4wDM	1936
Thorpeness	5	M/Rail (22209)	4wDM	1964
Orfordness	6	M/Rail (22211)	4wDM	1964

Stock
Locally designed and built covered coach and brake van
Small selection of wagons
Van body ex-Southwold Railway

Steam Centre

East Anglian Railway Museum

Essex

Member: AIRPS, TT, RM, MLOA, AIM, EATB, EETB
Adjacent to Chappel Viaduct which is the most spectacular railway structure in East Anglia
Location: Chappel & Wakes Colne Station, near Colchester CO6 2DS
OS reference: TL 898289
Chairman: Gordon V. Adams
Operating society/organisation: East Anglian Railway Museum, Chappel & Wakes Colne Station, Station Road, Wakes Colne, Essex CO6 2DS. Registered charity No 1001579
Telephone: Colchester (01206) 242524
Fax: (01206) 242524
Internet address: e-mail — earm@btinternet.com
Car park: On site
Access by public transport: Great Eastern Chappel & Wakes Colne station. Also Eastern National/Hedingham Omnibus service No 88 Colchester-Halstead. Sundays Eastern National No 88C Colchester-Halstead
On site facilities: Refreshments, comprehensive bookshop, museum, signalboxes, souvenir shop, picnic area, miniature railway, heritage centre and toilets
Public opening: Daily 10.00-16.30

Locomotives and multiple-units

Name	*No*	*Origin*	*Class*	*Type*	*Built*
A. J. Hill	69621	GER	N7	0-6-2T	1924
—	80151	BR	4MT	2-6-4T	1956
—	D2279	BR	04	0-6-0DM	1960
—	D3940	BR	08	0-6-0DE	1960
—	50599	BR	108	DMBS	1958
—	56491	BR	108	DTC	1960
—	51568	BR	108	DMCL	1959
—	52053	BR	108	DMCL	1960

Industrial locomotives

Name	*No*	*Builder*	*Type*	*Built*
Jubilee	—	Bagnall (2542)	0-4-0ST	1936
—	1074	Barclay (1047)	0-4-0ST	1905
Belvoir	—	Barclay (2350)	0-6-0ST	1954
—	2	M/Vick	0-4-0E	1912
Jeffery	2039	Peckett (2039)	0-4-0ST	1943
Penn Green	54	RSH (7031)	0-6-0ST	1941
—	AMW144	Barclay (333)	0-4-0DM	1938
—	23	Fowler (4220039)	0-4-0DH	1965
—	2029	Simplex (2029)	0-4-0PM	1920

Locomotive notes: 69621 is operational, 80151 approaching completion

Stock
4 ex-BR Mk 1s; 1 ex-BR sleeping coach; 1 ex-BR Mk 1 full brake; 1 ex-LNER Buffet car; 1 ex-LNER pigeon van; 1 ex-LNER TSO coach; 1 fully restored GER 6-wheel full brake; 1 GER 6-wheel family saloon; 1 GER fully restored 4-wheel coach; 1 ex-GER bogie coach; 1 MSL 6-wheel coach; 1 SR PMV; 1 ex-BR CCT; 1 ex-BR 13-ton open wagon; 2 ex-BR 16-ton mineral wagons; 1 Lomac wagon; 1 ex-LMS 12-ton open wagon; 3 Wickham Trolleys; 1 GWR Toad Brakevan; 1 ex-BR brake van; Somersham 'pump' trolley, 1 Grafton steam crane

Special events: Friends of Thomas the Tank Engine — 10-13 April; Volunteer day — 26 April; Steam Day — 24 May; Arts & Science Workshops for Children — 26-29 May; (half term, no trains); Model Railway Exhibition — 6/7 June; Meccano Exhibition — 11/12 July; Diesel Day & Bus Rally — 19 July; Steam Day — 26 July; Beer Festival — 9-12 September (no trains); Art Exhibition — 10/11 October (no trains); Halloween & Photographic Steam — 31 October (evening only); Santa Steamings/Victorian Christmas — 6, 12/13, 20 December
Family tickets: Available on all days (unlimited rides on steam days)
Special notes: Special steam days are held first Sunday of month March-August inclusive and October, plus Bank Holidays, Wednesdays and Sundays in August. Three restored signalboxes, large goods shed and restoration shed. Original Victorian country junction station. Schools days and Santa steamings. Disabled visitors welcome — prior advice appreciated. Guided tours by prior arrangement. Buffet open daily May-October
Membership details: Membership Secretary, 50 Ayr Way, Rise Park, Romford, Essex RM1 4UH
Membership journal: *Stour Valley Steam* — 3 times/year

Timetable Service

East Kent Railway

Kent

Member: AIRPS
The East Kent Light Railway Society was formed in 1985 with the aim of preserving the remaining 3-mile section of the Colonel Stephens' light railway which originally ran from Shepherdswell to Wingham. Passenger-carrying operations between Shepherdswell and Eythorne started during 1995 and 1996 saw the first steam on the line for over 30 years. A future extension to Tilmanstone is planned
Location: Shepherdswell (EKLR) Station, Shepherdswell, Dover, Kent
Operating society/organisation: East Kent Light Railway Society
Telephone: (01304) 832042 (answerphone, events and site)
Car park: At both Shepherdswell and Eythorne stations
Access by public transport: South Eastern trains to Shepherdswell station (adjacent). Bus — Stagecoach East Kent (limited service, not Sundays), Tel: (01227) 472082
On site facilities: Light refreshments, book and souvenir shop, plus 3.5/5in gauge steam railway. Picnic area and toilets
Public opening: Weekends and Bank Holidays Easter-Christmas (Sundays only during low season)
Special events: Easter Bunny Specials — 10-13 April; Teddy Bears' Picnic — 25 May; Gala Weekend — 25/26 July; Ghost Trains — 31 October and 1 November; Santa Specials weekends 29 November and weekends 5-21 December
Facilities for disabled: Limited access to buffet, and platforms at both stations
Membership details: Mr B. Hancock, 33 Beaufield, Whitfield, Dover, Kent CT16 3JW
Membership journal: *EKLRS Newsletter*

Multiple-units

Name	No	Origin	Class	Type	Built
—	65373	BR	2EPB	DMBS	1953
—	77558	BR	2EPB	DTS	1953

Industrial locomotives

Name	No	Builder	Type	Built
Spitfire	—	Barclay (1964)	0-4-0ST	1929
—	—	Barclay (2248)	0-4-0ST	1948
Richborough Castle	—	E/Electric (D1197)	0-6-0D	1967
Snowdon	—	Fowler (416002)	0-4-0DM	1952
—	—	V/Foundry (D297)/ Drewry (2583)	0-4-0DM	1951
St Dunstan	—	Avonside (2004)	0-6-0ST	1927
Dougal	—	V/Foundry (D77)/ Drewry (2251)	0-4-0DM	1947

Rolling stock
Leyland Experimental coach, LMS brake third, 2 x LMS full brake (BG), BR Mk 2A first brake, BR Mk 2 TSO and a selection of freight vehicles.

Owners
St Dunstan on long-term loan from British Coal
LMS BG the 33046 Fund
Leyland Experimental Coach the Nene Valley Railway
65373 & 77558 the EPB Preservation Group
BR Mk 2 coaches the EKRVCT

Timetable Service

East Lancashire Railway

Lancashire

Member: AIRPS
A very popular railway run by the East Lancs Railway Society in close co-operation with local authorities, the line won the 1987 ARPS award. Visit the line to find out the cause of the line's popularity and success
Location: Bolton Street Station, Bury, Lancashire BL9 0EY
OS reference: SD 803109
Publicity Director: Graham Vevers
Operating society/organisation: East Lancashire Railway Preservation Society
Telephone: 0161 764 7790
Access by public transport: Main line services to Manchester, Bolton, Rochdale and Burnley. Metrolink from central Manchester to Bury Interchange. Various bus services also operate to Bury, Ramsbottom or Rawtenstall from the main line stations listed
On site facilities: Refreshments normally available when trains are running. Buffet car service on most trains. Souvenir shop, transport museum
Length of line: Approximately 8 miles
Public opening: Steam and diesel-hauled services operate on Saturdays, Sundays and Bank Holidays throughout the year. Santa Specials (advanced booking only) in December
Special events: August — Teddy Bears' Picnic; Santa Specials — weekends in December; Diesel Enthusiasts' Weekend and Friends of Thomas the Tank Engine Days — please apply for details; Irwell Valley Diner, Wine & Dine Trains (advance booking only — please apply for details)
Special Notes: The Society re-opened the Bury-Summerseat-Ramsbottom section in 1987 and the Ramsbottom-Irwell-Rawtenstall section in 1991
Membership details: D. Flood
Membership journal: *The East Lancashire Railway News* — twice yearly
Marketing name: East Lancs

Locomotives and multiple-units

Name	*No*	*Origin*	*Class*	*Type*	*Built*
—	7229	GWR	7200	2-8-2T	1935
—	52322	L&Y	27	0-6-0	1896
—	2700	LMS	5P4F	2-6-0	1927
—	42765	LMS	5P4F	2-6-0	1927
—	45337	LMS	5MT	4-6-0	1937
—	5407	LMS	5MT	4-6-0	1937
Leander	5690	LMS	'Jubilee'	4-6-0	1936
—	46441	LMS	2MT	2-6-0	1950
—	46428	LMS	2MT	2-6-0	1948
—	47324	LMS	3F	0-6-0T	1926
Sir Nigel Gresley	60007	LNER	A4	4-6-2	1937
Duke of Gloucester	71000	BR	8P	4-6-2	1954
—	73156	BR	5MT	4-6-0	1956
—	80097	BR	4MT	2-6-4T	1954
Morning Star	92207	BR	9F	2-10-0	1959
—	45160	WD/TCCD	8F	2-8-0	1941
—	388	USATC	S160	2-8-0	1942
Sherwood Foresters	45060	BR	45	1Co-Co1	1961
—	D335	BR	40	1Co-Co1	1961
—	D345	BR	40	1Co-Co1	1961
Valiant	50015	BR	50	Co-Co	1967
Onslaught	D832	BR	42	B-B	1961
Western Prince	D1041	BR	52	C-C	1962
—	D2767	BR	—	0-4-0DH	1960
—	D2774	BR	—	0-4-0DH	1960
—	11506	BR	01	0-4-0DM	1956
—	D2062	BR	03	0-6-0DM	1959
—	D5054	BR	24	Bo-Bo	1960
—	D5705	BR	28	Co-Bo	1958
Royal Highland Fusilier	D9019	BR	55	Co-Co	1961
—	D7076	BR	35	B-B	1963
—	D7612	BR	25	Bo-Bo	1966
—	D9531	BR	14	0-6-0DH	1965
Gateshead	D1501	BR	47	Co-Co	1962
—	08479	BR	08	0-6-0DE	1958
—	7069	LMS	—	0-6-0DE	1936
—	51285	Cravens	105	DMBC	1958
—	51813	BRCW	110	DMBC	1961
—	51842	BRCW	110	DMCL	1961
—	56121	Cravens	105	DTC	1956
—	59701	BRCW	110	DMCL	1961
—	65451	BR	504	DMBS	1958
—	77172	BR	504	DTS	1958
—	79998*	BR	—	DMBS	1958
—	79999*	BR	—	DTCL	1958

*Battery-electric multiple-unit

Industrial locomotives

Name	*No*	*Builder*	*Type*	*Built*
Gothenburg	32	H/Clarke (680)	0-6-0T	1903
Phoenix	70	H/Clarke (1464)	0-6-0T	1921
—	1	Barclay (1927)	0-4-0ST	1927
—	DH16	Sentinel (10175)	4wDH	1964
—	—	Sentinel (10204)	4wDH	1964

Owners
D345 the Class 40 Preservation Society
Battery-electric MU on loan from Transperience

Name	No	Builder	Type	Built
MR Mercury	1	Hibberd (3438)	4wDM	1950
Winfield	—	M/Rail (9009)	4wDM	1948
—	4002	H/Clarke (D1076)	6wDM	1959

Stock
44 BR Mk 1 coaches; 1 GWR coach; 1 Bogie Guards coach; Cravens 50-ton steam crane RS1013/50 (1930), NER 5-ton hand crane DB915390 (1880) and Smiths 5-ton diesel crane (1939) plus over 80 goods vehicles

Timetable Service

East Somerset Railway

Somerset

Member: AIRPS, TT
Set up by the artist, David Shepherd, 'the man who loves giants', the railway line is home to *Black Prince* and *The Green Knight* housed in their 'traditional' shed. As one might expect, Cranmore station is well laid out and aesthetically pleasing. An art gallery is situated at Cranmore station where prints of his, and other artists', paintings can be bought. One of only two remaining all-steam railways in the country
General Manager: Vacant
Headquarters: East Somerset Railway, (Cranmore Railway Station) Shepton Mallet, Somerset BA4 4QP
OS reference: ST 664429
Telephone: Cranmore (01749) 880417
Fax: (01749) 880764
Main station: Cranmore
Car park: Cranmore — free
Refreshment facilities: Restaurant 'Whistle Stop' situated in car park offering lunches, snacks, teas, etc. Group catering by arrangement. Picnic areas at Cranmore, Merryfield Lane stations and depot. On train catering by arrangement. Private saloon trips
Souvenir shop: Cranmore
On site facilities: Museum, Victorian style engine shed and workshops, children's play area. Railway and wildlife prints for sale in art gallery
Depot: Cranmore West
Length of line: 2.75 miles
Passenger trains: Cranmore to Mendip Vale. Stations at Cranmore West, Merryfield Lane and Mendip Vale, unlimited train travel
Period of public operation: Open daily with trains running on Sundays in January, February, March and November. Wednesdays to Sundays in June and September. Daily in July and August. Saturdays and Sundays in April, May, October, (and December for Santa Trains only) plus all bank holidays and Wednesdays to Sundays during half term weeks. Also New Years' Day.

Last admission 30min before closing time. Each day ticket allows unlimited travel on all timetabled trains
Special events: Freight charters, Steam Dream, Music in the Engine Shed, dirty weekend
Facilities for disabled: Yes
Special Notes: Santa special steam trains weekends, and other days, in December. Footplate experience courses
Membership details: Please apply to above address, SAE for brochure
Membership journal: *East Somerset Railway Journal* — quarterly
Marketing name: The Strawberry Line

Locomotives

Name	No	Origin	Class	Type	Built
—	1450	GWR	1400	0-4-2T	1935
Nunney Castle	5029	GWR	'Castle'	4-6-0	1934
—	6634	GWR	5600	0-6-2T	1928
—	B110	LBSCR	E1	0-6-0T	1877
—	47493	LMS	3F	0-6-0T	1927
—	68846	GNR	J52	0-6-0ST	1899
The Green Knight†	75029	BR	4MT	4-6-0	1954
Black Prince†	92203	BR	9F	2-10-0	1959
—	D3998	BR	08	0-6-0DE	1960
—*	390	ZSR	7	4-8-0	1896

*3ft 6in gauge
†On loan to Great Central Railway

Industrial locomotives

Name	No	Builder	Type	Built
Lord Fisher	1398	Barclay (1398)	0-4-0ST	1915
—	705	Barclay (2047)	0-4-0ST	1937
Lady Nan	1719	Barclay (1719)	0-4-0ST	1920
—	4101	Dubs (4101)	0-4-0CT	1901

Stock
10 ex-BR Mk 1 coaches; 25 assorted wagons, mostly LMS and SR; Rhodesian Railways sleeping car 1808. Home to the 'Riviera' main line vehicles. Frequent main line visitors

Owners
D3998 on loan from Prism Rail

Steam Centre

Elsecar at Barnsley

South Yorkshire

The Elsecar Railway runs between Elsecar Workshop site and the canal basin at Hemingfield, through a scenic conservation area alongside the Elsecar branch of the Deane & Dove Canal
Location/headquarters: Elsecar Heritage Centre, Wath Road, Elsecar, Barnsley, South Yorkshire S74 8HJ
Telephone: (01226) 740203
Fax: (01226) 350239
Main station: Elsecar
Length of line: 1-mile, 20min journey
Car park location: On site
Access by public transport: Main line Elsecar from Sheffield, Huddersfield, Leeds
Refreshment facilities: On site
Souvenir shops: On site
On site facilities: Refreshments, souvenir shop, toilets

Industrial locomotives

Name	*No*	*Builder*	*Type*	*Built*
Countess Fitzwilliam	544996	R/Hornsby(382808)	4wDM	1968
Earl Fitzwilliam	1917	Avonside (1917)	0-6-0ST	1923
Earl of Stafford	2895	YEC (2895)	0-6-0DH	1963

Stock
3 ex-BR Mk 1 coaches

Museum: Attractions include 'The Power House' science centre, Science Track, Educational Workshops, 'Elsecar People' history exhibition, Bottle Collection, Hot Metal Press, Newcomen Beam Engine, working crafts people
Facilities for disabled: There are four disabled persons' toilets at different locations on the site. All buildings are fully wheelchair accessible at ground floor level

Public opening: Daily (except 25 December-1 January) 10.00-17.00
Special events: Include Friends of Thomas the Tank Engine and Victorian Christmas Fayre — contact for details
Special notes: Entrance to site is free. Charges made for some attractions ('passport' and family tickets available). Santa specials run during December

Timetable Service

Embsay & Bolton Abbey Steam Railway

North Yorkshire

Member: AIRPS, TT
Yorkshire's 'Friendly Line' operates from Embsay station built in 1888. The railway is very family-orientated with many events for children. The enthusiast is not forgotten with one of the finest collections of ex-industrial tank engines in Britain. The railway is currently constructing a new museum and workshop complex, and the line's extension to Bolton Abbey opened in 1997. Bolton Abbey station has been built to the original Midland Railway style. An atmosphere of the rural branch line prevails, which is operated by ex-industrial locomotives
Operating Committee: Stuart Bell
Business & Marketing Manager: Stephen Walker. Tel: (01756) 794727 (ext 21). Fax: (01756) 795189
Location: Embsay Station, Embsay, Skipton, Yorkshire BD23 6AX
OS reference: SE 007533

Locomotives and multiple-units

Name	*No*	*Origin*	*Class*	*Type*	*Built*
—	D2203	BR	04	0-6-0DM	1952
—	NCB 38 (D9513)	BR	14	0-6-0DH	1964
—	LEV2	Derby	—	Railbus	1984

Industrial locomotives

Name	*No*	*Builder*	*Type*	*Built*
Annie	9	Peckett (1159)	0-4-0ST	1908
Gladiator	8	H/Clarke (1450)	0-6-0ST	1922
Slough Estates No 5	—	H/Clarke (1709)	0-6-0ST	1939
Primrose No 2	S121	Hunslet (3715)	0-6-0ST	1952
Ann	—	Sentinel (7232)	4wVB	1927
Beatrice	7	Hunslet (2705)	0-6-0ST	1945
Airedale	3	Hunslet (1440)	0-6-0ST	1923
York No 1	—	Yorkshire (2474)	0-4-0ST	1949
—	140	H/Clarke (1821)	0-6-0T	1948
Illingworth	—	H/Clarke	0-6-0ST	—
Spitfire	S112	Hunslet (2414)	0-6-0ST	1942
Wheldale	S134	Hunslet (3168)	0-6-0ST	1944
—	69	Hunslet (3785)	0-6-0ST	1953
Monkton No 1	—	Hunslet (3788)	0-6-0ST	1953
—†	22	Barclay (2320)	0-4-0ST	1952
—	68005	RSH (7169)	0-6-0ST	1945
Thomas	4	RSH (7661)	0-4-0ST	1950
H. W. Robinson	—	Fowler (4100003)	0-4-0DM	1946

Operating society/organisation: Yorkshire Dales Railway Museum Trust
Telephone: Skipton (01756) 794727. 24hr Talking Timetable (01756) 795189
Car parks: Embsay and Bolton Abbey
Access by public transport: Pennine bus from Skipton
On site facilities: Souvenir shop — specialising in children's gifts, transport and industrial archaeological titles, plus model railway supplies
Catering facilities: Buffet and bar on most trains. Buffet on Embsay station; a tea room will open at Bolton Abbey during 1998. Evening catering trains will serve meals on selected dates. Special charters can be arranged. Meals for parties can be arranged on normal service trains (subject to advance booking). Please write for further details
Length of line: 4.5 miles
Public opening: Steam trains run every Sunday throughout the year, plus Saturdays in June and September then daily from late July until the end of August (except for Mondays and Fridays). Trains run regularly between 11.00 and late afternoon
Special events: Friends of Thomas the Tank Engine at Easter, Spring and August Bank Holidays and Santa Trains from mid-November until December
Special notes: Steam rides are on 4.5-mile line to the new station and picnic area at Bolton Abbey. Old Midland Railway buildings, fine collection of industrial locomotives
Membership details: Membership Secretary at above address
Membership journal: *Dale Steam, YDR News* — 4 times/year

Name	*No*	*Builder*	*Type*	*Built*
—	MDE15	Baguley/Drewry (2136)	4wDM	1938
—	887	R/Hornsby (394009)	4wDM	1955
—	—	Wickham (7610)	2w-2PMR	1957
—	—	Lister (9993)*	4wPM	1938
—	—	Lister (10225)*	4wPM	1938
—	—	R/Hornsby (175418)*	4wDM	1936
—	—	R/Hornsby*	4wDM	—
—	—	M/Rail (8979)*	4wDM	1946
—	—	M/Rail (5213)*	4wDM	1930
—	—	R/Hornsby	4wDM	1957
Meaford	—	Barclay (440)	0-4-0DH	1958
—	36	H/Clarke (D1037)	0-6-0DM	1958

† on loan to Swindon & Cricklade Railway during 1998
*2ft gauge

Stock
18 ex-BR Mk 1 coaches (SK, CK, 2xBCK, 5xTSO, 2xRMB, 1xBSO(T), 1xRBR and 1xSLS), 4 ex-LNER coaches; 2 SR parcels vans; Freight stock and service vehicles, SR and GW brakes

Timetable Service

Foxfield Steam Railway

Staffordshire

Member: AIRPS
The railway, built in 1893 to connect a colliery to the national system, closed in 1965, has been re-opened.
Chairman: Ian A. Rutherford
Headquarters: Foxfield Steam Railway, Blythe Bridge, Stoke-on-Trent
Telephone: (01782) 396210 (weekends), (01270) 874959 (weekdays)
Fax: (01270) 874959
Main station: Blythe Bridge (Caverswall Road)
OS reference: SJ 957421
Car park: Blythe Bridge
Access by public transport: Main line railway Blythe Bridge (400yd). PMT bus service to Blythe Bridge
Refreshment facilities: Blythe Bridge
Souvenir shop: Blythe Bridge
Passenger trains: Steam-hauled trains operate from Blythe Bridge (Caverswall Road) to Dilhorne Park

Industrial locomotives

Name	*No*	*Builder*	*Type*	*Built*
Whiston	—	Hunslet (3694)	0-6-0ST	1950
Wimblebury	—	Hunslet (3839)	0-6-0ST	1956
Roker	—	RSH (7006)	0-4-0CT	1940
Meaford No 2	2	RSH	0-6-0T	1951
Millom	—	Avonside (1563)	0-4-0ST	1908
Cranford	—	Avonside (1919)	0-6-0ST	1924
Lewisham	—	Bagnall (2221)	0-6-0ST	1927
Hawarden	—	Bagnall (2623)	0-4-0ST	1940
Wolstanton No 3	—	Bagnall (3150)	0-6-0DM	1960
Bagnall	—	Bagnall (3207)	0-4-0DH	1961
—	—	B/Peacock (1827)	0-4-0ST	1879
—	—	E/Electric (788)	4wBE	1930
Spondon No 2	—	E/Electric (1130)	4wBE	1939
—	6	R/Heath	0-4-0ST	1886
Henry Cort	—	Peckett (933)	0-4-0ST	1903
Lion	—	Peckett (1351)	0-4-0ST	1914
Ironbridge No 1	—	Peckett (1803)	0-4-0ST	1933
—	11	Peckett (2081)	0-4-0ST	1947
Moss Bay	—	K/Stuart (4167)	0-4-0ST	1920
Rom River	—	K/Stuart (4421)	6wDM	1929
—	1	Barclay (1984)	0-4-0F	1930
Meaford No 4	—	Barclay (486)	0-6-0DH	1964
Helen	—	Simplex (2262)	4wDM	1924
—	820	Drewry (2157)	4wDM	1941

and return
Family ticket: Available (2 adults + 2 children or 1 adult + 4 children)
Length of line: 2.75 miles
Period of public operation: Steam trains operate Sundays and Bank Holiday Mondays only, April-September inclusive between Blythe Bridge and Dilhorne Park.
Special events: Please contact for details. Santa Specials, weekends in December (advanced booking essential)
Facilities for disabled: Access to majority of facilities is on the level. For special requirements, prior notice is desirable
Membership journal: *Foxfield News* — quarterly

Name	*No*	*Builder*	*Type*	*Built*
Amoco	—	R/Hornsby (395305)	0-4-0DM	1956
Gas-oil	—	R/Hornsby (408496)	0-4-0DM	1957
Hercules	—	Ruston (242915)	4wDM	1946
—	—	R/Hornsby	0-4-0DE	—
Megan	—	Thomas Hill (103C)	0-4-0DH	1957
Marston	3	H/Leslie (3581)	0-6-0ST	1924
Thorntwaite & Everard				

Stock
5 coaches; 4 scenery vans (some converted for other uses); 29 assorted wagons, 16ton mineral wagons; 1 rail-mounted self-propelled diesel-electric crane

Timetable Service

Gartell Light Railway

Somerset

The line is fully signalled using a variety of upper and lower quadrant, colour light and shunting signals controlled by two full-size signal boxes. From Pinesway Junction to Park Lane the line runs along a half-mile section of the former Somerset & Dorset Railway trackbed. Work has started on an extension northwards towards Templecombe along the S&D trackbed, which will involve a flyover and the re-opening of the level crossing north of Pinesway junction. The line's first steam locomotive, a locally-built 0-4-2T, specially designed to cope with the steep gradients and sharp curves of the Common Lane-Pinesway Junction section of the line, is expected to enter service during the 1998 season
Location/headquarters: Gartell Light Railway, Common Lane, Yenston, Nr Templecombe, Somerset BA8 0NB
Telephone: (01963) 370752
General Manager: John Gartell
Main station: Common Lane
Other stations: Pinesway Junction, Park Lane (southern terminus)
Car park: Common Lane
OS reference: ST 718218
Access by public transport: 1.5 miles south-east of Templecombe railway station
Refreshment facilities: Trackside refreshment room adjacent to the station at Common Lane serving range of hot and cold snacks and drinks. Lakeside picnic area at Pinesway Junction
Visitor Centre: Common Lane
Souvenir shop: Common Lane
Museum: Common Lane — Templecombe Railway Museum (collection of artefacts, photographs, documents, models, etc recording the history of Templecombe station)
Depot: Common Lane (not open to public)
Facilities for disabled: Enclosed passenger coach with accommodation for one wheelchair. Wheelchair access to refreshment room via ramp
Period of public operation: 4, 25 May; 28 June; 26 July; 30 August; 27 September. 10.30-16.30
Special events: Traction engine display — 28 June; Santa Specials — 13, 20 December

Industrial locomotives
2ft gauge:

Name	*No*	*Builder*	*Type*	*Built*
Amanda	1	Lister (55070)	4wDH	1966
Andrew	2	R/Hornsby	4wDH	1964/5
Alan	3	Lister (42494)	4wDM	1956
Alistair	4	R/Hornsby (201790)	4wDM	1950
Alison	5	A/Kief (10)	4wDH	1983

Rolling stock — coaches: 3 fully enclosed bogie coaches, 3 covered open-sided bogie coaches (further fully enclosed coaches under construction)

Rolling stock — wagons: goods guards van, tool van, open wagon, bogie hopper, bogie open 2 bogie flats (bogie PW gang/tool van under construction)

Timetable Service

Gloucestershire Warwickshire Railway

Glos

Member: AIRPS
Part of an ambitious project to link Cheltenham racecourse with Stratford racecourse, much has been done to recreate the railway and buildings that made up this cross-country route. The railway is home to many owners of private locomotives and rolling stock, so from time to time the items on display may vary
Location: Toddington station, Toddington
OS reference: SO 050322
Operating society/organisation: Gloucestershire Warwickshire Steam Railway plc, The Station, Toddington, Cheltenham, Glos GL54 5DT
Telephone: Toddington (01242) 621405
Main station: Toddington
Other public stations: Winchcombe
Access by public transport: Public transport is very limited with occasional buses from Cheltenham, Stratford-on-Avon and Evesham only. Local bus service Castleways will answer timetable queries on (01242) 602949
Car park: On site
On site facilities: Sales, catering, narrow gauge rides, toilets
Length of line: 6.5 miles
Public opening: On non-operating days the station is unmanned but visitors are welcome. Public services weekends, Bank Holiday Mondays, between March and October. Some summer weekdays and Sundays throughout the year
Special events: Diesel Gala — 14/15 March; Teddy Bears' Picnic — 16/17 May; Friends of Thomas the Tank Engine — 20/21 June; 15/16 August; Schools Day — 26 June; Diesel Week — 20-24 July; Steam & Vintage Gala — 17/18 October; Diesel Gala — 6-8 November; Model Railway Exhibition — 14 November; Santa & Mince Pie Specials — December
Special notes: The site is being developed as the headquarters of the railway between Cheltenham and Stratford. The GWR owns the railway land between Cheltenham

Locomotives and multiple-units

Name	*No*	*Origin*	*Class*	*Type*	*Built*
—	2807	GWR	2800	2-8-0	1905
Raveningham Hall	6960	GWR	6959	4-6-0	1944
Owsden Hall	6984	GWR	6959	4-6-0	1948
Peninsular & Oriental SNCo	35006	SR	MN	4-6-2	1941
—	76077	BR	4MT	2-6-0	1956
—	03069	BR	03	0-6-0DM	1959
—	D2182	BR	03	0-6-0DM	1952
—	D9537	BR	14	0-6-0DH	1965
—	D9539	BR	14	0-6-0DH	1965
—	D9553	BR	14	0-6-0DH	1965
—	20137	BR	20	Bo-Bo	1966
—	26043	BR	26	Bo-Bo	1959
—	D5541	BR	31	A1A-A1A	1959
—	37215	BR	37	Co-Co	1964
—	45149	BR	45	1Co-Co1	1961
Goldcrest	47105	BR	47	Co-Co	1963
—	51134	BR	116	DMBS	1958
—	51147	BR	116	DMS	1958
—	51950	BR	108	DMBS	1960
—	52062	BR	108	DMC	1960

Industrial locomotives

Name	*No*	*Builder*	*Type*	*Built*
Byfield No 2	—	Bagnall (2655)	0-6-0ST	1941
Sir Robert Peel	—	Hunslet (3776)	0-6-0ST	1952
—	19	Fowler (4240016)	0-6-0DH	1964
—	21	Fowler (4210130)	0-4-0DM	1957
—	—	H/Clarke (D615)	0-6-0DM	1938
—	—	Hibberd (2893)	4wPM	1943
John	—	Peckett (1976)	0-4-0ST	1939

Stock
3 ex-GWR coaches; 23 ex-BR coaches; 1 ex-LMS coach; plus numerous wagons

Owners
2807 the Cotswold Steam Preservation Ltd
35006, 76077 the P & O Locomotive Society
26043 the Cotswold Mainline Diesel Group
D9537, D9539 and D9553 the Cotswold Diesel Preservation Group
37215 the Growler Group/Brush Type 4 Fund & GWR Diesel Dept
51134 and 51147 the Llanelli Railway Society

North Gloucestershire Railway
Industrial narrow gauge locomotives (2ft gauge)

Name	*No*	*Builder*	*Type*	*Built*
Isibutu	5	Bagnall (2820)	4-4-0T	1946
George B	—	Hunslet (680)	0-4-0ST	1898
Chaka	—	Hunslet (2075)	0-4-2T	1940
Justine	—	Jung (939)	0-4-0WT	1906
Brigadelok	—	Henschel (15968)	0-8-0T	1918
—	2	Lister (34523)	4wDM	1949
—	3	M/Rail (4565)	4wPM	1928
Spitfire	—	M/Rail (7053)	4wPM	1937

and Broadway and operates over 6.5 miles from Toddington to Gotherington with an intermediate station at Winchcombe.

Guest locomotives will be operating during the year.

Family tickets available. Railway postal service

Membership details: From above address

Membership journal: *The Cornishman* — quarterly

Name	No	Builder	Type	Built
—	1	R/Hornsby (166010)	4wDM	1932
—	L5	R/Hornsby (181820)	4wDM	1936
—	—	R/Hornsby (354028)	4wDM	1953

Stock

3 coaches; 11 wagons

Timetable Service

Great Central Railway

Leicestershire

Member: AIRPS, TT

The original Great Central Railway's extension to London in 1899 was the last main line to be built in this country, most of which was closed in the 1960s. Steam-hauled services operate through attractive rolling Leicestershire countryside, crossing the picturesque Swithland reservoir. The railway's aim is to re-create the experience of British main line railway operation in the days of steam. The images of a main line are backed up by a double track line with long trains hauled by large locomotives

Headquarters: Great Central Railway plc, Loughborough Central Station, Great Central Road, Loughborough, Leicestershire LE11 1RW

Telephone: Loughborough (01509) 230726

Main stations: Loughborough Central, Leicester North

Other public stations: Quorn & Woodhouse, Rothley

OS reference: SK 543194

Car park: Quorn, Rothley

Access by public transport: Loughborough main line station (0.75-mile). Trent, South Notts, and Midland Fox bus services to Loughborough bus station (0.75-mile). Some Midland Fox services pass bottom Great Central Road, 300yd. New 'Kinchbus' service to/from main line station every half-hour Monday-Saturday

Refreshment facilities: Licensed buffet car and light refreshments on all trains and at all stations. Saturday and Sunday lunches on 13.15 train; evening dining trains

Locomotives and multiple-units

Name	No	Origin	Class	Type	Built
—	5224	GWR	5205	2-8-0T	1924
Witherslack Hall	6990	GWR	'Hall'	4-6-0	1948
—	45231	LMS	5MT	4-6-0	1936
—	5305	LMS	5MT	4-6-0	1936
—	47406	LMS	3F	0-6-0T	1926
—	48305	LMS	8F	2-8-0	1943
—	1264	LNER	B1	4-6-0	1947
—	69523	LNER	N2	0-6-2T	1921
—	63601	GCR	8K	2-8-0	1919
Boscastle	34039	SR	WC	4-6-2	1946
Sir Lamiel	30777	SR	N15	4-6-0	1925
Brocklebank Line	35025	SR	MN	4-6-2	1948
The Green Knight	75029	BR	4MT	4-6-0	1954
—	92212	BR	9F	2-10-0	1959
—	13180	BR	08	0-6-0DE	1955
—	D3101	BR	08	0-6-0DE	1955
—	08788	BR	08	0-6-0DE	1960
—	D4067	BR	10	0-6-0DE	1961
—	D8098	BR	20	Bo-Bo	1961
—	31418	BR	31	A1A-A1A	1959
Great Gable	D4	BR	44	1Co-Co1	1959
—	D1705	BR	47	Co-Co	1965
—	51616	BR	127	DMBS	1959
—	51622	BR	127	DMBS	1959
—	59276	BR	120	TS	1958

Industrial locomotives

Name	No	Builder	Type	Built
Arthur Wright	D4279	Fowler (4210079)	0-4-0DE	1952
—	28	A/Barclay (400)	0-4-0DM	1956

Owners

69523 the Gresley Society
5305 the 5305 Locomotive Association
6990 the Witherslack Hall Locomotive Society
61264 the Thompson B1 Locomotive Society
92212 the 92212 Holdings Ltd
63601 on loan from the National Railway Museum
30777 on loan from the National Railway Museum (under custody of the 5305 Locomotive Association)
75029 on loan from the East Somerset Railway
D8098, 31418 and D1705 the Type 1 Locomotive Association

Above: **BR-liveried No 6990 *Witherslack Hall* rounds the curve at Kinchley on the Great Central Railway. This section has been restored to the original double track configuration.** ***John East***

Below: Bellerophon **leaves Tenterden on the Kent & East Sussex Railway. The locomotive was on loan from the Vintage Carriages Trust.** ***Alan P. Barnes***

on most Saturday nights and Wednesday nights May-September; please contact railway for dates and reservations (advance booking recommended). Picnic areas at Quorn and Rothley stations. Most trains carry griddle car serving all-day Great Central breakfast and other hot food. Private charter trains available on request
Souvenir shop: Loughborough
Museum: Loughborough
Depot: Loughborough
Length of line: 8 miles
Passenger trains: Loughborough-Leicester North
Period of public operation: Weekends throughout the year and Bank Holiday Mondays. Daily Easter week, and 18 May -25 September.

Guided tours available by prior arrangement. School/party visits a speciality — Tel: 01509 230726 for details
Special events: Diesel Gala — 2-5 April; Quorn & Woodhouse Station Classic Gala — 2-4 May; Diesel Running Day — 30 May, 15 August; Quorn Swapmeet/Tot Fair at Loughborough — 7 June; Midsummer Gala — 20/21 June; *Steam Railway* Gala — 8/9 August; Toy & Model Fair—16 August; AGM & Shareholders' Day — 22 August; Friends of Thomas the Tank — 22 August to 1 September and 17/18 October; Quorn Swapmeet — 6 September; Autumn Gala — 10/11 October; Bonfire Night at Quorn— 5 November; Santa Specials — start 28 November; Boxing Day Trains — 26 December; Christmas Gala & Mince Pie Specials — 27-31 December. Themed dining trains run — 15 April, 1 May, 5, 14 June, 14 July, 21 August, 18 September (please contact for details)
Facilities for disabled: Special carriage for wheelchair/disabled persons (advance notice required). Wheelchair access good at Quorn and Rothley, can be arranged at Loughborough with advance notification. Boarding ramps at all stations
Membership & share details: Share enquiries: Company Secretary, Great Central Railway plc
Membership: Membership Secretary, Main Line Steam Trust Ltd. Both c/o above address

Steam Centre | Great Whipsnade Railway | Bedfordshire

Location: Whipsnade Wild Animal Park, Dunstable, Bedfordshire LU6 2LF
Telephone: (01582) 872171 (extension 2270)
Fax: (01582) 872649
General Manager: Ian Gordon
Main station: Whipsnade Central
On site facilities: Car park (100yd), Souvenir shop, refreshments (30yds)
Period of public operation: January — no trains; February — half term; March — weekends only; April to July — daily (Weekdays diesels only/steam at weekends); August daily steam trains; September/October — daily (Weekdays diesels only/steam at weekends); November — no trains; December — steam, weekends & school holidays
Special events: Steam Weekend — 2-4 May (two engines in steam, traction engines, steam lorries, vintage cars and fire engines)
Facilities for disabled: Carriage designed for wheelchairs

Locomotives

Name	*No*	*Builder*	*Type*	*Built*
Chevalier	1	M/Wardle (1877)	0-6-2T	1915
Excelsior	2	K/Stuart (1049)	0-4-2T	1908
Superior	4	K/Stuart (4034)	0-6-2T	1920
Victor	—	Fowler (4160004)	0-6-0DM	1951
Hector	—	Fowler (4160005)	0-6-0DM	1951
Mr Bill	10	R/Hornsby (221625)	0-4-0DM	1944

Rolling stock: 10 carriages, 9 wagons

Steam Centre | Hollycombe Steam Collection | West Sussex

Member: TT
An extensive collection of working steam railways, traction engines including fairground rides, Bioscope, organs, the oldest Burrell Showman's engine *Emperor*, sawmill and engine from the paddle steamer *Caledonia*, set in woodlands and gardens
Location: Iron Hill, Hollycombe, near Liphook, Hants
OS reference: SU 852295
Operating society/organisation: Hollycombe Steam & Woodland Garden Society, Iron Hill, Midhurst Road, Liphook, Hants GU30 7LP
Telephone: Liphook (01428) 724900 (24hr answerphone)
Car park: On site
Access by public transport: Liphook main line station (1.5 miles)
On site facilities: Shop and refreshments, toilets, car park, *dogs allowed in car park only*
Length of lines: Standard gauge – quarter mile
2ft gauge 'Quarry Railway' – 1.5 miles
7.25in gauge – quarter mile

Public opening: Easter then Sundays and bank holidays only until 11 October. Daily 26-31 July; 16-31 August only

Industrial locomotives

Name	No	Builder	Type	Built
Caledonia	70	Barclay (1995)	0-4-0WT	1931*
Jerry M	38	Hunslet (638)	0-4-0ST	1895*
Commander B	50	H/Leslie (2450)	0-4-0ST	1899
—	16	R/Hornsby	4wDM	1941*

*2ft gauge

Steam Centre

Irchester Narrow Gauge Railway Museum

Northants

Member: AIRPS

The aims of the controlling trust are to acquire and preserve narrow gauge railway locomotives, rolling stock and exhibits associated with Northamptonshire and the East Midlands, to display the collection for the benefit of the public and to restore exhibits to working order so they may be demonstrated in a proper manner

Location: Within Irchester Country Park, 2 miles south of Wellingborough

Operating society/organisation: The Irchester Narrow Gauge Railway Trust, 71 Bedford Road, Cranfield, Bedford MK43 0EX

On site facilities: Shop, museum, demonstration line, picnic area

Access by public transport: Main line Wellingborough (Midland Road) station, buses to Irchester and Little Irchester

Industrial locomotives

Name	No	Builder	Type	Built
—	85*	Peckett (1870	0-6-0ST	1934
—	86*	Peckett (1871)	0-6-0ST	1934
—	87*	Peckett (2029)	0-6-0ST	1942
Cambrai	—*	Corpet (493)	0-6-0T	1888
—	ND3645*	R/Hornsby (211679)	4wDM	1941
—	—†	R/Hornsby (281290)	0-6-0DM	1949
—	ED10*	R/Hornsby (411322	4wDM	1958
—	—†	M/Rail (1363)	4wPM	1918
The Rock	—*	Hunslet (2419)	0-4-0DM	1941

* Metre gauge
† 3ft Gauge

Car Parks: Main park car parks

Toilets: Main park complex

Public opening: Every Sunday (summer 10.00-17.30, winter 10.00-16.00), at other times by arrangement. Steam and demonstration weekends are held on last full weekend of the month — March-October

Facilities for disabled: Museum and site on level, staff available if required

Membership details: Membership Secretary, 1 Wilby Street, Northampton NN1 5JX

Museum

Ironbridge Gorge Museum

Shropshire

The railway items form only a small part of the displays on two of the museum's main sites: Blists Hill and Coalbrookdale. The Blists Hill site offers an opportunity to see a number of industrial and other activities being operated in meticulously reconstructed period buildings. A working foundry and ironworks are just two of the exciting exhibits. The Ironbridge Gorge was designated a World Heritage Site in 1987

Location: Ironbridge, Shropshire

OS reference: SJ 694033

Operating society/organisation: Ironbridge Gorge Museum Trust, Ironbridge, Telford, Shropshire TF8 7AW

Telephone: Telford (01952) 433522

Car park: At the sites

Access by public transport: Various private bus companies, including Midland Red, Williamson's Shearings, Elcocks, Boultons. Please telephone (01952) 433522 for further details

Catering facilities: Licensed Victorian pub, sweet shop and tea rooms at the Blists Hill site, serving drinks and mainly cold snacks. Tea, coffee and light refreshments at the Museum of Iron, Coalbrookdale and Coalport China Museum

Industrial locomotives

Name	No	Builder	Type	Built
—	—	Sentinel/Coalbrookdale (6185)	0-4-0VBT	1925
—	—	Sentinel/M/Wardle (6155)	0-4-0VBT	1925
—	5	Coalbrookdale	0-4-0ST	1865

All locomotives are at the Museum of Iron & Iron Mighty, Coalbrookdale

Public opening: Main sites, including Museum of Iron and on Blists Hill, daily (except Christmas Eve and Christmas Day) 10.00-17.00, 10.00-18.00 during British Summer Time

Special notes: Tickets for all the sites or just for single sites available.

A full size working replica of Richard Trevithick's 1802 steam locomotive built by the Coalbrookdale Company will be operating at the Ironbridge Power Station on certain weekends throughout the year. For further details please telephone (01952) 432141

Timetable Service

Isle of Wight Steam Railway

Isle of Wight

Member: AIRPS, TT

Separated from the mainland by the Solent, the line's isolation encouraged the maintenance and retention of Victorian locomotives and coaching stock which still operate the line today. Its rural charm enhances its attraction for the island's holidaymakers during the summer season

Traffic manager: Terry Hastings
Headquarters: Isle of Wight Steam Railway, Haven Street station, Ryde, Isle of Wight PO33 4DS
Telephone: Station: Isle of Wight (01983) 882204
Main station: Haven Street
OS reference: SZ 556898
Other public stations: Wootton, Ashey and Smallbrook Junction
Car park: Haven Street
Access by public transport: 'Island Line' service from Ryde or Shanklin to Smallbrook Jct
Refreshment facilities: Light refreshments available
Souvenir shop: Haven Street
Museum: Small exhibits museum at Haven Street
Depot: Haven Street
Length of line: 5 miles
Passenger trains: Wootton-Smallbrook Jct
Period of public operation: 26, 29 March; April — Thursdays & Sundays plus daily 9-19 inc; May: —Sundays, Wednesdays, Thursdays until 24th then daily; June, July and August — daily; September – daily until 27th; October — Thursdays and Sundays
Special events: Steam Extravaganza — 28-31 August. Santa Specials, in December until Xmas (please write for details)
Facilities for disabled: Limited facilities, but can be catered for individually, or in groups (by prior arrangement), toilets available
Membership details: Membership Secretary at above address
Membership journal: *Wight Report* — quarterly

Locomotives

Name	*No*	*Origin*	*Class*	*Type*	*Built*
Freshwater	W8 (32646)	LBSCR	A1X	0-6-0T	1876
Newport	W11 (32640)	LBSCR	A1X	0-6-0T	1878
Calbourne	W24	LSWR	O2	0-4-4T	1891
—	D2554	BR	05	0-6-0DM	1956
—	D2059	BR	03	0-6-0DM	1959

Industrial locomotives

Name	*No*	*Builder*	*Type*	*Built*
Invincible	37	H/Leslie (3135)	0-4-0ST	1915
Ajax	38	Barclay (1605)	0-6-0T	1918
Royal Engineer	198	Hunslet (3798)	0-6-0ST	1953

Locomotive notes: *Ajax* is not on public display.

Owners
Royal Engineer on loan from Royal Corps of Transport Museum Trust

Stock
1 IWR coach; 4 LBSCR coaches; 3 SECR coaches; 2 LCDR coaches; 5 IWR coaches (bodies only); 5 LCDR coaches (bodies only); 1 LBSCR coach (body only); 1 crane; 1 ex-BR ballast tamper; 1 Wickham trolley; 30 wagons; 6 parcels vans; 2 ex-LT hoppers; 1 ex-BR Lowmac; 1 LSWR Road van; 1 cattle van (on loan from the National Railway Museum)

Timetable Service

Keighley & Worth Valley Railway

West Yorkshire

1968 saw the re-opening of the Worth Valley branch following the first sale of a standard gauge railway to a preservation society. Qualified volunteers have now managed and operated the KWVR every weekend, summer and winter for three decades. In September, re-enactments of the early days of the society with original locomotives and rolling stock will mark this significant event in Britain's railway preservation history. The KWVR is justifiably proud of having led the British independent railway movement in establishing the now ubiquitous late 1950s/early 1960s house style. Many have copied, but few succeed so well as the Worth Valley with totems, A5 handbills, period

posters, red uniform ties, hanging baskets, gas lights and coal fires. One of the most community-orientated independent railways, being the first to create a 'Resident's Railcard' discount fares scheme since copied by Regional Railways NE!
Chairman, Joint Management Committee: Brian A. Baker
Headquarters: Haworth Station, Keighley, West Yorkshire, BD22 8NJ
Telephone: Haworth (01535) 647777 24hr recorded timetable and information service; Haworth (01535) 645214 (other calls)
Main stations: Keighley, Ingrow West, Haworth, Oxenhope
Other public stations: Damems, Oakworth
OS reference: SE 034371
Car parks: Free at Keighley, Ingrow West, Oakworth, Oxenhope. Limited parking at Haworth (pay). Coaches at Ingrow West and Oxenhope only
Access by public transport: Fast and frequent electric Metro trains from Leeds, Bradford and Skipton to Keighley (joint station with KWVR) 2 adults and up to 3 half fares with a Metro Family Day Rover and the children travel free on KWVR trains. Regional Railways through services from Carlisle, Morecambe, Lancaster to Keighley station. Through bookings to 'Oxenhope KWVR' are available from any travel centre throughout Britain and allow one day's unlimited travel on KWVR. Regional Railways from Blackpool, Preston, Blackburn, Accrington, Burnley, Manchester to Hebden Bridge for connection via bus service 500 to Oxenhope (tel 01535 603284 for days of operation and timings). A large number of bus services, including National Express operate to Keighley
Refreshment facilities: Buffet Restaurant at Oxenhope. Buffet bar at Keighley (open when train service in operation). The only CAMRA-approved 'Real Ale' Bar operates on most steam trains (March-October). Wine and Dine by prior booking only — the 'White Rose Pullman' and 'West Riding Ltd'
Picnic areas: Keighley Station, Haworth Locomotive Depot, Oxenhope Station, Oxenhope picnic area
Viewing areas: Keighley (Garsdale) Turntable, Haworth Locomotive Depot
Souvenir shops: Keighley, Haworth and Oxenhope stations; Ingrow Vintage Carriage Museum
Museums: KWVR 'reserve

Locomotives and multiple-units

Name	*No*	*Origin*	*Class*	*Type*	*Built*
—	41241	LMS	2MT	2-6-2T	1949
—	43924	MR	4F	0-6-0	1920
—	45212	LMS	5MT	4-6-0	1935
Bahamas	45596	LMS	'Jubilee'	4-6-0	1935
—	48431	LMS	8F	2-8-0	1944
—	47279	LMS	3F	0-6-0T	1925
—	1054	LNWR	—	0-6-2T	1888
City of Wells	34092	SR	WC	4-6-2	1949
—	80002	BR	4MT	2-6-4T	1952
—	75078	BR	4MT	4-6-0	1956
—	78022	BR	2MT	2-6-0	1953
—	30072	SR	USA	0-6-0T	1943
—	5775	GWR	5700	0-6-0PT	1929
—	52044	L&Y	2F	0-6-0	1887
—	19*	L&Y	Pug	0-4-0ST	1910
—	51218	L&Y	Pug	0-4-0ST	1901
—	752	L&Y	—	0-6-0ST	1881
—	85	TVR	02	0-6-2T	1899
—	5820	USA TC	S160	2-8-0	1945
—	90733	MoS	WD	2-8-0	1945
—	68077	LNER	J94	0-6-0ST	1947
—	D226	BR	—	0-6-0DE	1956
—	D2511	BR	—	0-6-0DM	1961
—	D3336	BR	08	0-6-0DE	1954
—	D5209	BR	25/1	Bo-Bo	1963
—	D8031	BR	20	Bo-Bo	1960
—	50928	BR	108	DMBS	1959
—	51565	BR	108	DMC	1959
—	79962	W&M	—	Railbus	1958
—	79964	W&M	—	Railbus	1958

Industrial locomotives

Name	*No*	*Builder*	*Type*	*Built*
Hamburg	31	H/Clarke (697)	0-6-0T	1903
Nunlow	—	H/Clarke (1704)	0-6-0T	1938
Brussels	118	H/Clarke (1782)	0-6-0ST	1945
Southwick	—	RSH (7069)	0-4-0CT	1942
Fred	—	RSH (7289)	0-6-0ST	1945
Tiny	—	Barclay (2258)	0-4-0ST	1949
Merlin	231	H/Clarke (D761)	0-6-0DM	1951
—	1999*	Peckett (1999)	0-4-0	1941
Austins No1	—	Peckett (5003)	0-4-0DM	1961
—	MDHB No 32	Hunslet (2699)	0-6-0DM	1944

*Away on loan

Stock
30 coaches including examples of pre-Grouping types; BR Mk 1 stock including the oldest vehicle in existence, part of the prototype batch; a Pullman car, NER and L&Y observation cars

Owners
19, 752 and 51218 the L&YRPS Trust
75078 and 78022 the Standard 4 Preservation Society
Bahamas, Nunlow, Tiny the Bahamas Locomotive Society
1054 the National Trust
52044 the Bowers 957 Trust
34092 the *City of Wells* Syndicate

collection' at Oxenhope, Vintage Carriage Trust's carriage and locomotive museum at Ingrow Railway Centre. Both open when KWVR train services are in operation
Depots: Carriage and wagon — Oxenhope; Motive power/loco works — Haworth, 'Bahamas Locomotive Society' workshops at Ingrow Railway Centre
Length of line: 4.75 miles
Passenger trains: Early morning local shoppers' services worked by diesel railbus/diesel multiple-unit, otherwise all steam-hauled

Frequent bus service between Haworth station and Haworth village top on Sundays (May-September) and Bank Holidays, 11.15-17.15
Period of public operation: Steam-hauled passenger services every weekend and Bank Holiday throughout the year (in December diesel-hauled). Daily from mid-June to early September
Special events: Vintage Trains — 19, 26 April, 10, 17 May; Enthusiasts' Weekend — 2/3 May; Friends of Thomas the Tank Engine — 6/7 June; 30th Anniversary Weekend — 19/20 September; Diesel Day — 1 August; Heritage Diesel Service — 19-23 October; Santa Specials — 28/29 November, 5/6, 12/13, 19/20 December
Facilities for disabled: Wheelchairs accommodated in guard's compartments on trains. Please advise before visit to the Advanced Bookings Officer, c/o Haworth station
Special notes: Accompanied children under 5 years of age free. Children 5-15 and senior citizens at 50% discount. Family ticket available (2 adults + 3 children/senior citizen)
Membership details: Membership Secretary c/o above address
Membership journal: *Push & Pull* — quarterly
Marketing name: Worth Valley

Timetable Service

Kent & East Sussex Railway

Kent

Member: AIRPS, TT
The Kent & East Sussex Railway owes much of its charm to its origin as the world's first light railway. The tightly-curved line with steep gradients is typical of those country railways that were developed on shoestring budgets to bring the 'iron horse' to sparsely populated areas. Services operate over seven miles of line from the picturesque town of Tenterden to Northiam and the company has plans to extend to Bodiam in the future.

Pride of the line's coach fleet is the magnificently restored train of Victorian carriages built between 1860 and 1901
Company Secretary: Cathy Roberts
Headquarters: Tenterden Railway Co Ltd, Tenterden Town Station, Tenterden, Kent TN30 6HE
Telephone: Tenterden (01580) 762943 (24 hour talking timetable); Tenterden (01580) 765155 (office)
Main station: Tenterden Town
Other public stations: Rolvenden, Wittersham Road, Northiam
Car parks: Tenterden, Northiam
OS reference: Tenterden TQ 882336, Northiam TQ 834266
Access by public transport: Maidstone & District bus service No 400 from Ashford (Kent) main line station
Refreshment facilities: Tenterden

Locomotives and multiple-units

Name	*No*	*Origin*	*Class*	*Type*	*Built*
Bodiam	3	LBSCR	A1X	0-6-0T	1872
Sutton	32650	LBSCR	A1X	0-6-0T	1876
Knowle	2678	LBSCR	A1X	0-6-0T	1880†
—	1556	SECR	P	0-6-0T	1909
Wainwright	DS238	SR	USA	0-6-0T	1943*
Maunsell	65	SR	USA	0-6-0T	1943*
—	1638	GWR	1600	0-6-0PT	1951*
—	20	GWR	AEC	diesel railcar	1940
—	376	NSB	21c	2-6-0	1919*
—	D2023	BR	03	0-6-0DM	1958◊
—	D2024	BR	03	0-6-0DM	1958
—	11223	BR	04	0-6-0DM	1957
—	08108	BR	08	0-6-0DE	1955◊
—	D9504	BR	14	0-6-0DH	1964
—	D9525	BR	14	0-6-0DH	1965◊
Ashford	D6570	BR	33	Bo-Bo	1961
—	51571	BR	108	DMC	1959*
—	53971	BR	108	DMBS	1959*

Industrial locomotives

Name	*No*	*Builder*	*Type*	*Built*
Marcia	12	Peckett (1631)	0-4-0T	1923
Charwelton	14	M/Wardle (1955)	0-6-0ST	1917*
Holman F. Stephens	23	Hunslet (3791)	0-6-0ST	1952*
Rolvenden	24	Hunslet (3800)	0-6-0ST	1953*
Northiam	25	Hunslet (3797)	0-6-0ST	1953
—	40	BTH	Bo-Bo	1932
—	42	Hunslet (4208)	0-6-0DM	1948
Titan	—	R/Hornsby (423661)	0-4-0DM	1958*

*in passenger traffic
†due to enter traffic during 1998
◊in use for shunting/engineering trains

Town and Northiam. Also on many trains. Lunch and afternoon teas on many trains (advanced booking essential). Picnic areas at Tenterden, Wittersham Road and Northiam
Souvenir shop: Tenterden Town Station
Museum: Colonel Stephens' Railway Museum
Depot: Rolvenden
Length of line: 7 miles
Passenger trains: Tenterden-Northiam. Trains run: Sundays — March; Weekends, Bank Holidays and School Holidays — April to October; Tuesdays, Wednesdays & Thursdays — June & September; Daily — July & August; Santa Specials at weekends in December
Special events: Easter Steam Up & Family Fun Weekend — 10-13 April; Friends of Thomas the Tank — 2-4 May, 19/20 September; Bank Holiday Steam Up — 24/25 May; Father's Day Lunch & Tea — 14 June; Historic Transport Weekend — 20/21 June; Light Railway Gala & Steam Up — 25/26 July; Bank Holiday Steam Up — 30/31 August; Delivering the Goods Weekend — 24/25 October; Santa Special Steam Trains — 29 November, 5/6, 12/13, 18-24 December
Facilities for disabled: A special coach for disabled people, 'Petros', is conveyed in many trains (telephone for confirmation of availability), reserved parking at Northiam.
Toilets with disabled access at Tenterden and Northiam, and in 'Petros'
Special notes: Dining car service operates on most Saturday evenings April to October and selected Wednesdays in the summer. Roast lunch served most Sundays. Advance booking is essential for these trains. Santa Special services operate on each Saturday and Sunday in December. Advanced booking recommended
Membership details: New Members Secretary, c/o above address
Membership journal: *The Tenterden Terrier* — 3 times/year

Passenger stock in service
SECR family saloon; LNWR 6-wheel director's saloon; SECR 4-wheel full third; SR Maunsell CK; GER 6-wheel composite; District Railway 4-wheel full first; SR Maunsell non-descript brake-open; BR Mk 1 RU and 5 other BR Mk 1 coaches; Metro-Cammell Pullman Parlour Car

Stock
2 ex-SECR 'Birdcage' coaches; 2 ex-LSWR coaches; 1 GER observation car; 2 Pullman cars; 5 ex-SR Maunsell coaches; 3 steam cranes; large interesting collection of freight vehicles, totalling 51 vehicles

Kew Bridge Steam Museum

Steam Centre — London

The museum is housed in a magnificent 19th century Pumping Station and centres around the station's five world famous Cornish Beam Engines, two of which can be seen in steam every weekend. Originally used to pump West London's water supply for more than a century, one of them, the 'Grand Junction 90,' is the world's largest working beam engine. In surrounding buildings other large engines also work at weekends, demonstrate more modern steam and diesel pumping machinery.

A new gallery, opened in September 1997, reveals the fascinating history of London's water supply from Roman toilet spoons to the massive 'high-tec' London ring main.

Many Victorian waterworks had their own railway. At Kew Bridge this is demonstrated by a short line, operated by the Hampshire Narrow Gauge Railway Society. 1998 will see the return to steam of *Cloister* for the first time in 22 years
Location: 100yd from the north side of Kew Bridge, next to the tall Victorian tower
Operating group: Kew Bridge Engines Trust, Green Dragon Lane, Brentford, Middx TW8 0EN
Telephone: (0181) 568 4757 (information line)
Internet address: http://www.cre.canon.co.uk/~david e/kbsm
Car park: Free on site
Access by public transport: *Rail*:SouthWest Trains, Kew Bridge (from Waterloo via Clapham Junction); *Bus:* Nos 65, 237, 267, 391; *Tube:* Gunnersbury (District Line, then 237 or 267 bus), Kew Gardens (District Line, then 391 bus)
Length of line/gauge: About 100yd, 2ft gauge
Public opening: Museum: Daily 11.00-17.00. Railway: see below
On site facilities: Bookshop/toilets/car park. Refreshments available at weekends only
Facilities for disabled: Access to most of museum, including lower floor. Access via ramps and lift. Large print guide available and guide dogs welcome
Special note: Groups of 10 or more can be given guided tours and a 10% discount on admission charges. Special steaming can be arranged and touch tours are available for partially sighted groups. All groups must be pre-booked
Museum contact: Kew Bridge Engine Trust, c/o above address
Railway contact: HNGRS, 44 St Thomas' Avenue, Hayling Island, Hants PO11 0EX

Industrial locomotives
2ft gauge:

Name	*No*	*Builder*	*Type*	*Built*
Cloister	—	Hunslet (542)	0-4-0ST	1891
Wendy	1	Bagnall (2091)	0-4-0ST	1919
Alister	2	Lister (44052)	4wDM	1958

Other attractions: Museum displays a selection of stationary steam engines and associated water supply displays
Special events: The railway is scheduled to operate on: 28/29 March; 11-13, 25/26 April; 2-4, 23-25 May; 13/14, 25/26 June; 11/12, 25/26 July; 8/9, 29-31 August; 26/27 September; 3/4, 24/25 October; 7/8, 21/22 November

Museum

Kidderminster Railway Museum

Worcestershire

Established in an 1878 GWR warehouse, the museum houses an enormous collection of railway relics, photographs and documents, with a number of 'hands-on' exhibits.
Contact address: Station Drive, Comberton Hill, Kidderminster, Worcestershire DY10 1QX
General Manager: David Postle
Telephone: Kidderminster (01562) 825316
OS reference: SO 837763
Location: Adjacent to SVR station
Car park: SVR car park
Access by public transport: Kidderminster main line station, Midland Red bus service X92 to Kidderminster
Facilities for disabled: Ramp access for wheelchairs to ground level
Special events: Practical signalling courses using Museum and SVR resources
On site facilities: Souvenirs, refreshments
Public opening: Open on SVR operating days

Timetable Service

Kirklees Light Railway

West Yorkshire

Member: AIRPS
Location/headquarters: Clayton West, A636 Wakefield-Denby Dale road
Operating Society/organisation: Kirklees Light Railway, Park Mill Way, Clayton West, Nr Huddersfield HP8 9XJ
Telephone: (01484) 865727
Main station: Clayton West
Other station: Cuckoos Nest, Skelmanthorpe
Length of line: 2 miles, 15in gauge (extension proposed for 1998 opening)
Car park: Clayton West — free
Access by public transport: Bus No 235 from Huddersfield & Barnsley; 484 from Wakefield. Rail to Huddersfield, Wakefield or Denby Dale stations
Refreshment facilities: Clayton West
Souvenir shop: Clayton West
On site facilities: Toilets, swings, half-scale roundabouts, lake. HQ of Barnsley Society of Model Engineers
Facilities for disabled: Limited
Period of public operation: Winter— weekends & most school holidays. Summer — daily from Spring Bank Holiday to end August
Special events: Not advised

Locomotives

Name	*No*	*Builder*	*Type*	*Built*
Fox	—	Taylor	2-6-2T	1987
Badger	—	Taylor	0-6-4T	1991
Toby the Tram Engine	7	Taylor	0-4-0	1995
Jay	—	Taylor	4wD	1992

Rolling stock
2 rakes of four heated carriages, 4-wheel tool van, 4-wheel ballast/stone wagon, heavy bogie flat car for rail carrying

Timetable Service

Lakeside & Haverthwaite Railway

Cumbria

Member: AIRPS, TT
Originally this Furness Railway branch line carried passengers and freight from Ulverston to Lakeside but now the only part remaining is the 3.5-mile section from Haverthwaite to the terminus at Lakeside where connections are made with the lakeside steamers which ply the 10-mile length of Windermere
General Manager: M. A. Maher
Headquarters: Lakeside & Haverthwaite Railway Co Ltd, Haverthwaite Station, near Ulverston, Cumbria LA12 8AL
Telephone: Newby Bridge (015395) 31594
Main station: Haverthwaite
Other public stations: Intermediate station at Newby Bridge. Terminus at Lakeside
OS reference: SD 349843
Car parks: Haverthwaite, Lakeside

Access by public transport: Lakeside steamers on Windermere call at Lakeside. CMS bus to Haverthwaite
Refreshment facilities: Haverthwaite
Souvenir shop: Haverthwaite
On site facilities: Picnic area at Haverthwaite
Depot: All rolling stock at Haverthwaite
Length of line: 3.5 miles
Passenger trains: Steam-hauled Haverthwaite-Lakeside
Period of public operation: Easter then daily from early May to end of October.
Special events: Santa Specials (advance booking essential) please contact for details
Special notes: Combined railway/lake steamer tickets available, from the station at Haverthwaite and Lakeside steamers piers at Bowness and Ambleside. Lakeside steamer is operated by Windermere Lake Cruises Ltd
Membership journal: *The Iron Horse* — quarterly

Locomotives and multiple-units

Name	*No*	*Origin*	*Class*	*Type*	*Built*
—	42073	LMS	4MT	2-6-4T	1950
—	42085	LMS	4MT	2-6-4T	1951
—	8(D2117)	BR	03	0-6-0DM	1959
—	17(AD601)	LMS	—	0-6-0DE	1945
—	D2072	BR	03	0-6-0DM	1959
—	5643	GWR	5600	0-6-2T	1925
—	20214	BR	20	Bo-Bo	1967
—	D5301	BR	26	Bo-Bo	1958
—	52029	BR	107	DMS	1960
—	52071	BRCW	110	DMBC	1961
—	52077	BRCW	110	DMBC	1961

Industrial locomotives

Name	*No*	*Builder*	*Type*	*Built*
*Caliban**	1	Peckett (1925)	0-4-0ST	1937
Rachel	9	M/Rail (2098)	4wDM	1924
Repulse	11	Hunslet (3698)	0-6-0ST	1950
Princess	14	Bagnall (2682)	0-6-0ST	1942
Askam Hall	15	Avonside (1772)	0-4-0ST	1935
Alexandra	12	Barclay (929)	0-4-0ST	1902
David	13	Barclay (2333)	0-4-0ST	1953
Cumbria	10	Hunslet (3794)	0-6-0ST	1953
—	7	Fowler (22919)	0-4-0DM	1940
Fluff	16	Hunslet/Fowler	0-4-0DM	1937
—	20	Jones crane	0-4-0DM	1952
Sir James	21	Barclay (1550)	0-6-0F	1917
—	22	Fowler (4220045)	0-4-0DM	1967

*Under restoration at Steamtown, Carnforth

Stock
10 ex-BR Mk 1 coaches; 1 ex-LNER BG; 1 ex-BR Mk 1 miniature buffet coach, Royal saloon No 5 (built GER, Stratford 1898); Small selection of freight vehicles

Steam Centre

Lappa Valley Railway

Cornwall

Location/headquarters: Benny Halt, St Newlyn East, Nr Newquay, Cornwall TR8 5HZ
Telephone: 01872 510317
General Manager: Miss Amanda Booth
Main station: Benny Halt
Other station: East Wheal Rose, Newlyn Downs Halt
Car park: Benny Halt and Newlyn Downs Halt
Access by public transport: Bus service, Newquay to Truro and return. Western National and The Cornishman coaches to St Newlyn East. Signposted, half-mile walk from bus stop to railway. July and August – bus from Newquay to railway (3 times daily)
Refreshment facilities: Cafe at East Wheal Rose serving hot and cold food, snacks, hot & cold drinks; licensed with food
Souvenir shop: East Wheal Rose and Benny Halt
On site facilities: 15in, 10.25in and 7.25in gauge railways. Canoes, paddle boats, crazy golf, trikes, electric motorbikes, children's play area, brick path maze, listed engine house, walks and a video
Depot: Benny Halt
Facilities for disabled: Yes
Public opning: Easter to end of

Locomotives

Name	*No*	*Builder*	*Type*	*Built*
Muffin	2	Berwyn	0-6-0	1967
		rebuilt Tambling		1991
Zebedee	1	S/Lamb	0-6-4T	1974
		rebuilt Tambling		1990
Lappa Lady	3	Minirail	4w-4wDH	c1960
Dougal	—	Booth	4w-4wPM	1975

(all 15in gauge)
Also one 10.25in gauge diesel

Rolling stock
15in gauge — 10 passenger coaches
10.25in gauge — 4 passenger coaches, 2 wagons
7.25in gauge — 1 Mardyke APT set

October, usually daily but ring for early and late season opening days
Special notes: Entry by one all-in price, except for motorbikes.

Family tickets and reduced afternoon saver fares are available all days. Under 3s free

Timetable Service

Launceston Steam Railway

Cornwall

Industrial locomotives

Name	*No*	*Builder*	*Type*	*Built*
Lilian	—	Hunslet (317)	0-4-0ST	1883
Velinheli	—	Hunslet (409)	0-4-0ST	1886
Covertcoat	—	Hunslet (679)	0-4-0ST	1898
Sybil	—	Bagnall (1760)	0-4-0ST	1906
Dorothea	—	Hunslet (763)	0-4-0ST	1901
—	—	M/Rail (5646)	4wDM	1933
—	—	M/Rail (9546)	4wDM	1950

Locomotive notes: The three Hunslet locomotives (317/409/679) are expected to be in use during 1997.

Stock
1 electric inspection trolley; 4 bogie carriages and 1 4-wheel carriage

The railway runs through the beautiful Kensey Valley on a track gauge of 1ft 11.5in, following the trackbed of the old North Cornwall line. The locomotives formerly worked on the Dinorwic and Penrhyn railways in North Wales. Launceston station contains a museum of vintage cars and motorcycles and there is also a collection of stationary steam engines which are demonstrated at work. There are catering, gift shop and bookshop facilities. At the far end of the line there are pleasant walks and a shaded picnic area, adjacent to Newmills Farm Park. The covered rolling stock ensures an enjoyable visit whatever the weather
Location: Newport Industrial Estate, Launceston, Cornwall
OS reference: SX 328850
Operating Society/organisation: The Spice Settlement Trust Co Ltd, trading as the Launceston Steam Railway, Newport, Launceston
Telephone: (01566) 775665
Stations: Launceston-Hunts Crossing-New Mills
Car park: Newport Industrial Estate, Launceston
Length of line: 2.5 miles
Gauge: 1ft 11.5in
Access by public transport: Main line Gunnislake 13 miles, Plymouth or Bodmin 25 miles
On site facilities: Cafe and restaurant, transport museum, workshop tours, gift and bookshop, all situated at Launceston
Period of public operation: Easter holiday, then Tuesdays and Sundays until Whitsun. Daily (not Saturdays) Whitsun until end of September. Tuesdays and Sundays in October, also daily (except Saturday) during half-term week. Santa Specials every Saturday and Sunday in December, also Christmas Eve and Boxing Day
Public opening: Trains run from 11.00-16.30. Departures every 40min and more frequently if required. Unlimited riding on date of issue of ticket
Family ticket: Available, 2 Adults + 4 children
Journey time: Return 35min
Facilities for disabled: Easy access to all areas except bookshop and motorcycle museum. No toilet facilities for disabled. However, public toilets are reasonably accessible
Special events: Double-headed trains on Wednesdays in July and August (whenever possible). Demonstration freight trains (contact for details)

Steam Centre

Lavender Line

East Sussex

Member: AIRPS
The Lavender Line is centred around a typical country station, which unusually is situated in the village it was built to serve. The emphasis is on steam for passenger trains, although diesel power, including a unique Class 12, is represented. The next stretch of trackbed has just been purchased, whilst the present operating length will become double track. This will enable the popular footplate experience courses to operate at weekends. The running line is currently being extended. Planned works for the coming year include new shed roads, extra sidings and return to operation of Barclay 945. Additional rolling stock is expected.
Location: Isfield Station, Isfield, near Uckfield, East Sussex TN22 5XB. (Just off the A26)
OS reference: TQ 452171
Operating society/organisation: The Lavender Line Preservation Society
Telephone: Isfield (01825) 750515
Car park: On site
Access by public transport: Train to Uckfield or Lewes, then bus to Isfield

On site facilities: Professional catering, souvenir shop, museum. Private functions, weddings and parties catered for. Trackside path to picnic and viewing area
Length of line: 1-mile — extension under-way
Public opening: Steam-hauled trains Sundays and Bank Holidays all year round, plus Saturdays in July. Also open every day (except Mondays) in August. Site open 11.00-17.00
Footplate courses: Available on steam, diesel shunters or DMUs
Facilities for disabled: Access to site, platforms, museum, buffet, shop and for train rides; no wheelchair access to toilets at present
Special events: Firework display in September; Father Christmas on the four weeks before Christmas; Mother's and Father's Days; Easter Bunny Days. Plus may be more, please ring for details

Ticket price includes unlimited rides and visit to signalbox. Loco shed/workshop visits when accompanied by society member

Locomotives and multiple-units

Name	*No*	*Origin*	*Class*	*Type*	*Built*
—	15224	BR	12	0-6-0DE	1949
Sir Herbert Walker	73003	BR	73	Bo-Bo	1962
—	51656	BR	115	DMBS	1960
—	51677	BR	115	DMBS	1960

Industrial locomotives

Name	*No*	*Builder*	*Type*	*Built*
Annie	945	Barclay (945)	0-4-0ST	1904
Lady Ingrid	3	Barclay (2315)	0-4-0ST	1951
Blackie	68012	Hunslet (3193)	0-6-0ST	1944
—	15	Barclay	0-4-0DM	1945
—	16	Barclay	0-4-0DM	1945

Stock

3 ex-BR Mk 1 coaches; 1 ex-GWR 'Toad' brake van, 3 box vans, 2 coal trucks, 1 BR standard brake van, 1 LT hopper, 1 Lowmac, 1 dorm coach, 1 Sturgeon, 1 Conflat A, 1 Pipefit

Museum — Leeds Industrial Museum — Leeds

Location: The Leeds Industrial Museum, Armley Mills, Canal Road, Leeds LS12 2QF
OS reference: SE 275342
Operating society/organisation: Leeds City Council, Department of Leisure Services, The Town Hall, The Headrow, Leeds LS1 3AO
Curator: D. C. Rooke
Telephone: (0113) 263 7861
Car park: Cark park adjacent to the Museum
Access by public transport: Nos 14 or 5A from City Square, Leeds (outside the railway station)
Public opening: April-September: Tuesdays-Saturdays 10.00-16.00, Sundays 14.00-16.00. October-March: Tuesdays-Saturdays 10.00-16.00, Sundays 14.00-16.00. Closed Mondays (except Bank Holidays)
On site facilities: Museum shop, refreshments (vending machines), picnic area
Special notes: Facilities for the disabled (toilets, etc), lifts. Museum can be viewed by visitors in wheelchairs (most areas are accessible)
Details of locomotive and rolling stock: Locomotive collection includes steam, diesel, mines locomotives and a narrow gauge railway and engines

Industrial locomotives

Name	*No*	*Builder*	*Type*	*Built*
1ft 6in gauge				
Jack	—	Hunslet 684)	0-4-0WT	1898
Coffin	—	G/Bat (1326)	0-4-0BE	1933
2ft gauge				
Barber	—	T/Green (441)	0-6-2ST	1908
Cheetal	—	Fowler (15991)	0-6-0WT	1923
Simplex	—	M/Rail (1369	4wPM	1918
Hudson Fordson	—	Hudson (36863)	4wDM	1928
Layer	—*	Fowler (21294)	4wDM	1936
Hudson Hunslet	—	Hunslet (2959)	4wDM	1944
Resin	—	Hunslet (2008)	0-4-0DM	1939
Nacob	—*	Hunslet (5340)	0-4-0DM	1957
Sharlston	—†	H/Clarke (1164)	0-4-0DM	1959
Demtox	—†*	Hunslet (6048)	0-4-0DM	1961
2ft 1in gauge				
Fricl	—*	Hunslet (4019)	0-4-0DM	1948
Pitpo	—*	Hunslet	0-4-0	1955
Calverton	—*	H/Clarke (1368)	0-4-0DM	1965
2ft 6in gauge				
Ordnance	—	G/Bat (1877)	0-4-0BE	1943
Junin	—	H/Clarke (D557)	2-6-2DM	1930
Fimyn	—†	Hunslet (3411)	0-4-0DM	1947
2ft 8in gauge				
Ficol	—	Hunslet (3200)	0-4-0DM	1945
2ft 11in gauge				
Lurch	—	H/Clarke (D571)	4wDM	1932

Notes
*not currently on public display
†On loan to Red Rose Steam Society/Astley Green Colliery Museum
Simplex is on loan to Moseley Industrial Railway Museum

Name	No	Builder	Type	Built
3ft gauge				
Lord Granby	—*	H/Clarke (633)	0-4-0ST	1902
Cement	—*	Fowler (20685)	2-4-0DM	1935
Lofti	—*	Hunslet (4057)	0-6-0DM	1953
3ft 6in gauge				
Progress	—	H/Clarke (D634)	0-6-0DM	1946
Festival of Britain	—	H/Clarke (D733)	0-6-0DM	1951
Standard gauge				
Hodbarrow	—*	Hunslet (299)	0-4-0ST	1882
Aldwyth	—	M/Wardle (865)	0-6-0ST	1882
Capper	—	Fowler (22060)	0-4-0DM	1938
Fort William	—*	Fowler (22893)	0-4-0DM	1940
Trecwn	—	Hunslet (2390)	0-4-0DM	1941
Elizabeth	—	H/Clarke (1888)	0-4-0ST	1958
Southam No 2	—*	H/Clarke (D625)	0-4-0DM	1942
Luton	—	G/Bat (1210)	0-4-0BE	1930
Smithy Wood	—*	G/Bat (2543)	0-4-0WE	1955

Timetable Service

Leighton Buzzard Railway

Bedfordshire

Member: AIRPS, TT
Built in 1919, this is one of England's foremost narrow gauge centres. In places, this line bears the air of a Continental roadside tramway, running as it does behind the backs of houses before it passes into the open countryside; there is no denying the quaintness of its engines or the friendliness of the little trains and their staff
General Manager: J. Horsley
Headquarters: Leighton Buzzard Railway, Page's Park station, Billington Road, Leighton Buzzard LU7 8TN
OS reference: Page's Park SP 928242
Telephone: (01525) 373888, 24hr answerphone with service and event details
Main station: Page's Park (A4146, Leighton Buzzard)
Other public stations: Halts at Vandyke Road and Stonehenge Works
Car park: Page's Park
Access by public transport: Leighton Buzzard main line station then by bus to town centre
Refreshment facilities: Page's Park. Picnic area by station. Cafe for hot & cold snacks, refreshments and ice creams
Souvenir shop: Page's Park
Depots: Page's Park and Stonehenge Works

Locomotives

Name	No	Builder	Type	Built
—	740	O&K	0-6-0T	1907
—*	—	Baldwin (778)	4-6-0T	1917
Berlin	—	Freudenstein (73)	0-4-0WT	1901
Alice	—	Hunslet (780)	0-4-0ST	1902
Peter Pan	—	K/Stuart (4256)	0-4-0ST	1922
Chaloner	1	de Winton	0-4-0VBT	1877
Pixie	2	K/Stuart (4260)	0-4-0ST	1922
Rishra	3	Baguley (2007)	0-4-0T	1921
Doll	4	Barclay (1641)	0-6-0T	1919
Elf	5	O&K (12740)	0-6-0WT	1936
Falcon	7	O&K (8986)	4wDM	1939
Gollum	8	Ruston (217999)	4wDM	1943
Madge	9	O&K (7600)	4wDM	1934
Haydn Taylor	10	Simplex (7956)	4wDM	1945
P. C. Allen	11	O&K (5834)	0-4-0WT	1912
Carbon	12	Simplex (6012)	4wPM	1930
Arkle	13	M/Rail (7108)	4wDM	1937
—	14	Hunslet (3646)	4wDM	1946
Tom Bombadil	15	Hibberd (2514)	4wDM	1941
Thorin Oakenshield	16	Lister (11221)	4wDM	1939
Damredub	17	Simplex (7036)	4wDM	1936
Feanor	18	M/Rail (11003)	4wDM	1956
—	19	M/Rail (11298)	4wDM	1965
—	20	M/Rail (60s317)	4wDM	1966
Festoon	21	Simplex (4570)	4wPM	1929
Fingolfin	22	under construction	—	—
—	23	Ruston (164346)	4wDM	1932
Ad-a-Cab	25	Simplex (7214)	4wDM	1938
Yimkin	26	Ruston (203026)	4wDM	1941
Poppy	27	Ruston (408430)	4wDM	1957
RAF Stanbridge	28	Ruston (200516)	4wDM	1940
Creepy	29	Hunslet (6008)	4wDM	1963
—	30	M/Rail (8695)	4wDM	1941
—	31	Lister (4228)	4wDM	1931
—	32	Ruston (172892)	4wDM	1934

Length of line: 3 miles, 2ft gauge
Journey time: Single 25min, return 65min
Passenger trains: Page's Park-Stonehenge Works
Group discounts and packages such as Birthday Breaks, Schools Specials, Twilight Trains available
Period of public operation: Sundays 15 March-11 October; Good Friday; Easter Saturday; Bank Holiday Mondays 13 April, 4, 25 May, 25 August; Wednesdays 27 May-26 August; Thursdays 6-27 August; Saturdays 2, 23 May, 1-29 August, 5 September
Special events: Industrial Train Displays — 15 March, 19 April, 17 May, 28 June, 19 July, 16 August, 20 September; Quarry Excavator Demonstrations — 5 July, 2 August; Demonstration freight train runs— 15 March, 19 April, 7 June, 13 September; Easter steam weekend — 10-13 April; Teddy Bears' Outing — 29 March; Heritage weekend — 27/28 June; Model Mania — 2 August; Autumn Steam Up — 5/6 September (includes photographic cavalcade on Saturday); Mad Hatter's Tea Party— 27 September; Steam Show — 3 October; Xmas Trains Weekends 5-20 December
Facilities for disabled: Access to shop, buffet, platform and toilets. Wheelchairs can be conveyed on trains
Special notes: Visiting steam locomotives expected during 1998
Membership details: Membership secretary, c/o above address
Membership journal: *Chaloner* — quarterly
Marketing name: England's Friendly Little Line

Name	*No*	*Builder*	*Type*	*Built*
—	33	Hibberd (3582)	4wDM	1954
Red Rum	34	M/Rail (7105)	4wPM	1936
—	35	Hunslet (6619)	0-4-0DM	1966
Caravan	36	Simplex (7129)	4wDM	1938
—	37	Ruston (172901)	4wPM	1934
—	38	Lister (37170)	4wDM	1951
T. W. Lewis	39	Ruston (375316)	4wDM	1954
—	40	Ruston (283507)	4wDM	1949
—	41	Hunslet (2536)	4wDM	1941
—	42	Ruston (223692)	4wPM	1944
—	43	Simplex (10409)	4wDM	1954
Kestrel	44	Simplex (7933)	4wDM	1941
—	46	Ruston (209430)	4wPM	1942
—	47	Hudson (38384)	4wDM	1930
—	48	Hunslet (RFST2)	4wDM	1952
—	—	M/Rail (1377)	4wPM	1918
—	—	M/Rail (11297)	4wDM	1965

* on loan from Amberley Museum

Dismantled for spares: M/Rail 4805, 5613, 5612, 5603; Ruston 218016 converted to brake vans: M/Rail 5608, 5875

Locomotive notes: 1, 2, 4, 5, 11, *Alice* and *Peter Pan* are potentially operational during 1998.

Stock
10 coaches and a number of miscellaneous vehicles

Museum

Liverpool Museum

Liverpool

A fine selection of vehicles in a traditional 'stuffed and mounted' display. *Lion* is on display throughout the year and is no longer steamed.
Location: William Brown Street, Liverpool
Curator: Sharon Brown
Operating society/organisation: National Museums and Galleries on Merseyside, William Brown Street, Liverpool L3 8EN
Telephone: (0151) 207 0001
Car parks: Public car parks nearby
Access by public transport: Adjacent Lime Street stations (main line and Merseyrail). Numerous bus routes
On site facilities: Cafe, shop
Public opening: Monday to Saturday 10.00-17.00. Sundays 12.00-17.00
Special notes: Transport gallery within large general museum. Facilities for disabled visitors
Journal: *The Guide,* published twice yearly covering entire activities of National Museums & Galleries on Merseyside

Locomotives

Name	*No*	*Origin*	*Class*	*Type*	*Built*
Lion	57	L&MR	—	0-4-2	1838

Industrial locomotives

Name	*No*	*Builder*	*Type*	*Built*
—	1	Avonside (1465)	0-6-0ST	1904

Stock
LOR electric coach of 1893
L&MR replica coach built Derby 1929

Museum

London Transport Museum

London

Member: AIRPS, TT
Spectacular displays of buses, trams and trains reveal a fascinating story of travel, people and the history of London itself. Special exhibitions, family activities, actors, videos and working models all bring the story to life
Location: Covent Garden, London WC2E 7BB
OS reference: TQ 303809
Operating society/organisation: London Regional Transport
Telephone: (0171) 379 6344. (24hr [0171] 836 8557)
Access by public transport: Underground to Covent Garden, Leicester Square or Charing Cross. Buses to Strand/Aldwych
On site facilities: Museum shop, lecture theatre, photo and research libraries (by appointment), resource centre and café
Public opening: Daily 10.00-18.00 (except Fridays 11.00-18.00) (last admissions 17.15). Closed 24-26 December. Reduced admission prices for children, students, senior citizens, registered disabled, UB40 holders and pre-booked parties. Family season ticket available
Facilities for disabled: Disabled toilets available, wheelchair access to all displays. Reduced admission for registered disabled visitors and person accompanying them. Please advise in advance if a party of disabled visitors would like to visit
Special notes: Visitors can put themselves in the driving seat of a bus, a tube simulator, there are also 'hands-on' demonstrations of signals and points. In addition to the vehicles and rolling stock there are models, signs, posters, photographs, audio-visual displays and a 1906 Otis lift car. The museum runs a full programme of events and activities in addition to temporary exhibitions on a variety of topics. In addition to the vehicles on display there is a growing reserve collection
Membership details: Details from the Friends of the London Transport Museum

Locomotives

Name	*No*	*Origin*	*Class*	*Type*	*Built*
—	23	Met Rly	A	4-4-0T	1866
John Hampden	5	Met Rly		Bo-Bo	1922

Industrial locomotives

Origin	*Builder*	*Type*	*Built*
Wotton Tramway	A/Porter (807)	0-4-0TG	1872

Electric stock
4248 District Rly Q23 stock driving motor coach 1923
11182 LPTB 1938 stock driving motor coach
400 Met Rly bogie stock coach 1899
30 City & South London Rly 'Padded Cell' coach 1890
Great Northern Piccadilly & Brompton Railway 'Gate stock' car 1906 (sectioned)

Stock
1 Met Rly milk van; 3 electric trams; 3 horse buses; 7 motorbuses; 1 trolleybus; 1 horse tram; 1 petrol-electric bus chassis; 1 tram/trolleybus tower wagon

Steam Centre

Mangapps Farm Railway Museum

Essex

Mangapps recreates the atmosphere of a rural light railway. Featuring a large museum collection, strong in items of East Anglian interest, railway signalling and goods rolling stock. Other features include original station buildings from Mid-Suffolk Light, Great Eastern and Midland & Great Northern Railways.
Superintendent of the Line: John Jolly
Commercial Manager: June Jolly
Location: Mangapps Farm Railway Museum, Southminster Road, Burnham-on-Crouch, Essex CM0 8QQ. (Entrance on B1021, 1-mile north of Burnham)
Telephone: (01621) 784898
Access by public transport: Burnham station approx 1 mile
On site facilities: Station, car park, souvenir shop, toilets, amenity and picnic areas
Refreshment facilities: teas and light refreshments
Length of line: Three quarter-mile
Public opening: Weekends & Bank Holidays all year (except 25/26 December, and daily during Easter and summer school holidays. Closed January/February. Steam trains operate 1st Sunday of March to December, every Sunday during August & December
Opening times: 13.00-17.30 diesel days; 11.30-17.30 steam days
Special events: Friends of Thomas the Tank Engine; Gala Day — 7 July; Santa Specials — during December; Steam Special — 1 January 1999

Locomotives and multiple-units

Name	No	Origin	Class	Type	Built
—	D2089	BR	03	0-6-0DM	1960
—	03399	BR	03	0-6-0DM	1961
—	D2325	BR	04	0-6-0DM	1961
—	11104	BR	04	0-6-0DM	1953
—	54287	BR	121	DTS	1960
—	22624	LT	R38	DMS	1938

Industrial locomotives

Name	No	Builder	Type	Built
Minnie	—	F/Walker (358)	0-6-0ST	1878
Brookfield	—	Bagnal (2613)	0-6-0PT	1940
Demelza	—	Bagnall (3061)	0-6-0ST	1954
Elland	No 1	H/Clarke (D1153)	0-4-0DM	1959
—	—	S/Henshaw (7502)	4wDM	1966
—	226	Drewry (2180)/ V/Foundry (5261)	0-4-0DM	1945

Timetable Service

Mid-Hants Railway

Hampshire

Member: AIRPS
Originally built as the Winchester to Alton link, the Mid-Hants Railway became known as the Watercress Line through regularly carrying this local produce to London markets. Now restored, the line runs from its BR connection at Alton through rolling countryside to its terminus at Alresford. Large and powerful locomotives work impressively over the steeply inclined route, known to railwaymen as 'the Alps'. No 31625 entered traffic for the first time in September 1996. Nos 30499, 35018 and 41312 are expected to be the next locomotives to enter service
Chief Executive: Margaret Parker
Headquarters: Mid-Hants Railway PLC, Alresford Station, Alresford, Hants SO24 9JG
Telephone: Alresford (01962) 733810
Fax: (01962) 735448
Talking timetable: (01962) 734866
Internet address: http://www.itoeye.co.uk
Main station: Alresford
Other public stations: Ropley, Medstead & Four Marks, Alton
OS reference: Alresford SU 588325, Ropley SU 629324
Car park: Alresford-HCC, pay & display (free Sundays & Bank Holidays). Alton station pay & display

Locomotives

Name	No	Origin	Class	Type	Built
—	30499	LSWR	S15	4-6-0	1920
—	30506	LSWR	S15	4-6-0	1920
—	31625	SR	U	2-6-0	1929
—	31806	SR	U	2-6-0	1926
—*	31874	SR	N	2-6-0	1925
Bodmin	34016	SR	WC	4-6-2	1945
Tangmere††	34067	SR	BB	4-6-2	1947
249 Squadron	34073	SR	BB	4-6-2	1948
Swanage	34105	SR	WC	4-6-2	1950
Shaw Savill†	35009	SR	MN	4-6-2	1942
British India Line	35018	SR	MN	4-6-2	1945
—	41312	LMS	2MT	2-6-2T	1952
—	73096	BR	5MT	4-6-0	1956
—	76017	BR	4MT	2-6-0	1954
Franklin D. Roosevelt	701	USATC	S160	2-8-0	1944
—	D3358	BR	08	0-6-0DE	1957
—	D5353	BR	27	Bo-Bo	1961
—	D6513	BR	33	Bo-Bo	1960
Captain Bill Smith RNR	33109	BR	33	Bo-Bo	1960
—	D6593	BR	33	Bo-Bo	1962
—	33208	BR	33	Bo-Bo	1962
—	45132	BR	45	1Co-Co1	1961

*Currently running as No 5 *James*
†Currently under restoration at Swindon Railway Workshop
††Currently under restoration at Riley Engineering, East Lancs

Industrial locomotives

Name	No	Builder	Type	Built
—	4	Fowler (22889)	0-4-0DM	1939
Thomas	1	Hunslet (3781)	0-6-0T	1954
Barbara	—	Hunslet (2890)	0-6-0ST	1943

Stock
3 steam cranes; 1 Plasser & Theurer AL250 lining machine; 26 ex-BR Mk 1 coaches; 15 ex-BR Mk 2 coaches; 4 ex-SR coaches; 1 ex-LSWR coach; 2 ex-LMS coaches; Numerous goods vehicle

Access by public transport: *South West Train services* — just over 1hr from London. Through ticketing arrangements available from Waterloo and all main line stations. Alternatively, travel to Winchester station and take the bus to Alresford from nearby City Road.
Bus services – operated by Stagecoach (01256) 464501, or dial 100 and ask for freefone County Bus Line
Refreshment facilities: Buffet service on most trains; 'West Country' buffet at Alresford; 'T-Junction' picnic/barbeque area at Ropley; tea/coffee available at Alton when information office open
Catering facilities: The 'Countryman' pre-booked Sunday lunch trains. The 'Watercress Belle' operates on certain Saturday evenings April-October. Early booking is essential, please telephone to confirm seat availability for both trains. Real Ale trains — certain special events and Saturday evenings featuring beers from local breweries
Souvenir shops: Alresford, Alton and Ropley — which also specialises in secondhand books
On-site facilities: Picnic area and viewing facilities at Ropley, including children's playground
Depot: Ropley
Length of line: 10 miles
Passenger trains: Phone Talking Timetable (01962 734866) to confirm details. Sundays February; Weekends and Bank Holidays March to end October; mid-week June/July; daily July to first week September. Santa Specials (bookings commence end of August)
Journey time: Round trip 1hr 40min max
Special events: Friends of Thomas the Tank Engine — 10-19 April 8-16 August inclusive; Real Ale Trains (including Saturday Evening) — 25/26 April, 23-25 May, 18/19 July, 19/20 September, 24/25 October; 9th Model Railway Exhibition (in Alton) — 3/4 May; Enthusiast Event — 23-25 May; Country Market/Craft Fair, Austin Car Display — 7 June; Father's Day and Watercress William's Birthday and Singer Car Display — 21 June; Morris Day (cars and dancers) along with Real Ale — 5 July; Bus Rally — 19 July; 1940s Weekend — 12/13 September; Open Day (the chance to see behind the scenes) — 27 September; Teddy Bears' Day — 4 October; Somerset & Dorset Weekend — 24/25 October; Santa Specials — 5/6, 12/13, 19-24 December
Facilities for disabled: Toilets at Ropley and 100yd from Alresford station. Passengers in fixed wheelchairs can be carried in the brake compartment of all trains. Ramps are provided to ease entry to trains
Membership details: Membership Secretary, c/o above address

Owners
30499 and 30506 the Urie Locomotive Society
34105 the 34105 Light Pacific Group
76017 the Standard 4 Locomotive Group

Diesel Centre — Mid-Norfolk Railway — Norfolk

Member: AIRPS
A scheme to preserve part of the former Great Eastern line from Wymondham to Wells-next-the-Sea. The section from Wymondham to Dereham has been purchased and initial services will operate from Dereham to Yaxham. Re-opening to Wymondham is anticipated during 1998.
Headquarters: The Railway Station, Station Road, Dereham, Norfolk NR19 1DF
Main station: Dereham
Telephone: (01362) 690633 (answerphone)
Car park: At Dereham
Museum: A 'Goods Handling Throughout the Ages' will be developed in Dereham goods shed
Souvenir shop: Dereham
Refreshment facilities: Dereham and *Railway Buffet*
Access by public transport: Bus from Norwich and Kings Lynn
Period of public operation: Regular trains from Dereham to Yaxham and will extend to Wymondham. Occasional demonstration freight trains
Membership details: Stuart Moye, 21 The Brambles, Ware, Herts SG12 0XU
Membership journal: *The Blastpipe* (four times a year)

Locomotives & multiple-units

Name	*No*	*Origin*	*Class*	*Type*	*Built*
—	20069	BR	20	Bo-Bo	1961
—	37099	BR	37	Co-Co	1962
—	51073	Gloucester	119	DMBC	1958
—	51503	M/Cam	101	DMC	1959
—	51572	BR	108	DMC	1959
—	54224	BR	108	DTC	1959
—	55009	Gloucester	122	DMBS	1958
—	56301	Gloucester	100	DTC	1957

Industrial locomotives

Name	*No*	*Builder*	*Type*	*Built*
—	—	R/Hornsby (497753)	0-4-0DE	1963

Locomotive notes: 20069, 20206, and DMU 55009 are in service. DMUs 51572 and 54224 are expected to enter service during 1998

Rolling stock 5 BR Mk 2 coaches. Selection of freight wagons

Above: **National Railway Museum-owned No 46229** ***Duchess of Hamilton*** **climbs 'the Alps' as it makes its way from Alton to Medstead on the Mid-Hants Railway. No 46229 has since been repainted into BR green.** ***Alan P. Barnes***

Below: **With track relaid within the station area at Dereham the Mid-Norfolk Railway was able officially to re-open the section from there to Yaxham.** ***Sir Berkeley*****, owned by the Vintage Carriages Trust, was on loan for the first few weeks.** ***Sir Berkeley*** **and 'bubble car' No 55009 are seen during the first weekend of operation.** ***Alan C. Butcher***

Museum

Mid-Suffolk Light Railway

Suffolk

Location: Wetheringsett, Nr Stowmarket, Suffolk IP14 5PW
OS reference: TM 129659
Operating organisation: Mid-Suffolk Light Railway Company
Telephone: 01449 766899
Car park: On site
Access by public transport: Main line Stowmarket (8 miles); by bus from Ipswich on summer Sundays
On site facilities: Souvenir shop, refreshments, railway walk, railwayana and photographic exhibition, toilets and picnic area
Period of public opening: Sundays and Bank Holidays, Easter to end September
Special events: Subject to confirmation, please enquire locally
Special notes: Museum dedicated to Mid-Suffolk Light Railway. Original MSLR restored buildings and artefacts. Reproduction MSLR ticket on entry. *Railway World* award winner
Membership details: Membership Secretary, 4 Felix Road, Stowupland, Stowmarket, Suffolk IP14 4DD
Society journal: *Making Tracks:* quarterly MSLRS Newsletter

Industrial locomotives

Name	*No*	*Builder*	*Type*	*Built*
—	1604	H/Clarke (1604)	0-6-0ST	1928

Rolling stock

2 GER ventilated vans, 1 GER non-ventilated van, Moy private owner coal wagon (conversion of BR open wagon), GER 5-compartment third, GER 2-compartment brake third, GER 3-compartment first, BR tube wagon, nondescript flat wagon, LNER brake van, 3 GER coach bodies, NER milk van body, LMS horse box body

Steam Centre

Middleton Railway

Leeds

Members: AIRPS, TT
This is a preserved section of one of the world's oldest railways, authorised by Act of Parliament in 1758, and also the first to be re-opened by volunteers
Headquarters: Middleton Railway Trust Ltd, Moor Road, Leeds LS10 2JQ
Telephone: (0113) 271 0320 (Ansaphone) or (0113) 271 1089 after 6pm
Main station: Moor Road, Hunslet
OS reference: SE 302309
Car parks: Tunstall Road/Moor Road (free)
Access by public transport: Any bus from Corn Exchange to Tunstall Road, walk down the road, across Waterway and the MR is on the right, walking time 5min
Souvenir shop: Moor Road
Museum: Depot now open 10.00 to 18.00 during season (10.00 to 16.00 during winter). There is no charge for admission to site
Length of line: 1.25 miles
Passenger trains: Sunday trains all steam operated. Saturday services may be diesel hauled. Special trains operate on request, contact J. Wickinson. Tel: (0113) 271 9785

Locomotives

Name	*No*	*Origin*	*Class*	*Type*	*Built*
—	1310	NER	Y7	0-4-0T	1891
—	54	LNER	Y1	0-4-0VB	1933
—	385	DSB	HsII	0-4-0WT	1893
—	7401	LMS	—	0-6-0DM	1932

Industrial locomotives

Name	*No*	*Builder*	*Type*	*Built*
John Blenkinsop	—	Peckett (2003)	0-4-0ST	1941
—	—	H/Clarke (1208)	0-6-0ST	1916
Henry de Lacy II	—	H/Clarke (1309)	0-4-0ST	1917
—	67	H/Clarke (1369)	0-6-0T	1919
Mirvale	—	H/Clarke (1882)	0-4-0ST	1955
Brookes No 1	—	Hunslet (2387)	0-6-0ST	1941
Windle	—	Borrows (53)	0-4-0WT	1909
Matthew Murray	—	Bagnall (2702)	0-4-0ST	1943
Arthur	—	M/Wardle (1601)	0-6-0ST	1901
—*	—	Brush (91)	0-4-0DE	1958
—	No 6	H/Leslie (3860)	0-4-0ST	1935
Carroll	—	H/Clarke (D631)	0-4-0DM	1946
—	—	Hunslet (1786)	4wD	1935
Mary	—	H/Clarke (D577)	0-4-0DM	1932
—	—	Fowler (3900002)	0-4-0DM	1945
—	—	Fowler (4200038)	0-4-0DH	1966
—		Sentinel (10252)	0-4-0DH	1966
—	—	Thomas Hill (138C)	0-4-0DH	1963
Rowntrees No 3†	—	R/Hornsby (441934)	4wDM	1960

*On loan from BSC Orb Works, Newport
†On loan from North Yorkshire Moors Railway

Period of public operation: Every Saturday, Sunday and Bank Holiday Monday from 1 April to 23 October. Saturday service — 13.30, 14.13, 15.00, 15,45, 16.30. Sunday service — every 30min, 13.00-16.30. Trains depart from Moor Road at 11.00, 11.45, 12.30, 13.00 then every 30min until 16.30. Winter steam service — Sundays 13.00 to 16.30
Special events: Please contact for details

Stock
2 CCTs converted for passenger use Nos 1867 and 2048; CCT as stores van No 2073; Norwegian brake coach; Various goods vehicles; 5-ton Booth rail crane; 1 3-ton Smith steam crane; 1 3-ton Isles steam crane; 7.5 ton steam crane

Owners
1310, 385 the Steam Power Trust

Facilities for disabled: Access very good
Special notes: It was the first standard gauge railway to be opened by volunteers, in June 1960. The railway terminates in a large car park and a nature trail has been provided by the local council

Timetable Service

Midland Railway Centre

Derbyshire

Member: AIRPS, TT
The Centre is a rapidly developing Preservation Scheme with a difference. The massive 57 acre Museum site and 35 acre Country Park enables the Centre to become 'More Than Just a Railway' as its publicity says. The seven road Matthew Kirtley Museum allows much of the historic collection to be on display and most of the locomotives to be stored and displayed under cover. A miniature railway (3.5 and 5in gauge) and a rarrow gauge line (2ft gauge) carry passengers and the rarrow gauge line is being extended into the Country Park. A new development is the Brittain Pit Farm Park, with its wide variety of livestock. And of course there is a 3.5-mile standard gauge line complete with Midland signals, three restored signalboxes, Butterley station, the scenic delights of Butterley Reservoir and Golden Valley!

1998 will be a year of celebration: 75 years since the Grouping to form the London Midland & Scottish Railway; 50 years since Nationalisation of the LMS to form British Railways; 25 years since the formation of the MRT. 100 years since St Saviour's Church was first completed, it has since been re-erected at the Centre. The narrow gauge extension to Newmill Inn (subject to Railway Inspectorate approval) should open at Easter. A start has been made on the new Historical Model Railway Society's headquarters building
Location: Midland Railway Centre, Butterley Station, near

Locomotives and multiple-units

Name	*No*	*Origin*	*Class*	*Type*	*Built*
Princess Elizabeth	6201	LMS	8P	4-6-2	1933
Princess Margaret Rose	46203	LMS	8P	4-6-2	1935
Duchess of Sutherland	6233	LMS	8P	4-6-2	1938
—	44027	LMS	4F	0-6-0	1924
—	44932	LMS	5MT	4-6-0	1945
—	45491	LMS	5MT	4-6-0	1943
—	47564	LMS	3F	0-6-0T	1928
—	47327	LMS	3F	0-6-0T	1926
—	47357	LMS	3F	0-6-0T	1926
—	47445	LMS	3F	0-6-0T	1927
—	158A	MR	—	2-4-0	1866
—	53809	S&DJR	7F	2-8-0	1925
—	73129	BR	5MT	4-6-0	1956
—	80080	BR	4MT	2-6-4T	1954
—	80098	BR	4MT	2-6-4T	1955
—	92214	BR	9F	2-10-0	1959
—	92219	BR	9F	2-10-0	1959
—	D2138	BR	03	0-6-0DM	1960
—	08590	BR	08	0-6-0DE	1959
—	12077	BR	11	0-6-0DE	1950
—	D8001	BR	20	Bo-Bo	1957
—	20205	BR	20	Bo-Bo	1967
Traction	20227	BR	20	Bo-Bo	1967
—	D7671	BR	25	Bo-Bo	1967
—	31108	BR	31	A1A-A1A	1959
—	5580	BR	31	A1A-A1A	1960
—	33201	BR	33	Bo-Bo	1962
—	37190	BR	37	Co-Co	1964
Aureol	40012	BR	40	1Co-Co1	1959
Great Gable	D4	BR	44	1Co-Co1	1959
Royal Tank Regiment	45041	BR	45/1	1Co-Co1	1962
—	45133	BR	45/1	1Co-Co1	1961
—	46045	BR	46	1Co-Co1	1963
—	47401	BR	47	Co-Co	1963
—	47417	BR	47	Co-Co	1963
Sir Edward Elgar	50007	BR	50	Co-Co	1967
Tulyar	55015	BR	55	Co-Co	1961
Western Lady	D1048	BR	52	C-C	1962
Electra	27000	BR	EM2	Co+Co	1953
—	50019	BR	114	DMBS	1956
—	55966	BR	127	DPU	1959
—	55976	BR	127	DPU	1956

Ripley, Derbyshire DE5 3QZ
OS reference: SK 403520
General Manager: John Hett
Operating society/organisation: Midland Railway Trust Ltd
Telephone: Ripley (01773) 747674, Visitor Information Line (01773) 570140.
Fax: (01773) 570271
Car park: Butterley station on B6179 1-mile north of Ripley
On site facilities: Museum, award winning country park, Brittain Pit Farm Park, souvenir shops, miniature railway, narrow gauge railway, garden railway, model railways
Refreshment facilities: Butterley station suffet, Johnson Buffet (Swanwick), on-train bars and extensive 'Wine and Dine' trains. 'The Midlander' (details from above address)
Length of line: Standard gauge 3.5 miles, narrow gauge 0.8-mile
Public opening: Every Sunday and Bank Holiday Monday from 25 January. Every Saturday from 24 January to 7 November and 28 November to 27 December. Every Wednesday from 1 April to 29 October (except 11 June). Daily: 21 February to 1 March, 7-19 April, 23-31 May, 22-25 June, 14 July to 7 September, 24 October to 1 November. On other dates the centre will be open for static display.
Golden Valley Light Railway: open throughout (subject to DoT approval) and running weekends, Bank Holiday Mondays and Wednesdays April to October and daily 25 July to 7 September.
Butterley Park Miniature Railway: operates Sundays and Bank Holiday Mondays Easter to October.
Journey time: Approximately 1hr
Special events: Spring Diesel Gala— 28/29 March; Easter Eggstravaganza — 7-19 April; Spring on the Farm — 18/19 April; Nostalgia Weekend — 25/26 April; Diesel & Steam Weekend — 25/26 April, 16/17 May, 20/21 June, 18/19 July, 10/11 October; Freight Train Days — 25 April, 17 May, 20 June, 14 July, 10 October; Edwardian Gala — 2-4 May; Friends of Thomas the Tank Engine — 23-31 May, 1-9 August; Model Railway Exhibition — 6/7 June; Father's Day — 21 June; Schools

Name	*No*	*Origin*	*Class*	*Type*	*Built*
—	56006	BR	114	DTC	1956
—	59609	BR	127	TC	1959
—	79018	BR	—	MBS	19??
—	79612	BR	—	DTC	19??
—	29663	M/Cam	—	TC	1931
—	29666	M/Cam	—	TC	1931
—	29670	M/Cam	—	TC	1931
—	56171	Wickham	109	DMBS	1957
—	50416	Wickham	109	DMBS	1957

Locomotive notes: In service 80080, 80098, 47327, 20001, 20227, 46045, 08590, 5580, Class 114 DMU, D4, 47401, D2138, 40012, 12077, 45133, 55015 and D7671. Under restoration 6201, 44027, 47357, 53809, 73129, 92214, 45491, 44932, Wickham unit, 127 unit. Awaiting repairs or stored 31108, 47417, 47445, 92219. Boiler and frames only 47564. Static display 158A, 6233, 27000

Industrial locomotives

Name	*No*	*Builder*	*Type*	*Built*
Gladys	—	Markham (109)	0-4-0ST	1894
Stanton	24	Barclay (1875)	0-4-0CT	1925
Lytham St Annes	—	Peckett (2111)	0-4-0ST	1949
Brown Bailey	4	N/Wilson (454)	0-4-0ST	1894
Castle Donnington	1	RSH (7817)	0-4-0ST	1954
—	27	RSH (7086)	0-6-0ST	1943
Neepsend		Sentinel (9370)	4wVBT	1947
Andy	2	Fowler (16038)	0-4-0DM	1923
—	RS9	M/Rail (2024)	0-4-0DM	1921
—	RS12	M/Rail (460)	0-4-0DM	1912
Boots	2	Barclay (2008)	0-4-0F	1935
Castle Donnington	2	Barclay (416)	0-4-0DM	1957
Boots	—	R/Hornsby (384139)	0-4-0DE	1955
*Handyman**	—	H/Clarke (573)	0-4-0ST	1900
*Rothwell Colliery**	—	H/Clarke (D718)	0-6-0DM	1950
—	—	H/Clarke (D1152)	0-6-0DM	1959
Albert Fields	—	H/Clarke (D1114)	0-6-0DM	1958
—†	—	Deutz (10249)	4wDM	1932
Campbell Brick Works†	—	M/Rail (60S364)	4wDM	1968
—†	—	Lister (3742)	4wDM	1931
—†	—	M/Rail (5906)	4wDM	1932
—†	—	M/Rail (11246)	4wDM	1963
—†	2	O/Koppel (7529)	0-4-0WT	1914
—†	—	O/Koppel (5215)	4wDM	1936
Wheal Jayne†	19	BEV	4wBE	1985
—†	—	Ruston (7002/0567/6)	4wDM	1966
Berryhill†	—	Ruston (222068)	4wDM	1943
Hucknall Colliery†	3	Ruston (480678)	4wDM	1961
—†	—	Hunslet (7178)	4wDH	1971
Calverton Colliery†	22	H/Clarke (1117)	0-6-0DM	1958
Welbeck Colliery††	—	H/Clarke	0-6-0DM	—
Linby Colliery††	—	H/Clarke (DM647)	0-6-0DM	1954
—†	—	Lister (53726)	4wDM	1963
—†	—	SMH (40SD529)	4wDM	1983
—†	NG24	Baguley/ Drewry (3703)	4wBE	1974
Claverton No 7†	7	Hunslet (8911)	4wDM	1980
—†	RS202	SMH (102T20)	4wDH	19xx
—§	—	Chrzanow (3226)	0-6-0T	1954
—§	—	Chrzanow (1983)	0-6-0T	1949
*Princess Elizabeth***	6201	H/Clarke (D611)	4-6-2DM	1938
*Princess Margaret Rose***	6203	H/Clarke (D612)	4-6-2DM	1938

*3ft gauge †2ft gauge ††2ft 4in gauge §2ft 6in gauge **21in gauge

Week 22-25 June; Open Day — 27/28 June; Free for Registered Disabled — 25/26 July; Narrow Gauge Railway Gala and Garden Railway Festival — 15/16 August; Victorian Gala — 29-31 August; Autumn Diesel Gala — 12/13 September; Introduction to Model Railways — 19/20 September; Railways & Film Weekend — 26/27 September; Stationary Engine Display — 3/4 October; Branchline Weekend — 17/18 October; Oswald the Talking Engine's Birthday Party — 26 October-1 November; Fireworks Night — 7 November; Santa Specials 28/29 November, 5/6, 12/13, 17, 19-24 December; Mince Pie Specials — 26 December-1 January
Facilities for disabled: Toilets, special coach, access to shop and cafeteria, special weekend
Membership details: J. Hett, at above address
Membership journal: *The Wyvern* — quarterly
Marketing names: 'More than just a railway'; Golden Valley Light Railway (narrow gauge); Butterley Park Miniature Railway (miniature line)

Locomotive notes: In service: Boots, *Castle Donnington No 2,* NG24, Ruston 222068, SMH (40SD529 & 102T20), *Calverton Col No 22,* Lister, Deutz 10249, *Albert Fields,* M/Rail 60S364. Under restoration: *Andy* RS12, *Princess Margaret Rose.* Awaiting repairs or stored on display: Stanton, RS9, Hunslet 7178, M/Rails 5906/11246. Static display *Gladys,* 4, Boots No 2, *Handyman,* Sentinel 9370, both Chrzanows, *Lytham St Annes*

Stock

Numerous carriages, wagons and cranes. Museum display includes MR Royal saloon, MR 4-wheeled coach, MR brake third, LD&ECR all third, BR horsebox, LMS travelling Post Office, L&YR family saloon, MR motor carvan, MR bogie brake third, restored freight vehicles, and much more

Owners

6201 the 6201 Princess Elizabeth Society Ltd
158A, 44027 on loan from the National Railway Museum
53809 the 13809 Preservation Group
47357, 47327, 47445, 47564, 73129 Derby City Council
6233, 46203, 80080, 80098 the Princess Royal Class Locomotive Trust
55015 the Deltic Preservation Society
D4, 45041 and 46045 the Peak Locomotive Preservation Co Ltd
D7671 Derby Industrial Museum

Museum | Monkwearmouth Station Museum | County Durham

The Museum is one of Britain's finest neo-classical stations and was built in 1848 to commemorate the election of George Hudson as MP for Sunderland. Restored features include the booking office, unchanged since it was installed in 1866, waiting shelter on the west platform and siding area
Location: North Bridge Street, Sunderland
Telephone: (0191) 567 7075
OS reference: NZ 396576
On site facilities: Car parking on museum forecourt, shop
Access by public transport: 10min walk from Sunderland Central station. Served by several bus routes from Sunderland city centre, Newcastle and South Shields
Public opening: Daily 1 January-31 December (except New Year's Day, Good Friday, Christmas Day, Boxing Day). Monday-Friday 10.00-17.00. Saturday 10.00-16.30. Sunday 14.00-17.00. Free admission.
Access for disabled: Ramped access, suitable for wheelchair users

Rolling stock

NER brake van 1915, LNER CCT van 1939

Museum | Moseley Railway Museum | Cheshire

The collection concentrates on diesel and petrol power with some battery units and one steam outline locomotive. Emphasis is placed on operational locomotives and stock which, by prior appointment, can be observed and photographed performing the tasks for which they were originally designed. There are a number of unique running exhibits, including the Kent Construction petrol locomotive and a single-cylinder diesel Simplex. Petrol-powered locomotives dating back to 1918 form a key part of the working locomotive fleet. Passenger train rides and demonstration goods trains are always available on official open days The museum will be re-locating in 1998
Location: Grounds of Ridge Danyers College, Northdowns Road, Cheadle, Cheshire SK8 5HA

OS reference: SJ 864871
Operating society: The Moseley Industrial Narrow Gauge Tramway Museum Society (MTM), c/o 63 Honford Road, Brownley Green, Wythenshawe, Manchester M22 9PE
Telephone (0161) 485 2588 or (01663) 766992
Internet details: e-mail: mitm@djr12ecg.demon.co.uk
Web site: http://www.djr12ecg.demon.co.uk/mitm.html
Car park: Extensive, free, adjacent to the museum buildings
Station: One boarding area adjacent to the museum. Other request stops
Length of line and gauge: Approximately one third of a mile, 2ft gauge
Access by public transport: Nearest main line station Cheadle Hulme (10min walk). Bus from Manchester 157, bus from Stockport 368/369, ask for Cheadle Adult Education Centre/Ridge Danyers College
On site facilities: Free access and parking, a small selection of hot and cold drinks and other refreshments, access to all site. Visitor centre, with photographic and other displays
Period of public operation: Throughout the year. Second Sunday of every month plus any other time by appointment. 11.00-17.00 (dusk in winter) until Easter 1998. Thereafter phone for details
Train services: Return journey (round trip) approximately 20min
Facilities for the disabled: The museum operates the same policy as Stockport Education Authority. Every effort is made to accommodate disabled persons
Special events: Please contact for details or see Internet details
Special notes: Museum buildings and displays are now open
Membership details: C/o 11 Ashwood Road, Disley, Stockport, Cheshire SK12 2EL

Industrial locomotives

Name	*No*	*Builder*	*Type*	*Built*
Billet	1	W/Rgers (C6717)	4wBE	1963
Cable Mill	2	W/Rgers (C6716)	4wBE	1963
—	3	M/Rail (8878)	4wDM	1944
—	5	R/Hornsby (223667)	4wDM	1943
—	6	M/Rail (9104)	4wPM	1942
—	7	M/Rail (8663)	4wDM	1941
—	8	Kent	4wPM	c1926
—	9	M/Rail (4565)	4wPM	1928
—	10	M/Rail (7552)	4wDM	1948
Ald Hague	11	Hiberd (3465)	4wPM	1954
—	13	M/Rail (11142)	4wDM	1960
Knothole Worker	14	M/Rail (22045)	4wDM	1959
Ursula	15	Hunslet (7325)	4wDM	1973
—	18	H/Hunslet (6299)	4wDM	1964
—	21	M/Rail (8669)	4wDM	1941
—	23	Lister (52031)	4wDM	1960
—	29	R/Hornsby (195846)	4wDM	1939
—	30	R/Hornsby (2327914)	4wDM	1946
—	31	Lister (3834)	4wPM	1931
—	32	L/Blackstone (52885)	4wDM	1962
—	33	Wickham (4091)	2w-2PMR	1946
—	34	Wickham (4164)	2w-2PMR	1948
PMW 2214	35	Wickham (4131)	2w-2PMR	1947
Commercial	36	R/Hornsby (280865)	4wDM	1949
—	37	R/Hornsby (260719)	4wDM	1948
Kenneth	38	R/Hornsby (223749)	4wDM	1944
LR 2832	39	M/Rail (1111)	4wPM	1918
Chaumont	44	Hudson (LX1002)	4wDH	1968
Mavis	46	R/Hornsby (7002/0967/6)	4wDM	1968
—	47	M/Rail (1369)	4wDM	1918

Stock
Nearly 80 items of rolling stock including Groudle Glen and Corris-type replica coaches under construction

Museum

Museum of Army Transport

East Yorkshire

Member: TT
Operating a substantial network of railways in wartime, the Army is still responsible for railways feeding MoD depots in this country. Not only does the Museum hold extensive archives and display some fascinating maps, drawings and photographs, it contains some very interesting stock from the former military railways
Location: Museum of Army Transport, Flemingate, Beverley, East Yorkshire HU17 0NG
OS reference: TA 041392
Operated by: The Museum of Army Transport Ltd (Charitable Status Company)
Telephone: Hull (01482) 860445
Car park: Yes, 1.25 acres
Access by public transport: Rail: 10min walk from Beverley station. Bus: served by East Yorks Motor Service

On site facilities: Museum — The Royal Corps of Transport Collection of road, rail, sea, air and movement control artefacts. Licensed cafeteria. Shop in building. Lavatories, including special for disabled. Large car and bus park
Facilities for disabled: The Museum is on one floor. This allows viewing of all vehicles. Access is available by ramp into the Armoured Train. Access is not possible into the Beverley aircraft, the railway locos and the signalbox frame
Public opening: 10.00-17.00 every day except 24-26 December. Group discount rate for parties of 20 or more
Special notes: Please bear in mind that while what is reported here deals with railways, other parts of this extensive museum cover movement by road, sea and air
Honorary Railway (and Port) Consultant: Major J. A. Robins (Retd)

Locomotives

Name	*No*	*Builder*	*Type*	*Built*
Woolmer	—	Avonside (1572)	0-6-0ST	1910
Waggoner	92	Hunslet (3792)	0-6-0ST	1953
Rorke's Drift	—	Drewry (2047)	0-4-0DM	1934
Lyddia	AD41†	R/Hornsby (191646)	4WDM	1933
—	110	R/Hornsby (411319)	4wDM	1958
—	1035	Wickham Rail Car	4w	1958
—	3282*	Wickham Target Trolley	4w	1943
—	WD2182†	M/Rail (461)	4wDM	1917
—	LOD 758009†[1]	M/Rail	4wDM	1941-3
—	LOD 758220†[2]	M/Rail	4wDM	1941-3
—	LOD 758228†	M/Rail (8667)	4wDM	1941
—	LOD 758028†	M/Rail (8855)	4wDM	1943
—	RTT 767182†	Wickham Target Trolley	4w	WW2

*2ft 6in gauge
†2ft gauge
[1]Fitted with air-brake for use with passenger stock
[2]Stored on site, may be moving

Rolling stock
Collection of various rolling stock items including Lord Kitchener's coach (c1885), a World War 1 Armoured Train gun truck and a World War 2 ramp wagon

A 2ft gauge system based on the ADLR of World War 1, some 200yd long, and worked by World War 2 Simplex rail tractors operated by volunteers, on Saturday and Sunday afternoons and at other times as advertised locally during the summer. Intending travellers should check the line is operating.

Museum

The Museum of Science & Industry in Manchester

Manchester

Based in the buildings of the world's oldest passenger railway station (dating from 1830), the Museum has colourful hands-on galleries that amuse, amaze and entertain. There are train rides on Sundays (please ring for details) and visitors can find out about our industrial past, walk through a Victorian sewer complete with sounds and smells, and hunt an alien!
Location: Liverpool Road, Castlefield, Manchester (off Deansgate near Granada studios)
OS reference: SJ 831987
Operating society/organisation: The Museum of Science and Industry in Manchester, Liverpool Road, Castlefield, Manchester M3 4FP
Telephone: (0161) 832 2244
Car parks: On site, plus parking in the area (Museum car park £1.50)

Locomotives and multipe-units

Name	*No*	*Origin*	*Class*	*Type*	*Built*
Pender	3††	IoMR	—	2-4-0T	1873
Novelty	Replica of 1829 locomotive using some original parts				1986
—	3157†	PR	—	4-4-0	1911
—	2352§	SAR	GL	4-8-2+2-8-4	1929
Ariadne	1505 (27001)	BR	EM2 (77)	Co-Co	1954
Hector	26048	BR	EM1 (76)	Bo-Bo cab only	1952
*Planet**	—	Replica	—	2-2-0	1992

Industrial locomotives

Name	*No*	*Builder*	*Type*	*Built*
Lord Ashfield	—	Barclay (1964)	0-4-0ST	1929
—	258	E/Electric (1378)	4wBE	1944
—	—	Fowler	0-4-0D	1952

*Replica of 1830-built locomotive
††Ex-Isle of Man Railways, 3ft gauge, sectioned (B/Peacock 1255)
†Ex-Pakistan Railways, 5ft 6in gauge (V/Foundry 3064)
§Ex-South African Railways, 3ft 6in gauge (B/Peacock 6693)

Rolling stock
BR Mk 2 SO E5241, 1966
Replica M&BR 1st class carriage c1840 using original fragments

Access by public transport: Manchester Victoria, Piccadilly, Oxford Road and Deansgate main line stations. GM bus 33. G-Mex Metrolink station

On site facilities: Oldest passenger railway station, weekend train rides, listed buildings containing exhibitions about science, industry, aviation, space, water supply and sewage disposal, gas and electricity. Xperiment! the hands-on science centre and the 'Out of this world' space gallery. World's largest collection of working steam mill engines in the Power Hall, demonstrated every afternoon. Xpressions coffee shop, Kites Cafe and Mosaics gift shop

2 replica L&MR 2nd class carriages c1835
c1908 L&YR ambulance carriage re-built 1923 as Medical Examination Car, LMS No 10825 (under restoration)
B955209 20-ton goods brake van, BR (Ashford), 1962
B782903 4-wheeled covered goods van, BR (Wolverton), 1961
B783709 4-wheeled covered goods van, BR (Wolverton), 1962
3-plank loose coupled goods wagon, MSLR (Dukinfield)?, c1890

Owners
Novelty on loan from the National Railway Museum, York
MSLR Wagon on loan from G. Maskin
Industrial locomotives (except Fowler) on loan from PowerGen

Public opening: Daily except 24-26 December, including Saturdays and Sundays, 10.00-17.00. Entrance in Lower Byrom Street. Admission charged

Special notes: Good wheelchair access, toilets for the disabled, lecture and conference facilities

Museum

National Railway Museum

North Yorkshire

Members: AIRPS, TT, MLSOG
Location: National Railway Museum, Leeman Road, York YO2 4XJ
OS reference: SE 594519
Operating society/organisation: Part of the National Museum of Science and Industry
Telephone: York (01904) 621261
Car park: Available on site at £2.50 per day. Coach parking is available — pre-booking required
Access by public transport: The Museum is within a few minutes' walking distance of the railway and bus stations in York. The York City & District Bus Service operates to the door
On site facilities: Museum shop, restaurant and toilets. Reference library (free by appointment)
Public opening: Daily 10.00-18.00. Closed 24-26 December
Facilities for disabled: Most areas of the museum are accessible
Special notes: The Museum has been open since 1975 and has welcomed over 19 million visitors.

It offers the visitor two extensive exhibition halls, the Great Hall and the South Hall, which house the world's premier collection of railway related material.

The Great Hall displays are on the theme of railway technology. There is a magnificent display of railway locomotive development round the turntable. Signalling, the permanent way, the modern railway and the Channel Tunnel are also represented. The displays reflect the future, the present and the past and include a full-sized model of the nose cone of a state of the art Transmanche Super Train operating between England and the Continent. Displays on the operation of the railways, tape/slide presentations can be found on the Balcony Galleries. A new exhibition 'Moving Things: The Mail' opened in October 1996

The South Hall illustrates the concept of travel by train — for passengers and freight. Several trains are drawn up at platforms with a number of footplates and carriages open to visitors. The vehicles displayed range from the superb Royal carriages to humble freight wagons.

Magician's Road, the children's activity centre, provides visitors with hands-on experience of various aspects of railway operation.

The Museum's extensive reference library (including the photographic and drawings collections) continues to be free to all booked enquirers every weekday from 10.30-17.00.

The tables which follow indicate the whereabouts (display, on loan, in store) of the National Railway Collection. It must be emphasised that the appearance of any particular item on public display cannot be guaranteed. If it is vital to discover the exact whereabouts of a specific item, enquirers should contact the Museum in York before the trip

The National Railway Museum is open for evening hire for private viewings and celebrations; menus and details are available on request.

Details of membership of the Museum's support group, including free entry and a quarterly newsletter are available from: The Secretary, Friends of the National Railway Museum, c/o the above address.

Locomotives — Steam

Name	*No*	*Origin*	*Builder*	*Class*	*Type*	*Built*
Agenoria	—	Shutt End Colliery	Foster/Raistrick	—	0-4-0	1829
Columbine	1868	LNWR	Crewe	—	2-2-2	1845
Coppernob	3	FR	Bury, Curtis & Kennedy	—	0-4-0	1846
Pet	—	LNWR	Crewe	—	0-4-0ST	1865
Aerolite	66	NER	Gateshead	X1(LNER)	2-2-4T	1869
—	1	GNR	Doncaster	—	4-2-2	1870
Bauxite	2	Hebburn Works	B/Hawthorn	—	0-4-0ST	1874
—	910	NER	Gateshead	E6	2-4-0	1875
Boxhill	82	LB&SCR	Brighton	A1	0-6-0T	1880
Gladstone	214	LB&SCR	Brighton	—	0-4-2	1882
Wren	—	LYR	B/Peacock	—	0-4-0ST	1887
—	1008	LYR	Horwich	—	2-4-2T	1889
Hardwicke	790	LNWR	Crewe	—	2-4-0	1892
—	563	LSWR	Nine Elms	T3	4-4-0	1893
—	1621	NER	Gateshead	M	4-4-0	1893
—	245	LSWR	Nine Elms	M7	0-4-4T	1897
—	673	MR	Derby	—	4-2-2	1899
—	737	SECR	Ashford	D	4-4-0	1901
—	251	GNR	Doncaster	C1	4-4-2	1902
—	1000	MR	Derby	4	4-4-0	1902
—	87	GER	Stratford	J69	0-6-0T	1904
—	1217	GER	Stratford	J17	0-6-0	1905
—	2818	GWR	Swindon	2800	2-8-0	1905
Lode Star	4003	GWR	Swindon	'Star'	4-6-0	1907
Butler Henderson	506	GCR	Gorton	'Director'	4-4-0	1920
—	485	LNWR	Crewe	G2/Super D	0-8-0	1921
Cheltenham	925	SR	Eastleigh	V/Schools	4-4-0	1934
—	2500	LMS	Derby	4P	2-6-4T	1934
—	5000	LMS	Crewe	5MT	4-6-0	1935
—	KF7	Chinese Govt Rlys	Vulcan	KF	4-8-4	1935
Green Arrow	4771	LNER	Doncaster	V2	2-6-2	1936
Mallard	4468	LNER	Doncaster	A4	4-6-2	1938
Eustace Forth	15	—	RSH (7063)	—	0-4-0ST	1942
Winston Churchill	34051	SR	Brighton	BB	4-6-2	1946
Ellerman Lines	35029	BR(SR)	Sectioned	MN	4-6-2	1949
—	—	Imperial Paper Mills	Barclay	—	0-4-0F	1956
—	5500	BR	Brush	31	A1A-A1A	1957
Frank Galbraith	5	Tees-Side Bridge & Engineering Co	Sentinel	—	4wTG	1957
Evening Star	92220	BR	Swindon	9F	2-10-0	1960
Kings Own Yorkshire Light Infantry	55002	BR	E/Electric	55	Co-Co	1961
Rocket (replica)	—	—	Loco Enterprises	—	0-2-2	1979
Iron Duke (broad gauge replica)	—	GWR	RESCO	—	4-2-2	1985

Locomotives — Electric

Name	*No*	*Origin*	*Builder*	*Class*	*Type*	*Built*
—	75S	W&CR	Siemens (6)	—	Bo electric	1898
—	1	NER	BTH	—	Bo-Bo electric	1904
—	809	GPO	Green Bat	—	2w-2E	1931
—	26020	BR	Gorton/Metrovick	76	Bo-Bo Electric	1951
—	E3036	BR	N/British	84	Bo-Bo	1960

Locomotives — Diesel

Name	No	Origin	Builder	Class	Type	Built
—	—	—	Simplex (4217)	—	4wPM	1925
Hexhamshire	15	CEGB	A/Whitworth (D21)		0-4-0DE	1933
—	08064	BR	Darlington	08	0-6-0 DE	1953
BEA Carrington Station	3	CEGB	RSH (7746)	—	0-6-0 DM	1954
—	D8000	BR	E/Electric	20	Bo-Bo	1957
Deltic	—	E/Electric	E/Electric	—	Co-Co	1955
—	D200	BR	E/Electric	40	1Co-Co1	1958
—	03090	BR	—	03	0-6-0DM	1960
—	D2860	BR	YEC	02	0-4-0 DH	1960
Western Fusilier	D1023	BR	Swindon	52	C-C	1963
Glorious	50033	BR	E/Electric	50	Co-Co	1968
—*	41001	BR	Crewe	41	Bo-Bo	1972

*Stored at MoD Kineton

Rolling Stock Powered Units— Gas Turbine

1972 BR Advanced Passenger Train

Rolling Stock Powered Units — Electric

1915 LNWR Motor Open Third Brake No28249
1925 SR Motor Third Brake No S8143S
1937 SR Motor Third Open Brake No S11179S
1940 SR (W&C) Motor Driving Car No 61

Rolling Stock Powered Units — Diesel

1959 BR DMU Class 108 Nos 51562 & 51922
1975 Leyland Motors LEV-1 experimental railbus

Rolling Stock — Departmental

1850 GNR 4-wheel hand crane No 112
1890 GNR Locomotive Tender No 1002
1891 NER Snow Plough No DE900566
1899 GWR Hand Crane No 537
1904 MR Officers' Saloon No 2234
1906 NER Dynamometer Car No 902502
1907 NER Steam Breakdown Crane No CME 13
1907 Match Truck No DE942114
1911 GWR Track Testing Coach
1926 LNER Match Truck No DE320952
1931/2 LNER Petrol-driven platelayers' trolley No 960209
1936 GWR Ballast Wagon No 80659
1938 LMS Mobile test unit No 1, No 45053
1949 BR Matisa tamping machine No 74007
1949* GWR/BR Inspection Saloon No ADW80970
1955 GEC 12.5ton Coles Crane
1957 BR Track recording trolley No DX 50002 *Neptune*
1969 BR Plasser Tamping & Liner No 73010

Rolling Stock — Passenger

1834 B&WR 1st & 2nd composite
1834 B&WR 2nd class
1834 B&WR 3rd class
1842 L&BR Queen Adelaide's Saloon
1845 S&DR 1st/3rd Composite No 59
1850 NER Brake End (body only)
1851 ECR 1st class No 1
1860 Cornwall Rly broad gauge coach (body only)
1861 NBR Port Carlisle branch 'dandy car'
1869 LNWR Queen Victoria's Saloon
1872 NLR Directors' Saloon No 1032
1885 MR 6-wheel composite brake No 901
1885 WCJS 8-wheel TPO No 186
1887 GNR Brake Van No 848
1887 GWR 6-wheel tricomposite No 820
1897 Lynton & Barnstaple Rly brake composite No 6992
1898 ECJS 3rd class No 12
1899 Privately owned Duke of Sutherland's Saloon No 57A
1900 LNWR (ex-WCJS) Dining Car LMS 76
1902 LNWR King Edward's Saloon No 800
1902 LNWR Queen Alexandra's Saloon No 801
1903 LSWR Tricomposite brake No 3598
1905* LNWR Corridor 1st Brake 5154 (Royal Train)
1905* LNWR Corridor 1st Brake 5154 (support vehicle)
1908 ECJS Royal Saloon No 395
1913 Pullman Car Co 1st class parlour car *Topaz*
1914 MR Dining car No 3463
1920* LNWR Royal Saloon No 45000
1925 LMS 3rd class vestibule No 7828
1928 LMS 3rd Sleeping Car No 14241
1930 L&MR 1st *Huskinson* (replica)
1930 L&MR 1st *Traveller* (replica)
1930 L&MR 2nd (replica)
1930 L&MR 2nd (replica)
1934 GWR Buffet Car No 9631
1936 CIWL Night Ferry sleeping car No 3792
1937 LNER Buffet Car No 9135
1938 GJR TPO (replica)
1941 LMS Royal Saloon 799
1945* GWR Royal Saloon No 9006
1955 BR Lavatory composite No E43046
1960* BR Griddle car No Sc1100
1960 Pullman Car Co 1st class Parlour car No 326 *Emerald*
1962* BR Prototype Mk II 1st class corridor No 13252
1962 BR Mk II 2nd brake corridor No 35468
1962* BR Mk II 1st corridor No 21274
1969 BR Mk IIb 2nd open No 5455
1985 GWR 2nd (broad gauge replica)
1985 GWR 3rd (broad gauge replica)

Rolling Stock — Freight & Non Passenger Carrying

1815 Little Eaton (Derby Canal) Gangroad Wagon
1815 Peak Forest Canal Tramway Wagon No 174

1816	Grantham Canal Tramway Truck
1826	Cramlington Colliery Chaldron Wagon
1828	Dandy Cart
1840	Stratford & Moreton Tramway wagon
1850	South Hetton Colliery chaldron wagon No 1155
1870	Seaham Harbour Colliery Chaldron Wagon
1870	S&DR Chaldron Wagon (replica)
1889	Shell-Mex oil tank wagon No 512
1894	LSWR Brake van No 99
1895	LSWR Open carriage truck No 5830
1901	Shell/BP Tank Wagon No 3171
1902	NER 20-ton wooden hopper wagon No 4551
1907	NER 16ton bogie stores van No 041273
1908	LNWR Open Carriage Truck No 11275
1912	LB&SCR Open wagon No 27884
1912	LSWR Gunpowder van No KDS61209
1912	NER Sand wagon No DE14974
1912	GNR 8-ton van No E432764
1914	GWR Shunters' truck No W94988
1917	Shell tank wagon No 3171
1917	MR 8ton open wagon
1917	GCR Box Van
1917	LNWR Box Van
1917	NER Box Van
1920	GNR double bolster wagon
1920	GCR single bolster wagon
1924	LMSR Van
1926	GWR Fitted open wagon No 108246
1927	LNER 40 ton flat wagon No DE633433
1928	ICI Nitric acid tank wagon No 14
1931	GWR Fruit Van No 112884
1931	Stanton Iron Works 12ton wagon
1933	LMSR 20ton Goods Brake Van No 295987
1933	PLM Train Ferry Van No 475014
1935	SR Bogie goods brake van No 56297
1935	GWR Motor car van No 126438
1936	LMSR 3 Plank Open Wagon No 472867
1936	LMS Tube wagon No 499254
1937	GWR Siphon bogie milk van No 2775
1937	LMSR Milk Tank Wagon No 44057
1938	GWR 20ton Goods Brake Van No DW56518
1938	LMS Single bolster wagon No 722702
1940	WD Warflat No 161042
1944	LMS Lowmac No M700728
1944	GWR 13ton open wagon No DW143698
1946	SNCF 16ton mineral wagon No ADB192437
1946	LNER 20ton hopper wagon No E270919
1949	BR Bogie bolster D No B941000
1950	BR 24-ton iron ore hopper wagon No B436275
1950	BR 20ton Weltrol No B900805
1951	ICI Liquid chlorine tank wagon No 47484
1951	BR(SR) Show cattle wagon No S3733S
1951	BR 8ton cattle wagon No B893343
1952	BR 30ton bogie bolster wagon No B943139
1954	BR 27ton Iron Ore Tippler No B383560
1954	National Benzole oil tank wagon No 2022
1955	BR china clay tip wagon No B743141
1957	BR Horse box No S96369
1959	BR Conflat No B737725
1960	BR Banana Van No B882593
1960	BR 25ton Weltrol WP No ADB 900916
1961	BR Presflo cement wagon No B873368
1961	BR 30ton bogie bolster No B923123
1962	BR Speedfreight container No BA 4324B
1965	BR Boiler Wagon Nos DB902805, DB902806, DB902807, DB902808
1966	Milk Marketing Board 6-wheel tank No 42801
1970	Phillips Petroleum 100-ton GLW tank wagon No PP85209
1970	BR 2,000gal Road/Rail Milk Tank No ADM707111
1979	S&DR Chaldron wagon (replica)

*Stored at MoD Kineton

Items on Loan from the NRM
Locomotives

Original type/No/Name	*Location*	*Builder*	*Built*
Wylam Colliery	Science Mus	—	1813
Hetton Colliery 0-4-0	Beamish	G. Stephenson	1822
SDR 0-4-0 *Locomotion*	Darlington	R. Stephenson & Co	1825
L&MR 0-2-2 *Rocket*	Science Mus	R. Stephenson & Co	1829
L&MR 0-4-0 *Sans Pareil*	Science Mus	T. Hackworth	1829
L&MR 0-2-2 *Novelty*	Museum of Science & Technology (Manchester)	Braithwaite & Ericsson	1829
SDR 0-6-0 No 24 *Derwent*	Darlington Nth Rd Mus	A. Kitching	1845
LNWR 2-2-2 No 3020 *Cornwall*	Crewe	Crewe	1847
Wantage Tramway 0-4-0WT No 5 *Shannon*	Didcot Rly Ctr	G. England	1857
LNWR 0-4-0ST 1439	East Lancs	Crewe	1865
MR 2-4-0 No 158A	Midland Rly Ctr	Derby	1866
South Devon Rly 0-4-0WT *Tiny*	South Devon Rly	Sara	1868
LSWR 2-4-0WT No 0298	South Devon Rly	B/Peacock	1874
NER 0-6-0 No 1275	Darlington	Duds & Co	1874
NER 2-4-0 No 910	Darlington Nth Rd Mus	Gateshead	1875
NER 2-4-0 No 1463	Darlington Nth Rd Mus	Gateshead	1885
C&SL Bo electric No 1	London Trans Mus	B/Peacock	1890
S&MR 0-4-2WT *Gazelle*	Col Stephens Rly Mus	Dodman	1893
GER 2-4-0 No 490	Bressingham	Stratford	1894
GWR 0-6-0 No 2516	Swindon GWR Mus	Swindon	1897
TVR 0-6-2T No 28	Dean Forest	TVR	1897

Original type/No/Name	*Location*	*Builder*	*Built*
GNR No 990 *Henry Oakley*	Bressingham	Doncaster	1989
LSWR 4-4-0 No 120	Bluebell Rly	Nine Elms	1899
GNR 0-6-0ST No 1247	East Somerset	S/Stewart	1899
GWR 4-4-0 No 3440	Swindon	Swindon	1903
LT&SR 4-4-2T No 80 *Thundersley*	Bressingham	R. Stephenson	1909
GCR 2-8-0 No 102	Great Central	Gorton	1911
NSR 0-4-0wE No 1	Churnet Valley	Bolton	1917
WD No 1377 (2ft Gauge)	LBR	Simplex	1918
NER 0-8-0 No 901	North York Moors Rly	Darlington	1919
NSR No 2	Cheddleton	Stoke	1922
GWR 4-6-0 No 4073 *Caerphilly Castle*	Didcot	Swindon	1923
LMS 0-6-0 No 4027	Midland Rly Ctr	Derby	1924
GWR 2-2-2 *North Star* (replica)	Swindon GWR Mus	R. Stephenson	1925
SR 4-6-0 No 777 *Sir Lamiel*	GCR	N/British	1925
SR 4-6-0 No 850 *Lord Nelson*	Eastleigh†	Eastleigh	1926
LMS 2-6-0 No 2700	East Lancs	Derby	1934
GWR No 6000 *King George V*	Swindon GWR Mus	Swindon	1927
LMS4-6-2 No 46229 *Duchess of Hamilton*	East LAncs	Crewe	1938
SR 0-6-0 No C1	Bluebell Rly	Eastleigh	1942
GWR 0-6-0PT No 9400	Swindon GWR Mus	Swindon	1947
BR 4-6-2 No 70013 *Oliver Cromwell*	Bressingham	Crewe	1951
BR Bo-Bo No E5001	Hastings	Eastleigh	1958

†Private site

Powered Units

NER electric parcels van No 3267, G. Stephenson Mus
SR 2BIL unit, No 2090, Hastings (private site)
GWR diesel railcar No 4, Swindon GWR Mus
LMS electric motor brake 2nd No 28361, (in store)
LMS electric driving trailer composite No 29896, (in store)
BR APT-P pre-production Advanced Passenger Train, Kineton (motor car only)
BR Magnetic LEV prototype, Science Museum (Wroughton store)

Departmental Stock

1908 LNWR match truck, No 284235, Steamtown
1908 LNWR steam crane, No 2987, Steamtown
1932 LMS Ballast plough brake van No 197266, Embsay
1937 SR Match Truck No ADB975672, NYMR
1949 BR(LMS) Dynamometer car No 3, No 45049, East Lancs

Passenger Stock

1846 SDR 1st & 2nd composite No 31, Darlington Nth Rd Mus
1850 SDR 3rd No 179, Timothy Hackworth Mus, Shildon
1850 NER 4-wheel coach body, Darlington
1905 LNWR Corridor 1st Brake No 5155 (Royal Train), Kineton
1908 ECJS Passenger Brake van LNER No 109, Kineton
1908 ECJS Passenger Brake van LNER No 396, Bressingham
1910 GCR Open 3rd class No 666, Great Central Railway
1925 GWR 3rd class dining car No 9653, Severn Valley Rly
1925 GWR 3rd class dining car No 9654, Severn Valley Rly
1936 LNER 3rd Open, No 13254, Great Central
1937 LMS corridor 3rd class brake No 5987, Steamtown
1941 LMS Royal saloon No 798, Glasgow Museum of Transport
1945 GWR Royal Saloon No 9007, West Somerset
1950 BR (LMS) 3rd brake, No 27093, Midland Rly Ctr
1960 Pullman Car Co 1st class Kitchen car No 311 *Eagle,* NYMR

Freight & Non-Passenger Carrying Stock

1909 GWR Girder Wagon Set (Pollen E) Nos DW84997, 84998, 84999, 85000, Didcot
1917 GWR Hydra-D No 42193, Didcot Railway Ctr
1920 LSWR Lowmac, No DE563024, NYMR
1922 LB&SCR cattle truck No 7116, Isle of Wight Steam Rly
1933 LMSR gunpowder van, No 288824, NYMR
1939 SR postal sorting van No 4920, Nene Valley Rly
1941 LNER 20 ton brake van, No 246710, NYMR
1945 GWR 25 ton machine truck, Embsay
1948 BR(SR) 12-ton shock absorbing wagon No 14036, NYMR
1949 BR 40-ton Gane-A No DB996724, North Staffs
1950 BR 12-wheel well wagon, No KDB901601, East Lancs
1955 BR 16ton mineral wagon No B227009, Middleton
1959 BR Fish van No B87905, Hull
1970 S&D Chaldron wagon (replica), Shildon

Tram Service — National Tramway Museum — Derbyshire

Member: AIRPS, TT
An experience of living transport history with vintage horse-drawn, steam and electric trams running through a recreated townscape of authentic buildings, stone setts, iron railings and historic street furniture. The heart of the Museum is its collection of over 70 vintage trams and you can enjoy the thrill of travelling on the scenic mile-long track
Location: Crich, near Matlock, Derbyshire DE4 5DP
OS reference: SK 345549
Manager: John Miller
Operating society/organisation: Tramway Museum Society
Telephone: (01773) 852565
Car park: Site; coach parking also available
Access by public transport: Nearest stations: Cromford (main line) or Alfreton (main line) then by bus; or Whatstandwell (main line) and steep uphill walk
On site facilities: Souvenir shop, bookshop and picnic areas. 1-mile electric tramway. Tramway period street, depots, displays, exhibitions and video theatre. Large exhibition hall now open, with new interpretive display depicting the history of the tram and Turn of the Century Trade Exhibition
Refreshment facilities: Hot and cold snacks and meals
Public opening: From 4 April — daily (except 24th); May — daily except Fridays; June, July August — daily; September, October — daily except Fridays; PLUS special 'Holiday Friday' openings 29 May, 4 September, 23, 30 October. Open: 10.00 to 17.30 (18.30 Saturdays/Sundays/Bank Holidays) plus longer opening times in peak season and some special events.
Special events: a Yesterday Mayday — 25 May; Tram-jam-boree — 7 June; Funtasia — 12 July; National Festival of Transport — 30/31 August; The Final 'Mane' Event — 6 September; In Living Memory — 13 September; Starlight Special — 25 October; Treasure Trail — 26 October-1 November
Family tickets: Available
Facilities for disabled: Access available for most of site, Braille guide book available
Special notes: Crich houses the largest collection of preserved trams in Europe and has a 1-mile working tramway on which restored electric trams are regularly operated. Special events are arranged at weekends and Bank Holidays throughout the season. Part of tram line occupies route of narrow gauge mineral railway built by George Stephenson
Membership details: From above address
Membership journal: *The Journal* — quarterly

Locomotives

Name	*No*	*Builder*	*Type*	*Built*
—	—	B/Peacock (2464)	0-4-0VB tram loco	1885
—	—	E/Electric (717)	4wE	1927
*Rupert**	—	R/Hornsby (223741)	4wDM	1944
*GMJ**	—	R/Hornsby (326058)	4wDM	1952
—*	—	R/Hornsby (373363)	4wDM	1954

*Not on display

Also some 70 trams (including examples from Czechoslovakia, Germany, The Netherlands, Portugal, USA and South Africa), about a third of which have been restored to working order

Museum — National Waterways Museum — Glos

Member: AIRPS
Location: Gloucester Docks signposted
OS Reference: SO 826183
Operating society/Organisation: National Waterways Museum Charitable Trust Ltd, Llanthony Warehouse, Gloucester Docks, Gloucester GL1 2EH.
Tel: (01452) 318054
Fax: (01452) 318066
Curator: Tony Conder
Volunteer co-ordinator: David McDougall (Keeper of Collections)
Car parks: Outside museum, free coach parking
Access by public transport: Main line Gloucester station, 1-mile
On site facilities: Tea room, souvenir and book shop (canal-related with some railway literature). School room/children's holiday activities. Working demonstrations vary. Tug rides (summer weekends). Trip boats and other museums in docks
Facilities for disabled: Full facilities, lifts, ramps, toilets. All indoor displays, quaysides and tea room accessible. Floating exhibits

Industrial locomotives

Name	*No*	*Builder*	*Type*	*Built*
—	1	A/Barclay (2126)	0-4-0F	1942

Ex-Gloucester Corporation, Castle Meads Power Station, Gloucester Docks. Under restoration for static display

Rolling stock
William Balmforth of Rodley crane, c1880. Small collection of GW, Midland, LMS and BR vans. Sharpness Docks open wagons and Gloucester-built flat wagon

not accessible
Public opening: Daily, except Christmas Day, 10.00-17.00. Admission charged
Special events: Horses weekend; preservation, modellers' & craft events; leisure learning courses (send for leaflet)
Membership details: 'Friends' support organisation. Membership Secretary, c/o Museum address, Volunteers active in restoration/fundraising. Winter Meetings programme.
Membership journal: *Llanthony Log* — quarterly

Timetable Service

Nene Valley Railway

Cambs

Member: AIRPS, TT
This unique railway's collection includes locomotives and coaches from 10 countries and two continents. It is a regular location for TV and film makers — from films like *Goldeneye* with Pierce Brosnan as 007 to TV — *Hannay*, *London's Burning* — to commercials for cars, beer and soft drinks. The railway and the pleasant Cambridgeshire countryside have doubled for locations as diverse as Russia and Spain
General Manager: Mr M. A. Warrington
Headquarters: Nene Valley Railway, Wansford Station, Stibbington, Peterborough, Cambs PE8 6LR
Telephone: Stamford (01780) 784444; Talking Timetable (01780) 784440
Main station: Wansford
Other public stations: Orton Mere, Ferry Meadows, Peterborough NVR (10min walk from city centre)
OS reference: TL 903979
Car park: Wansford, Orton Mere, Ferry Meadows, Peterborough NVR
Access by public transport: Buses from Peterborough to Orton Mere and Ferry Meadows
Refreshment facilities: Wansford, Orton Mere. Bar coach on most trains
Souvenir shops: Wansford, Orton Mere, Ferry Meadows, Peterborough
Museum: Wansford
Depot: Wansford
Length of line: 7.5 miles
Passenger trains: Yarwell Mill-Wansford-Orton Mere-Peterborough NVR
Period of public operation: Open all year at Wansford (loco yard). Services operate every Sunday January-end October; Weekends April-end October; Wednesdays May-end August; every day (except Mondays mid-July-end August)
Special events: Gala Weekend — 28/29 March; Easter Holiday Specials (with *Thomas* at Wansford) — 10-13 April; May Day Bank Holiday (with *Thomas* at Wansford) — 2-4 May; *Thomas*

Locomotives

Name	No	Origin	Class	Type	Built
Mayflower	1306	LNER	B1	4-6-0	1948
92 Squadron	34081	SR	BB	4-6-2	1948
City of Peterborough	73050	BR	5MT	4-6-0	1954
—	D2122	BR	03	0-6-0DM	1959
—	D3871	BR	08	0-6-0DE	1960
—	D9516	BR	14	0-6-0DH	1964
—	D9523	BR	14	0-6-0DH	1964
—	14029 (D9529)	BR	14	0-6-0DH	1965
Atlantic Conveyor	D306	BR	40	1Co-Co1	1960
—	64.305-6	DB	64	2-6-2T	1936
—	7173	DB	52	2-10-0	1943
—	656	DSB	F	0-6-0T	1949
—	101	SJ	B	4-6-0	1944
—	1178	SJ	S	2-6-2T	1914
—	3.628	Nord	3500	4-6-0	1911
—	51401	BR	117	DMS	19??
—	51347	BR	117	DMBS	19??

Industrial locomotives

Name	No	Builder	Type	Built
—	—	Avonside (1945)	0-6-0ST	1926
Toby	—	Cockerill (1626)	0-4-0VBT	1890
Muriel	—	E/Electric (1123)	0-4-0DH	1966
Rhos	—	H/Clarke (1308)	0-6-0ST	1918
Derek Crouch	—	H/Clarke (1539)	0-6-0ST	1924
Thomas	—	H/Clarke (1800)	0-6-0T	1947
Jacks Green	—	Hunslet (1953)	0-6-0ST	1939
—	75006	Hunslet (2855)	0-6-0ST	1943
—	—	R/Hornsby (294268)	4wDM	1951
Doncaster	—	YEC (2654)	0-4-0DE	1957
—	11	Rebuilt Hill	4wD	1963
Stanton No 50	—	YEC (2670)	0-6-0DE	1958
—	DL83	R/Royce (10271)	0-6-0DH	1967

Stock
14 BR Mk 1 coaches; Wagons Lits sleeping car, Italian-built; Wagons Lits dining car, Belgian-built; 6 coaches from Denmark; 1 coach from France; 4 coaches from Belgium; 3 steam rail cranes; SR Travelling Post Office; TPO coach M30272M; 20 12ton Vanfits plus items of freight stock

Owners
34081 the Battle of Britain Locomotive Preservation Society
73050 Peterborough City Council

Above: **Swedish State Railways' No 101 at the head of a demonstration freight train at Orton Mere on the Nene Valley Railway.** ***John East***

Below: Sir Nigel Gresley **in early British Railways blue livery at Goathland whilst on loan to the North Yorkshire Moors Railway.** ***Alan P. Barnes***

Birthday Weekend — 26-28 June. *Thomas* will also be out and about on 1/2, 29-31 August, October half-term and Santa Specials in December (phone for details)
Facilities for disabled: Ramp access to all stations and shops. Full toilets in Wansford station, souvenir shop. Disabled persons and helpers are eligible for concessionary fares. Passengers can be assisted on and off trains
Membership details: Bill Foreman, c/o above address
Membership journal: *Nene Steam* — 3 times/year; *Nene Staff* (workers' newsletter) — 6 times/year
Marketing name: Britain's International Steam Railway

Timetable Service

North Norfolk Railway

Norfolk

Member: AIRPS, TT
Part of the former Midland & Great Northern Joint Railway, other elements of the LNER have crept in in the guise of the 'B12' and a Gresley buffet car. The GER 'J15' is being restored. Guest locomotives can be viewed at various times throughout the year. The line runs through beautiful coast, wood and heathland scenery with a nature trail running along its side between Weybourne and Kelling Heath
General Manager: John Tinkler
Headquarters: North Norfolk Railway, Sheringham station, Sheringham, Norfolk NR26 8RA
Telephone: Sheringham (01263) 822045. Talking timetable: (01263) 825449
Fax: (01263) 823794
Main station: Sheringham
Other public stations: Weybourne, Kelling Heath Park, Holt
OS reference: Sheringham TG 156430, Weybourne TG 118419
Car parks: Sheringham, Weybourne, Holt
Access by public transport: By train to Sheringham station (200 yd)
Refreshment facilities: Sheringham, Weybourne
Souvenir shops: Sheringham, Weybourne, Holt
Museum: Sheringham
Depot: Weybourne
Length of line: 5.25 miles
Passenger trains: Steeply graded, Sheringham-Weybourne-Holt

Locomotives and multiple-units

Name	*No*	*Origin*	*Class*	*Type*	*Built*
—	564	GER	J15	0-6-0	1912
—	8572	LNER	B12	4-6-0	1928
—	D3935	BR	08	0-6-0DE	1961
—	12131	BR	11	0-6-0DE	1952
—	D5207	BR	25	Bo-Bo	1962
Holt Pioneer	D5386	BR	27	Bo-Bo	1962
Mirage	D6732	BR	37	Co-Co	1962
—	79960	W&M	—	Railbus	1958
—	79963	W&M	—	Railbus	1958
—	Car 87*	M/Cam	5BEL	TPS	1932
—	Car 91*	M/Cam	5BEL	DMPBS	1932
—	51346	P/Steel	117	DMBS	1959
—	51388	P/Steel	117	DMS	1959
—	59516	P/Steel	117	TCL	1960

*Ex-'Brighton Belle' Pullman cars, converted to locomotive-hauled

Industrial locomotives

Name	*No*	*Builder*	*Type*	*Built*
Ring Haw	—	Hunslet (1982)	0-6-0ST	1940
—	3809	Hunslet (3809)	0-6-0ST	1954
—	68009	Hunslet (3825)	0-6-0ST	1953
Birchenwood	4	Bagnall (2680)	0-6-0ST	1944
—	10	E/Electric (C8431)	0-4-0DH	1963
Wissington	—	H/Clarke (1700)	0-6-0ST	1938
—	—	Bagnall (2370)	0-6-0F	1929

Stock
7 ex-LNER coaches; Small number of wagons

Owners
564 and 61572 the Midland & Great Northern Railway Society

Period of public operation: Not advised. Please contact for details
Special events: Not advised. Please contact for details
Facilities for disabled: Specially adapted Pullman Car available, advanced booking essential
Membership details: Midland & Great Northern Joint Railway Society, Clive Morris, c/o above address
Membership journal: *Joint Line* — quarterly
Marketing name: The Poppy Line

Museum

North Woolwich Old Station Museum

London

No expense has been spared in the very imaginative restoration of this attractive Victorian terminus building overlooking the Thames. Railway artefacts, documents, drawings, etc, are well displayed in glass cases or on the walls, the stock being stabled in the platform area. Convenient for the new City airport and connections for the Docklands Light Railway

Location: North Woolwich Old Station Museum, Pier Road, North Woolwich, London E16 2JJ
OS reference: TQ 433798
Organisation: Newham Museum Service
Telephone: (0171) 474 7244
Car park: Only in adjoining streets
Public transport: Main line North London Link. Buses: 101, 69 and 473
Facilities: Museum shop
Public opening: Open April to September, Saturdays 10.00-17.00, Sundays 10.00-17.00. Mondays to Wednesdays (school summer holiday only) 13.00-15.00. Winter — closed
Admission: Free

Locomotives

Name	*No*	*Origin*	*Class*	*Type*	*Built*
—	229	GER	209	0-4-0ST	1876

Industrial locomotives

Name	*No*	*Builder*	*Type*	*Built*
—	—	Hibberd (3294)	4wDM	1948
—	—	Peckett (2000)	0-6-0ST	1942

Stock

1 ex-LNER coach; 2 compartment sections of LTSR coach; NLR Luggage Van; 1 ex-Royal Arsenal Ammunition Van (18in gauge)

Timetable Service

North Yorkshire Moors Railway

North Yorkshire

Member: AIRPS, TT

This 18-mile line runs through the picturesque North York Moors National Park and is host to an extensive collection of main line locomotives

Financial & Commercial Director: Ken Kitching
Headquarters: Pickering Station, Pickering, North Yorkshire YO18 7AJ
Telephone: Pickering (01751) 472508 for passenger enquiries, charter and dinner bookings
Main station: Pickering
Other public stations: Grosmont, Goathland, Levisham
OS reference: Pickering NZ 797842, Levisham NZ 818909, Goathland NZ 836013, Grosmont NZ 828053
Car parks: Grosmont, Goathland, Levisham, Pickering
Access by public transport: Main line service to Grosmont from Whitby and Middlesbrough. Bus services Malton-Pickering, York or Scarborough-Pickering and Whitby-Goathland and Pickering
Refreshment facilities: Available

Locomotives and multiple-units

Name	*No*	*Origin*	*Class*	*Type*	*Built*
George Stephenson†	44767	LMS	5MT	4-6-0	1947
Eric Treacy	45428	LMS	5MT	4-6-0	1937
—	65894	NER	P3	0-6-0	1923
—	2238	NER	T2	0-8-0	1918
—	901	NER	T3	0-8-0	1919
Blue Peter†	60532	LNER	A2	4-6-2	1948
—†	62005	LNER	K1	2-6-0	1949
—	69023	LNER	J72	0-6-0T	1951
—	3814	GWR	2884	2-8-0	1940
—	6619	GWR	5600	0-6-2T	1928
—	30841	SR	S15	4-6-0	1936
Repton	30926	SR	V	4-4-0	1934
Hartland	34101	SR	WC	4-6-2	1950
—	75014	BR	4MT	4-6-0	1951
—	80135	BR	4MT	2-6-4T	1956
Dame Vera Lynn	3672	MoS	WD	2-10-0	1943
—	90775	MoS	WD	2-10-0	1943
—	2253	USATC	S160	2-8-0	1942
—	D2207	BR	04	0-6-0DM	1953
—	08556	BR	08	0-6-0DE	1959
—	D5032	BR	24	Bo-Bo	1959
—	24061	BR	24	Bo-Bo	1960
—	D7541	BR	25	Bo-Bo	1965
—	D7628	BR	25	Bo-Bo	1965
Lion	50027	BR	50	Co-Co	1961
Alycidon†	55009	BR	55	Co-Co	1961

†Not on site

on most trains and at Grosmont, Goathland and Pickering
Souvenir shops: Pickering, Goathland, Grosmont
Museum: Situated at locomotive depot, Grosmont
Depot: Grosmont
Length of line: 18 miles
Passenger trains: Steam-hauled services Grosmont-Pickering. Pullman evening dining service and 'Moorlander' Sunday lunch service run regularly. GWR and NER saloons are also available for special occasions (eg wedding parties, conferences, etc)
Special events: Throughout the season, ring for details
Period of public operation: Daily 21 March-1 November, Santa Specials and other Xmas services in December/January
Facilities for disabled: The NYMR welcomes disabled visitors and special attention will gladly be provided if advanced notice is given
Special notes: Operates through North York Moors National Park

Industrial locomotives

Name	*No*	*Builder*	*Type*	*Built*
—	29	Kitson (4263)	0-6-2T	1904
—	5	R/Stephenson (3377)	0-6-2T	1909
Stanton	No 44	Yorkshire (2622)	0-4-0DE	1956
No 21	—	Fowler (4210094)	0-4-0DH	1954
Antwerp	—	Hunslet (3180)	0-6-0ST	1944
—	12139	E/Electric (1553)	0-6-0DE	1948
—	16	Drewry	0-4-0DM	1941
—	2	R/Hornsby (421419)	4wDM	1958
—	3*	R/Hornsby (441934)	4wDM	1960
—	1	Vanguard (129V)	0-4-0DM	1963
—	2	Vanguard (131V)	0-4-0DM	1963

*On loan to Middleton Railway

Stock
36 x BR Mk 1, 4 x Pullman, 2 x BR XP64, 1 x BR Mk 2, 3 x GUV, 7 x Gresley, 6 x Thompson, 1 x GW Saloon, 1 x SR Bulleid, 3 x LMS, 1 x GCR Barnum, 1 x GNR Brake, 3 x NER, 2 x H&BR, 2 x diesel cranes, 2 x 45ton steam cranes, over 40 wagons.

Owners
90775 and 30841 Essex Locomotive Society
62005, 2238, 65894, 69023 the North Eastern Locomotive Preservation Group
60532 on loan to the North Eastern Locomotive Preservation Group
63460 on loan from the National Railway Museum
75014 75014 Locomotive Operators Group
Antwerp the National Coal Board
55009 the Deltic Preservation Society
21, 44 British Steel Corporation
29 Lambton 29 Syndicate
5, 926, 2253, 3814, 6619, 34101 and 80135 private

Steam Centre

Northampton & Lamport Railway

Northants

Member: AIRPS
Headquarters: Pitsford & Brampton Station, Pitsford Road, Chapel Brampton, Northampton NN6 8BA
Location: About 5 miles north of Northampton, Pitsford Road off A5199 (A50) or A508
General Manager: Mr R. Faulkner
Operating company: Northampton Steam Railway Ltd
Operating society: Northampton & Lamport Railway Preservation Society
Telephone: (01604) 820327 (mainly Sundays, recorded announcements other times)
Car parks: On site
Access by public transport: None
On site facilities: NLR sales shop, toilets, buffet coach
Length of line: Three quarters of a mile at present. Work on southern extension to start shortly

Locomotives and multiple-units

Name	*No*	*Origin*	*Class*	*Type*	*Built*
—	3862	GWR	2884	2-8-0	1942
Castell Dinas Bran	25035	BR	25	Bo-Bo	1963
—	26010	BR	26	Bo-Bo	1959
—	D5401	BR	27	Bo-Bo	1962
The Royal Artilleryman	45118	BR	45	1Co-Co1	1962
—	51367	BR	119	DMBS	1959
—	54495	BR	108	DTCL	1960
—	55001	BR	122	DMBS	1958
—	55003	BR	122	DMBS	1958
—	13004	SR	4DD	DMBS	1949

Industrial locomotives

Name	*No*	*Builder*	*Type*	*Built*
Colwyn	45	Kitson (5470)	0-6-0ST	1933
—	2104	Peckett (2104)	0-4-0ST	1948
Vanguard	5374	Chrzanow (5374)	0-6-0T	1959
—	17646	Chrzanow (5387)	0-6-0T	1959
Bunty	146C	Fowler (4210018)/ rebuilt T/Hill	0-4-0DM	1950 1964
—	1	R/Hornsby (275886)	4wDM	1949
Sir Gyles Isham	764	R/Hornsby (319286)	0-4-0DM	1953

Public opening: Every Sunday from 1 March to 29 November, plus Santa Specials
Special events: Easter — 12-14 April; Spring Diesel Gala — 9/10 May; Friends of Thomas the Tank Engine — 23-25 May, 26/27 September; Teddy Bears' Weekend — 22-24 August; Steam Gala — 12/13 September; Autumn Diesel Gala — 3/4 October; Santa Specials — 5/6, 12/13, 18/19, 24 December; Mince Pie Specials 27/28 December, 1 January; Diesel service 2nd Sunday of month except April/September

Stock
Coaches: 1 BR Mk 1 FK; 2 BR Mk 1 TSO; Mk 1 BSO; 1 BR Mk 1 BSK; 1 BR Mk 1 SK; 1 BR Mk 1 CK; 1 BR Mk 1 RBR; 1 Mk 2 BSO (trolley buffet); 1 Mk 2 SO; 1 SR CCT van; 1 BR Mk 1 Suburban CL; 1 BR Mk 1 NAV; 2 BR NJV; 1 BR NAV; 2 SR PMV; 1 GWR full brake; 1 LMS CCT
Wagons — A number of various wagon types

Owners
Colwyn the Colwyn Preservation Society
17646 the Northampton Locomotive Co
54495 & 51367 the Northampton & Lamport Railway DMU Group

Membership details: Mr I. Rivett, Pitsford & Brampton Station, Pitsford Road, Chapel Brampton, Northampton NN6 8BA
Membership journal: *Premier Line* — 4 times a year

Steam Centre

Northamptonshire Ironstone Railway Trust

Northants

Location: Hunsbury Hill Industrial Museum, Hunsbury Hill Country Park, Hunsbury Hill Road, Camp Hill, Northampton
OS reference: SP 735584
Operating organisation: Northamptonshire Ironstone Railway Trust Ltd
Contact: C. Osborne, 11 Hillside Way, Weston Favell, Northampton NN3 3AW (Tel: [01604] 405970)
Access by public transport: Northampton Transport bus routes, 24, 25 to Camp Hill from Greyfriars bus station
On site facilities: Light refreshments, shop, toilets in car park. Children's play areas and picnic areas
Length of line: 2.25 miles with yard, engine shed and workshops, 2 stations and level crossing
Public opening: Museum and shed/yard for viewing most weekdays and weekends. Train service from Easter Sunday to end of September on Sundays and Bank Holiday Mondays plus December for Santa Specials. Parties can be catered for on weekdays by appointment
Times of opening: 10.00 to 16.00 for viewing with train service from 13.00 to 17.00
Facilities for the disabled: Passenger coach can accommodate wheelchairs
Special notes: Museum to the Ironstone Industry of Northamptonshire, the museum houses photographs, documents and other items connected with the ironstone undustry. The railway is laid on the old trackbed of the quarry system and partly on a new formation with remains of the quarry face and cuttings available for exploration
Membership details: Mr R. Coleman, c/o above address

Industrial locomotives

Name	*No*	*Builder*	*Type*	*Built*
Yvonne	—	Cockerill (2945)	0-4-0 Tram	1920
Vigilant†	—	Hunslet (287)	0-4-0ST	1882
Brill†	14	M/Wardle (1795)	0-4-0ST	1912
Belvedere◊	—	Sentinel (9365)	0-4-0TG	1946
Musketeer◊	—	Sentinel (9369)	0-4-0TG	1946
Hylton	—	Planet (3967)	0-4-0DH	1961
Lois	—	Fowler (422033)	0-4-0DH	1965
Muffin	46	R/Hornsby (242868)	4wDM	1946
—	16	Hunslet (2087)	0-4-0DM	1940
AMOCO	56	R/Hornsby	0-4-0DM	1956
Shire Lodge	53	R/Hornsby	0-4-0DM	1954
Sir Alfred	53	R/Hornsby (319214)	0-6-0DM	1953
—*	86	Peckett (1871)	0-6-0ST	1934
Northampton†	1	Bagnall (2565)	0-4-0ST	1934
—	—	Grafton	Steam crane	1934

* Meter gauge on loan to Irchester Country Park
◊ static display
† being rebuilt

Steam Centre

Nottingham Heritage Centre

Notts

Member: AIRPS
Location: On the A60 just south of Ruddington, 3 miles south of Nottingham city centre, off A52, 7 miles north of Loughborough. Signposted
Operating society/organisation: Great Central (Nottingham) Ltd, Nottingham Heritage Centre, Mere Way, Ruddington, Nottingham NG11 6NX
Telephone: (0115) 940 5905
Fax: (0115) 940 5905
Access by public transport: Buses from city centre and Broad Marsh (tel: [0115] 924 0000), via Nottingham Midland station
On site facilities: Car park, shop and cafe, picnic area and country park walks. 700m long passenger-carrying miniature railway. Extensive bus museum
Facilities for disabled: Accessible
Public opening: Steam Shuttle service Sundays & Bank Holidays Easter-mid October. 10.45-17.30
Membership details: Great Central Northern Development Association, c/o above address
Society journal: Quarterly

Locomotives and multiple-units

Name	*No*	*Origin*	*Class*	*Type*	*Built*
—	20094	BR	20	Bo-Bo	1961
—	20135	BR	20	Bo-Bo	1966
—	08885	BR	08	0-6-0DE	1962
—	13180	BR	08	0-6-0DE	1955
—	52060	BR	108	DMSL	1959
—	53645	BR	108	DMBS	1958
—	53926	BR	108	DMBS	1959
—	68088	LNER	Y7	0-4-0T	1927
—	45379	LMS	5MT	4-6-0	1937

Industrial locomotives

Name	*No*	*Builder*	*Type*	*Built*
—	54	H/Clarke (1682)	0-6-0ST	1937
—	1684	Hunslet (1684)	0-4-0T	1931
Powergen No 2	—	RSH (7818)	0-4-0ST	1954
—	56	RSH (7667)	0-6-0ST	1950
—	63	RSH (7761)	0-6-0ST	1954
Staythorpe	D2959	R/Hornsby	0-4-0DE	—

Rolling stock: 1 BR Mk 1 FO, 1 BR Mk 2 BSO, 1 BR Mk 2 BFK, 1 BR (ex-WR) cinema coach, GCR coach (body) CBL No 1663 (oldest surviving GCR coach, built 1903), Barnum coach, suburban coach, 1 LNER 45ton steam breakdown crane, 1 SR GUV, various goods wagons

Timetable Service

Paignton & Dartmouth Steam Railway

Devon

Member: AIRPS
The line from Paignton is the holiday line with steam trains running for seven miles in Great Western tradition along the spectacular Torbay coast to Churston and through the wooded slopes bordering the Dart estuary to Kingswear. The scenery is superb, with seascapes right across Lyme Bay to Portland Bill on clear days. Approaching Kingswear is the beautiful River Dart, with its fascinating craft, and on the far side, the 'olde worlde' town of Dartmouth and Britannia Royal Naval College, Butterwalk, Bayard's Cove and Dartmouth Castle

Locomotives and multiple-units

Name	*No*	*Origin*	*Class*	*Type*	*Built*
—	4555	GWR	4500	2-6-2T	1924
—	4588	GWR	4575	2-6-2T	1927
Goliath	5239	GWR	5205	2-8-0T	1924
—	6435	GWR	6400	0-6-0PT	1937
Lydham Manor	7827	GWR	7800	4-6-0	1951
Ardent	D2192	BR	03	0-6-0DM	1962
Volunteer	D3014	BR	08	0-6-0DE	1954
Mercury	D7535	BR	25	Bo-Bo	1965
Superb	50002	BR	50	Co-Co	1967
—	59003*	BR	116	TS	1957
—	59004*	BR	116	TS	1957
—	59488*	P/Steel	117	TCL	1959
—	59494*	P/Steel	117	TCL	1959
—	59503*	P/Steel	117	TCL	1959
—	59507*	P/Steel	117	TCL	1959
—	59513*	P/Steel	117	TCL	1959
—	59517*	P/Steel	117	TCL	1959

*Converted to locomotive-hauled vehicles

Director & General Manager: J. B. S. Cogar
Headquarters: Paignton Queen's Park station, Paignton, Devon
Telephone: Paignton (01803) 555872
Main station: Paignton Queen's Park
Other public stations: Goodrington, Churston, Kingswear (for Dartmouth)
OS reference: SX 889606
Car parks: Paignton municipal car park, Goodrington, Dartmouth (ferry to Kingswear)
Access by public transport: Adjacent to both Paignton main line station and Devon General bus station
Refreshment facilities: Paignton and Kingswear
Depot: Churston
Length of line: 7 miles
Passenger trains: Paignton-Kingswear, views of Torbay and Dart estuary, 495yd tunnel
Period of public operation: Easter to October
Facilities for disabled: Limited
Special events: Santa Specials — please see timetable and press for details
Membership details: Devon Diesel Society (Andy Matthews)
Membership journal: *Torbay Express* — quarterly

Stock
15 ex-BR Mk 1 coaches; 1 Pullman observation coach; 2 auto-coaches; 1 ex-GWR coach

Owners
50002 the Devon Diesel Society

Timetable Service

Peak Rail plc

Derbyshire

Member: AIRPS
Location: *Registered Office:* Matlock Station, Matlock, Derbyshire DE4 3NA
OS reference: Matlock SK 060738
Operating society/organisation: Peak Rail plc, Matlock Station, Matlock, Derbyshire DE4 3NA.
Telephone: (01629) 580381
Car parks: Matlock station, DFS Furniture Store at Darley Dale, Rowsley South station
Length of line: 4 miles — Matlock Riverside-Rowsley South
On site facilities: Shop at Matlock. Shops and buffets at Darley Dale and Rowsley South
Public opening: Not finalised, but will be every Sunday. Saturdays probably April-October. Midweek during summer. Timetable varies
Facilities for disabled: Darley Dale and Rowsley. Matlock Riverside unsuitable for disabled passengers
Period of public operation: Sundays: Throughout the year; Saturdays: April-October and December. 13-14 April; 25-26 May; 3, 10, 17, 24 June; 1, 8, 15, 22, 28-30 July; 4-6, 11-13, 18-20, 25-27, 31 August; 1-3 September; 28/29 October; 9, 16, 23 December
Special events: Members' & Shareholders' Day — 28 March; Steam into Spring — 11-13 April; Friends of Thomas the Tank Engine — 2-4 May; American Extravaganza — 23-25 May; Steam

Locomotives and multiple-units

Name	*No*	*Origin*	*Class*	*Type*	*Built*
—	48624	LMS	8F	2-8-0	1943
Penyghent	D8	BR	44	1Co-Co1	1959
3rd Carabinier	D99	BR	45	1Co-Co1	1961
—	51566	BR	108	DMSL	1959
—	51567	BR	108	DMSL	1959
—	51933	BR	108	DMBS	1960
—	53627	BR	108	DMBS	1958
—	53933	BR	108	DMBS	1959
—	54484	BR	108	DTC	1960
—	54504	BR	108	DTC	1960
—	59387	BR	108	TS	1958
—	977806	BR	108	DMBS	1958

Industrial locomotives

Name	*No*	*Builder*	*Type*	*Built*
Vulcan	—	V/Foundry (3272)	0-4-0ST	1918
The Duke	2746	Bagnall (2746)	0-6-0ST	1944
*Warrington**	150	RSH (7136)	0-6-0ST	1944

*At Darley Dale

Rolling Stock — coaches: 2 BR Mk 1 RMB; 1 BR Mk 1 SLF, 3 BR Mk 1 TSO, 2 BR Mk 1 SO, 1 BR Mk 1 BSOT, 3 BR Mk 1 SK, 1 BR Mk 1 BSK, 2 BR Mk 1 BG, 1 BR Mk 1 GUV, 1 BR Mk 2 SO, 1 BR Mk 2 BSO, 1 BR Mk 2 BFK, 1 LMS TK, 2 LMS BCK, 1BTK

Rolling stock — wagons: 1 MR brake van, 2 LMS brake vans, 1 LMS Shark brake van, 1 BR brake van, 1 Mess & Tool van, 1 Smith & Rodley 15ton diesel crane, 1 Sturgeon rail wagon, 1 Lowmac wagon, 2 Dogfish ballast hoppers, 1 mineral hopper wagon, 2 LMS 16ton fish vans, 1 SR PMV, 3 BR 12ton box van, 1 12ton van, 1 Shell tank wagon, 2 Esso tank wagons, 3 LNER wagons, 2 LMS wagons, 1 21ton mineral wagon, 2 ex-LMS match wagons, 1 Plasser & Theurer tamper, 1 Plasser & Theurer track slewer, 1 ex-LMR drain train water bowser, 2 Austrian ferry wagons

Owners
D8, the North Notts Loco Group
D99 & 45135 the 45135, Pioneer Diesel Loco Group
Vulcan the Vulcan Loco Trust

Traction Rally — 13/14 June; Comedy on Rails — 18/19 July; Anything Goes Weekend — 29-31 August; Members' & Shareholders' Day — 17 October; Ghost Trains & Halloween — 31 October; Santa Specials — 5/6, 9, 12/13, 16, 19/20, 23 December.

Dedicated diesel operating dates: 27 May, 20 June, 28 July, 6, 13, 20, 28 August, 12 September

Steam Centre — Plym Valley Railway — Devon

Member: AIRPS
A scheme dedicated to the restoration of services over the former GWR Marsh Mills-Plym Bridge line, a distance of 1.5 miles
Location: 5 miles from centre of Plymouth, Devon, north of A38. From Marsh Mills roundabout, take B3416 to Plympton, follow signs
OS reference: SX 517564
Operating society/organisation: Plym Valley Railway Co Ltd, Marsh Mills Station, Coypool Road, Marsh Mills, Plymouth, Devon PL7 4NL
Access by public transport: Buses from Plymouth, Nos 20, 20A, 21, 22A, 51 stop close to site
On site facilities: Shop and refreshments at Marsh Mills, Coypool (Sundays only)
Public opening: Sundays from 10.00, and other selected days
Length of line: Half-mile, plus sidings

Locomotives and multiple-units

Name	*No*	*Origin*	*Class*	*Type*	*Built*
—	75079	BR	4MT	4-6-0	1956
—	13002	BR	08	0-6-0DE	1953
—	51365	BR	117	MBS	1960
—	51407	BR	117	DMS	1960

Industrial locomotives

Name	*No*	*Builder*	*Type*	*Built*
—	3	H/Leslie (3597)	0-4-0ST	1926
—	—	T/Hill (125V)	4wDH	1963
—	—	Hibberd (3281)	4wDM	1948

Rolling stock: Self-propelled Smith & Rodley diesel crane of 1956

Special events: Please see press for details
Special notes: Visitors are advised that, at the moment, the railway and two locomotives are still under restoration. 3 working locomotives and DMU. Prospective visitors are advised to take the advice of their guides. Steam and diesel demonstration trains on some Sundays (tel: Alan Smith [01503] 250539)
Membership details: Pat Elbrolo, 75 Rigdale Close, Eggbuckland, Plymouth, Devon PL6 5PR
Membership journal: *Plym Valley News* — 3/year
Marketing name: The Woodland Line

Steam Centre — The Railway Age, Crewe — Cheshire

Location: Crewe Heritage Centre, Vernon Way, Crewe
OS reference: SJ 709552
Operating society/organisation: Crewe Heritage Trust Ltd
Telephone: (01270) 212130
Car park: On site, town centre, Forge Street, Oak Street,
Access by public transport: Main line Crewe
Refreshment facilities: Brief Encounter buffet
On site facilities: Gift shop, picnic area, children's corner, weekend train rides, standard gauge and miniature railway, exhibition hall, main line viewing area, 3 working signalboxes with hands-on visitor operation

Locomotives and multiple-units

Name	*No*	*Origin*	*Class*	*Type*	*Built*
—	03073	BR	03	0-6-0DM	1959
—	08375	BR	08	0-6-0DE	1957
—	D8233	BR	15	Bo-Bo	1963
—	37029	BR	37	Co-Co	1961
—	D120	BR	45	1Co-Co1	1961
Ixion	D172	BR	46	1Co-Co1	1962
—	D1842	BR	47	Co-Co	1965
—	47449	BR	47	Co-Co	1964
—	50008	BR	50	Co-Co	1968
—	E3003	BR	81	Bo-Bo	1960
—	82008	BR	82	Bo-Bo	1961
—	85101	BR	85	Bo-Bo	1961
—	18000	BR	—	A1A-A1A	1949
—	53986	BR	108	DMBs	1959
—	55032	P/Steel	121	DMBS	1960

Public opening: Daily 10.00-16.00, family tickets available. Please contact for details of events
Facilities for disabled: Toilets
Membership details: Heritage Centre Supporters Association, c/o above address
Notes: Steam locomotives passed for use over BR tracks are stabled between duties on the North Wales Coast and Settle & Carlisle lines

Industrial locomotives

Name	*No*	*Builder*	*Type*	*Built*
Robert	—	H/Clarke (1752)	0-6-0T	1943
—	—	K/Stuart (4388)	0-4-0ST	1926

Rolling stock
APT vehicle Nos 48103, 48106, 48602, 48603, 48606, 49002; 1 BR Mk 1 BSK; 2 BR brake vans

Timetable Service — Ravenglass & Eskdale Railway — Cumbria

Member: AIRPS
Originally built to serve iron ore mines in Eskdale, this delightful line makes an ideal 'tourist' line running as it does through wooded valleys and along rugged hillsides
General Manager: Steve Wood
Headquarters: Ravenglass & Eskdale Railway, Ravenglass, Cumbria CA18 1SW
Telephone: (01229) 717171
Fax: (01229) 717011
E-mail: rer@netcomuk.co.uk
Main station: Ravenglass
Other public stations: Muncaster Mill, Irton Road, The Green, Beckfoot, Eskdale (Dalegarth)
OS reference: SD 086964
Car parks: All stations
Access by public transport: Main line services to Ravenglass
Refreshment facilities: Ravenglass, Dalegarth. Bar meals at 'Ratty Arms'
Picnic areas: At both termini
Souvenir shops: Ravenglass, Dalegarth
Museum: Ravenglass
Length of line: 7 miles, 15in gauge
Passenger trains: Steam or diesel-hauled narrow gauge trains Ravenglass-Dalegarth
Period of public operation: Daily late March-late October. Limited winter service November-March
Family ticket: All day travel at reduced price
Special events: *River Esk* 75 years old, visiting locomotives — May Day Bank Holiday
Facilities for disabled: Special coaches for wheelchair passengers. Advance notice preferred. Wheelchair access to toilets and museum at Ravenglass; toilets, shop and cafe at Eskdale (Dalegarth)
Special notes: At Ravenglass the R&ER has two camping coaches and the company also operates the 'Ratty Arms' public house formed by conversion of the former BR station buildings. During the high summer, mid-July through August, five steam locomotives are normally in use Monday-Thursday.
Muncaster water mill is also worth a visit
Membership details: Mr N. Dickinson, 3 Clifton Terrace, Ravenglass, Cumbria CA18 1SE
Membership journal: *The R&ER Magazine* — quarterly
Marketing names: 'Ratty' or 'T' laal Ratty'

Locomotives

Name	*No*	*Builder*	*Type*	*Built*
River Irt	—	Heywood	0-8-2	1894
River Esk	—	Davey Paxman (21104)	2-8-2	1923
River Mite	—	Clarkson (4669)	2-8-2	1966
Northern Rock	—	R&ER	2-6-2	1976
Bonnie Dundee	—	K/Stuart (720)*	0-4-2	1901
Shelagh of Eskdale	—	R&ER/Severn-Lamb	4-6-4DH	1969
Quarryman	—	Muir-Hill (2)	0-4-0P/Paraffin	1928
Perkins	—	Muir Hill (NG39A)	0-4-4DM	1929
Silver Jubilee	—	R&ER	DMU	1977
Lady Wakefield	—	R&ER	B-B	1980
Synolda	—	Bassett-Lowke	4-4-2	1912
—	—	Greenbat (2782)	0-4-0BE	1957
Cyril	—	Lister	0-4-0DM	1987

*Rebuilt to 15in gauge 1981

Timetable Service — Romney, Hythe & Dymchurch Railway — Kent

Member: AIRPS
This line was built in 1926/27 as a one-third size miniature main line, and is by far the longest and most fully-equipped 15in gauge railway in the world. It carries not only daytrippers and holidaymakers but also children to and from the local school at New Romney.
Headquarters: Romney, Hythe & Dymchurch Railway, New Romney Station, Kent TN28 8PL
Telephone: (01797) 362353/363256
OS reference: TR 074249

Main station: New Romney
Other public stations: Dymchurch, Jefferstone Lane, New Romney, Romney Sands, Dungeness
Car parks: Hythe, Dymchurch, New Romney, Dungeness
Access by public transport: Folkestone Central station (Connex South Eastern) and then bus to Hythe (4 miles) or Rye station (Connex South Eastern) and then bus to New Romney (8 miles)
Refreshment facilities: Cafeterias at New Romney and Dungeness, picnic area at New Romney. Also an observation coach on certain trains
Souvenir shops: Hythe and New Romney (plus Dymchurch and Dungeness in main season)
Toy and Model Museum: New Romney, with displays of old, and not so old, toys; plus two large operating model railways
Depot: New Romney
Length of line: 13.5 miles, 15in gauge
Passenger trains: Train frequency depends on the time of year: maximum frequency is 45 minutes
Period of public operation: Trains run daily from Good Friday until last Sunday in September. Also run at weekends in March and October. Out of season the school train departs New Romney at 15.00 with limited public accommodation (Monday-Friday, term times only)
Special events: Steam & Diesel Gala — 10 May; Friends of Thomas Day — 5 July, 5/6 September. Santa Specials in December (pre-booking essential)
Special notes: Senior citizen concession Fridays, Saturdays, Sunday (return journey for single fare). Family tickets available from New Romney station only. The 'Romney Toy and Model Museum' at New Romney. Special trains can be run at most times by prior arrangement. Parties can be catered for at New Romney and Dungeness cafés
Facilities for disabled: Ramps at level crossings at all stations for easy access. Special wheelchair coach available on any train by prior arrangement. Stair lift between cafe and 'Toy & Model Museum'. Disabled toilets at Hythe, Dymchurch and New Romney
Internet addresses: RHDR web site is on: http:\\www.i-way.co.uk\~tburgess\rhdr.html\rhdr
RHDR e-mail is: 106104.245@compuserve.com
Membership details: RH&DR Association, 26 Norman Close, Battle, East Sussex TN33 0BD
Membership journal: *The Marshlander* — quarterly

Locomotives

Name	No	Builder	Type	Built
Green Goddess	1	Davey Paxman	4-6-2	1925
Northern Chief	2	Davey Paxman	4-6-2	1925
Southern Maid	3	Davey Paxman	4-6-2	1926
The Bug	4	Krauss (8378)	0-4-0TT	1926
Hercules	5	Davey Paxman	4-8-2	1926
Samson	6	Davey Paxman	4-8-2	1926
Typhoon	7	Davey Paxman	4-6-2	1926
Hurricane	8	Davey Paxman	4-6-2	1926
Winston Churchill	9	YEC (2294)	4-6-2	1931
Doctor Syn	10	YEC (2295)	4-6-2	1931
Black Prince	11	Krupp (1664)	4-6-2	1937
John Southland	12	TMA Birmingham	Bo-Bo	1983
—	14	TMA Birmingham	Bo-Bo	1989
—	PW1	M/Rail (7059)	4wDM	1938
—	PW2	RH&DR	4wPM	1965
Redgauntlet	PW3	RH&DR	4wPM	1975

Stock
42 saloon bogie coaches; 12 open bogie coaches; 3 semi-open coaches; 5 luggage/brake saloons; 1 Parlour car; 1 mess coach; 40 assorted wagons

Steam Centre | Ruislip Lido Railway | London

Member: AIRPS
The 12in gauge line is operated by enthusiast volunteers as an attraction within Ruislip Lido, a country park which is maintained by the London Borough of Hillingdon
Location: Ruislip Lido, Reservoir Road, Ruislip, Middlesex
Operating society/organisation: Ruislip Lido Railway Society Ltd, Membership Secretary, Mrs S. E. Simmons, 9 Wiltshire Lane, Eastcote, Pinner, Middx HA5 2LH
Telephone: (0181) 866 9654
Car park: Available at Lido
Access by public transport: Ruislip Underground station (Metropolitan and Piccadilly lines) then by bus H13 (Monday-Saturday), 331 nearby (Daily). Lido is off the A4180 road
Refreshment facilities: New family pub/restaurant (Brewers Fayre) on site. Picnic areas also

Locomotives

Name	No	Builder	Type	Built
Robert	3	Severn-Lamb	B-2 DH	1973
Lady of the Lakes	5	Ravenglass & Eskdale Railway	B-B DM	1985
Graham Alexander	7	Severn-Lamb	B-B DM	1990

Locomotive notes: All locomotives are available for service and a steam locomotive is under construction

Stock
6 open coaches; 9 closed coaches; miscellaneous service stock

available
Length of line: 1.5-mile single journey, 3 miles return including new extension now open which terminates beside main entrance to car park
Public opening: The line is open Sundays throughout the year; Tuesdays, Wednesdays, Thursdays and Saturdays in April, May, June, September and October. Every day in July and August, also daily during most Hillingdon school holidays.
24-hour recorded train information service (01895) 622595
Journey time: Single 20min, return 40min
Facilities for disabled: Wheelchair passengers can travel on all trains
Membership details: c/o above address
Membership journal: *Woody Bay News* — 3 issues per year

Steam Centre

Rutland Railway Museum

Rutland

Member: AIRPS
This museum is dedicated to portraying the railway in industry, particularly iron ore mining, and has a wide range of industrial locomotives and rolling stock. Indeed, its collection of quarry freight rolling stock is probably the most comprehensive in the country and regular demonstrations are a feature of the 'steam days'.
Location: Cottesmore Iron Ore Mines Siding, Ashwell Road, Cottesmore, near Oakham, Rutland — museum situated mid-way between villages of Cottesmore and Ashwell, approximately 4 miles north of Oakham (locally signposted)
OS reference: SK 886137
Operating society/organisation: Rutland Railway Museum, Cottesmore Iron Ore Mines Siding, Ashwell Road, Cottesmore, Nr Oakham, Rutland LE15 7BX
Telephone: Oakham (01572) 813203
Car park: Free car park on site
Access by public transport: Nearest main line station, Oakham. Blands bus service, Leicester-Oakham-Cottesmore. Bartons buses, Nottingham-Melton Mowbray-Oakham-Ashwell, Corby/Peterborough-Oakham-Ashwell (services 117 and 125).
On site facilities: Free train rides, demonstration freight trains, refreshments, toilets, museum, shop, picnic sites, demonstration line with lineside walk and viewing areas, static displays of over 30 steam and diesel locomotives; over 50 wagons, vans and coaches (believed to be the largest collection of preserved quarry freight stock in the UK)
Length of line: Three-quarter-mile

Locomotives and multiple-units

Name	*No*	*Origin*	*Class*	*Type*	*Built*
NCB No 7	(D9518)	BR	14	0-6-0DH	1964
BSC45	(D9520)	BR	14	0-6-0DH	1964
—	D9555	BR	14	0-6-0DH	1965
—	54274	BR	108	DTC	1959

Industrial locomotives

Name	*No*	*Builder*	*Type*	*Built*
Firefly	—	Barclay (776)	0-4-0ST	1896
Uppingham	—	Peckett (1257)	0-4-0ST	1912
BSC No 2	—	Barclay (1931)	0-4-0ST	1927
Dora	—	Avonside (1973)	0-4-0ST	1927
Elizabeth	—	Peckett (1759)	0-4-0ST	1928
Singapore	Yard No 440	H/Leslie (3865)	0-4-0ST	1936
Swordfish	—	Barclay (2138)	0-6-0ST	1941
Drake	—	Barclay (2086)	0-4-0ST	1940
Sir Thomas Royden	—	Barclay (2088)	0-4-0ST	1940
Carlton No 3	—	Barclay (352)	0-4-0DM	1941
Salmon	8410/39	Barclay (2139)	0-6-0ST	1942
—	1	Barclay (415)	0-4-0DH	1957
—	20-90-01	Barclay (499)	0-4-0DH	1965
—	8	Bagnall (3209)/ RSH (8364)	0-4-0DH	1962
Coal Products No 6	—	Hunslet (2868) (Rebuilt Hunslet 3883 1963)	0-6-0ST	1943
—	8	Peckett (2110)	0-4-0ST	1950
—	3	N/British (27656)	0-4-0DH	1957
—	—	R/Hornsby (305302)	4wDM	1951
—	—	R/Hornsby (306092)	4wDM	1950
—	—	R/Hornsby (347747)	0-6-0DM	1957
—	20-90-02	R/Hornsby (504565)	0-4-0DH	1965
Hays	—	R/Hornsby (544997)	0-4-0DE	1969
Phoenix	—	Hibberd (3887)	4wDM	1958
Janus	No 28	YEC (2791)	0-6-0DE	1962
—	1382	YEC (2872)	0-6-0DE	1962
—	65	Hunslet (3889)	0-6-0ST	1964
Betty	8411/04	R/Royce (10201)	0-4-0DH	1965
—	D21	R/Royce (10270)	0-6-0DH	1967
—	BSC 1	E/Electric (D1049)	0-6-0DH	1965
—	—	E/Electric (D1231)	0-6-0DH	1967
—	No 1	Hunslet (6688)	0-4-0DH	1968
—	CEGB 24	T/Hill (188c) (Rebuild of Sentinel 9597/1955)	4wDH	1967
—	24	Hunslet (2411)	0-6-0ST	1941
—	7	Sentinel (9376)	4wVBT	1947
—	21	H/Clarke (D707)	0-6-0DM	1950
—	10	T/Hill (234v)	4wDH	1971

Passenger trains: Regular shuttle service operates on open days (approximately every 15min)
Public Opening: Open weekends or by arrangement, some weekdays (please telephone prior to visit). Open 11.00-17.00. (Leaflets available, SAE please)
Special events: Please contact for details
Facilities for disabled: Site relatively flat. Members willing to assist.
Special notes: The museum houses an extensive collection of industrial locomotives and rolling stock typifying past activity in local ironstone quarries, nationwide mines and factories. A demonstration line approximately three quarters of a mile long has been relaid on the former MR Cottesmore mineral branch (originally built to tap local ironstone quarries), on which restored locomotives and stock are run. Among the latter is the body of the only surviving Wisbech & Upwell Tramway coach and the last diesel locomotive built for BR service at Swindon Works
Membership details: Membership Secretary, c/o above address

Name	*No*	*Builder*	*Type*	*Built*
—	ROF No 1	T/Hill (132c)	0-4-0DH	1963
		(Rebuild of Fowler 22982/1942)		
—	4	Fowler (4240012)	0-6-0DH	1961
—	—	Fowler (4240015)	0-6-0DH	1962

Locomotive notes: In service *Dora,* 7, BSC45, D9555, 1832, *Betty, Janus*, 1, *Pheonix*, CEGB No 24, No 1 and BSC 1.

Stock
2 coaches; 4 brake vans; 14 covered goods vans; 57 wagons (includes rakes of wagons as used in local ironstone and industrial railways); 2 rail cranes

Museum — Science Museum — London

Built on land acquired with the profits from the Great Exhibition of 1851, the Science Museum was one of the first to include industrial archaeology. The Land Transport Gallery is closed for the whole of 1998 pending a comprehensive redisplay. *Puffing Billy* remains on display; Stephenson's *Rocket* forms part of a large Science Museum touring exhibition of Japan during 1998. Other large exhibits are temporarily dispersed to other sites
Location: South Kensington
OS reference: TQ 268793
Operating society/organisation: Science Museum, Exhibition Road, South Kensington, London SW7
Telephone: (0171) 938 8000
Access by public transport: South Kensington Underground station
Catering facilities: Cafe on ground floor, tea, coffee, sandwiches, etc. Picnic area in basement
On site facilities: Book shop, toilets on most floors
Public opening: Daily 10.00-18.00. Closed 24-26 December
Special events: All organised by the National Railway Museum, York, which is part of the Science Museum. Telephone (01904) 621261 for details
Facilities for disabled: Toilets on most floors, ramp and lifts to all floors. Parties should contact before arrival if extra assistance is required
Special notes: Static exhibits only in Land Transport Gallery

Locomotive

Name	*No*	*Origin*	*Class*	*Type*	*Built*
Puffing Billy	—	Wylam Colliery	—	0-4-0	1813

Locomotive note: Restored to static display condition

Timetable Service — Seaton & District Electric Tramway — Devon

Member: AIRPS
Devon's unique narrow gauge electric tramway, operating on the trackbed of the former Seaton branch line between Seaton, Colyford and Colyton. Panoramic views of the beautiful Axe Valley and estuary. An unforgettable experience for the family
Location: Harbour Road Car Park, Seaton; Swan Hill Road, Colyford; Station Road, Kingsdon, Colyton
OS reference: SY 252904
Operating society/organisation: Seaton & District Electric Tramway Co, Riverside Depot, Harbour Road, Seaton, Devon EX12 2NQ
Telephone: Seaton (01297) 20375/21702
Fax: Seaton (01297) 625626
Access by public transport: Local bus service from Axminster railway station (South West Trains),

Locomotives

Name	*No*	*Builder*	*Type*	*Built*
Claude	—	R/Hornsby (435398)	4wDM	1959

Sidmouth and Lyme Regis serve Seaton, Colyford and Colyton. Bus enquiries (01392) 382800
On site facilities: Gift shops, tea rooms, children's playground, picnic area
Length of line: 3 miles, 2ft 9in gauge
Period of public operation: Daily 4 April-1 November; Santa Specials in December; private hire available all year round
Special events: 4th Annual Bus & Vintage Vehicle Rally — 6 June; Official launch of Exeter Corporation Tramways Car No 19 — 26 September; Enthusiasts' Day — 27 September
Times: Trams every 20 minutes, 09.40-17.20 (until 20.40 13 June-5 September)
Fares: Single, return and rover tickets available. Discounts for local residents, families and parties of 20 or more. Prices on application
Facilities for disabled: Tramcar No 17 carries up to 12 wheelchairs (by prior arrangement). Disabled toilets at Seaton and Colyton
Special notes: Tram driving lessons are offered every Friday and Saturday during the season, please contact for details. Services operated by open-top double-deck bogie cars with enclosed single-deck saloon cars during inclement weather

Seaton Tramway No 4 is based on the Blackpool Tramway's 'boat' design. *S&DET*

Timetable Service

Severn Valley Railway

Worcestershire

Member: AIRPS, TT
The railway hosts more main line engines than any other preserved line in the country, enjoying the back-up of a large volunteer and professional workforce and extensive engineering workshops and equipment. Railway travel like it used to be
General Manager: Alun Rees
Operating Superintendent: John F. Hill
Headquarters: Severn Valley Railway Co Ltd, Railway Station, Bewdley, Worcs DY12 1BG
Telephone: Bewdley (01299) 403816; 24hr timetable — Bewdley (01299) 401001
Main stations: Bridgnorth, Bewdley, Kidderminster Town
Other public stations: Arley, Highley, Hampton Loade, Northwood Halt, Country Park Halt
OS reference: Bridgnorth SO 715926, Bewdley SO 793753

Locomotives and multiple-units

Name	*No*	*Origin*	*Class*	*Type*	*Built*
The Great Marquess	61994	LNER	K4	2-6-0	1938
Union of South Africa	60009	LNER	A4	4-6-2	1937
Gordon	AD600	LMR	WD	2-10-0	1943
—	43106	LMS	4MT	2-6-0	1951
—	46443	LMS	2MT	2-6-0	1950
—	46521	LMS	2MT	2-6-0	1953
RAF Biggin Hill	45110	LMS	5MT	4-6-0	1935
—	47383	LMS	3F	0-6-0T	1926
—	48773	LMS	8F	2-8-0	1940
—	2968	LMS	5P4F	2-6-0	1933
—	813	GWR	—	0-6-0ST	1901
—	2857	GWR	2800	2-8-0	1918
—	5164	GWR	5101	2-6-2T	1930
—	4150	GWR	5101	2-6-2T	1947
—	5764	GWR	5700	0-6-0PT	1929
—	7714	GWR	5700	0-6-0PT	1930
—	4566	GWR	4500	2-6-2T	1924
Bradley Manor	7802	GWR	'Manor'	4-6-0	1939
Erlestoke Manor	7812	GWR	'Manor'	4-6-0	1939
Hinton Manor	7819	GWR	'Manor'	4-6-0	1939
Hagley Hall	4930	GWR	'Hall'	4-6-0	1929
—	1501	GWR	1500	0-6-0PT	1949
—	7325	GWR	4300	2-6-0	1932

Car parks: At all main stations
Access by public transport: Midland Red bus service 192 to Kidderminster and Bewdley and 125 & 297 to Bridgnorth. Rail service to Kidderminster (main line) with immediate connections to SVR station. Through tickets available from all manned main line stations
Refreshment facilities: At most stations, but not on all operating days and on most trains. Fully licensed bars at Bridgnorth and Kidderminster Town
Souvenir shops: Bridgnorth, Kidderminster Town
Depots: Bridgnorth (locomotives), Bewdley and Kidderminster (stock)
Model railways: At Bewdley, Kidderminster and Hampton Loade
Length of line: 16.5 miles
Passenger trains: Steam-hauled trains running frequently from Kidderminster Town to Bewdley and Bridgnorth. Diesel-hauled service on limited occasions as advertised
Period of public operation: Weekends year round, Santa Steam Specials in late November and December. Daily service mid-May to early October and all Bank Holidays and school hoildays. Open for limited viewing at other times
Special events: Model Engineering Weekend — 18/19 April; Spring Steam Gala — 25/26 April; Heavy Horse Weekend — 16/17 May; 1940s Weekend — 4/5 July; Friends of Thomas the Tank Weekend — 5/6 September; Autumn Steam Gala — 18-20 Sepember; Diesel Gala — 9/10 October; Classic Vehicle Day — 1 October; Santa Specials — 29 November, 5/6, 12/13, 19/20, 24 December; Mince Pie Specials — 26 December-3 January 1999
Facilities for disabled: Facilities available, special vehicle available to carry wheelchairs by prior arrangement. Disabled people's toilets at Kidderminster and Bridgnorth
Special notes: A number of special enthusiasts' weekends and special events are held when extra trains are operated. In addition, supplementary trains with diesel haulage are run as advertised. 'Severn Valley Limited' and 'Severn Valley Venturer'

Name	*No*	*Origin*	*Class*	*Type*	*Built*
—	80079	BR	4MT	2-6-4T	1954
—	78019	BR	2MT	2-6-0	1954
—	75069	BR	4MT	4-6-0	1955
Greyhound	D821	BR	42	B-B	1960
Western Ranger	D1013	BR	52	C-C	1962
Western Courier	D1062	BR	52	C-C	1963
—	D3022	BR	08	0-6-0DE	1952
—	D3586	BR	08	0-6-0DE	1953
—	12099	BR	11	0-6-0DE	1952
—	D7029	BR	35	Bo-Bo	1962
—	D7633	BR	25	Bo-Bo	1965
—	D5410	BR	27	Bo-Bo	1962
Hood	50031	BR	50	Co-Co	1968
Ark Royal	50035	BR	50	Co-Co	1968
Exeter	D444	BR	50	Co-Co	1968
—	51935	BR	108	DMBS	1960
—	51941	BR	108	DMBS	1960
—	52064	BR	108	DMC	1960
—	56208	BR	108	DTCL	1958
—	59250	BR	108	TBS	1958

Industrial locomotives

Name	*No*	*Builder*	*Type*	*Built*
Warwickshire	—	M/Wardle (2047)	0-6-0ST	1926
The Lady Armaghdale	—	Hunslet (686)	0-6-0T	1898
—	—	Ruston (319290)	0-4-0DM	1953
Alan	—	R/Hornsby (414304)	0-4-0DM	1957
William	—	R/Hornsby (408297)	0-4-0DM	1957

Stock

27 ex-GWR coaches; 13 ex-LMS coaches; 24 ex-BR Mk 1 coaches; 8 ex-LNER coaches; Numerous examples of ex-GWR, LMS and other freight vehicles and two 30-ton steam cranes

Owners

813 the GWR 813 Fund
1501 the 15xx Fund
2857 the 2857 Fund
2968 the Stanier Mogul Fund
61994 the family of the late Earl of Lindsay
4150 the 4150 Locomotive Fund
4566 the 4566 Fund
5164 the 51xx Fund
5764, 7714 the Pannier Tank Fund
46521, 60009, 78019 and D1013 are private
7325 the Great Western (SVR) Association
7802 and 7812 the Erlestoke Manor Fund
7819 the Hinton Manor Fund
43106 the Ivatt 4 Fund
46443 the SVR 46443 Fund
47383 the Manchester Rail Travel Society
48773 the Stanier 8F Locomotive Society
50031, 50035 and D444 the 50 Fund
75069 the 75069 Fund
80079 the Passenger Tank Fund
AD600 the Royal Corps of Transport Museum Trustees
D821 and D7029 the Diesel Traction Group
D1062 the Western Locomotive Association
D3022 the Class 08 Society
D5410 Sandwell Metropolitan Council
D7633 the SVR/PW Fund
4930 and 45110 the SVR(H) plc

Restaurant Car service operates on Sundays and as required on other occasions. Advanced booking required. Charter trains with or without dining facilities can be arranged
Membership details: Mrs Pauline Stribblehill, c/o above address
Membership journal: *Severn Valley Railway News* — quarterly
Share details: Mr Alun Rees, c/o above address

Steam Centre

Sittingbourne & Kemsley Light Railway

Kent

Member: AIRPS, TT
The Sittingbourne & Kemsley Light Railway is part of the 2ft 6in gauge railway built to convey paper and other materials between mills at Sittingbourne and Kemsley and the Dock at Ridham on the banks of the Swale. The first section of the line opened in 1906 and two of the engines then in use remain on the line today.

The railway is now leased from U.K. Paper Group and is operated as a tourist attraction. Passenger trains are normally steam-hauled and are formed of a varied selection of open and covered coaches. For the first half mile of the journey the train twists and turns through Milton Regis on a concrete viaduct which was one of the first reinforced concrete structures to be built
Operating Manager: Malcolm Burton
Headquarters: Sittingbourne & Kemsley Light Railway Ltd, Kemsley Down, Kent
Telephone: Sittingbourne (01795) 424899 (talking timetable) or (01634) 852672 (other enquiries)
Main station: Sittingbourne
Car park: Sittingbourne
Party bookings and enquiries: M. Burton, 85 Balmoral Road, Gillingham, Kent ME7 4QG
Access by public transport: Sittingbourne main line station, A2 and M2 roads
OS reference: Sittingbourne TQ 905643, Kemsley Down TQ 920662
Refreshment facilities: Kemsley Down

Locomotives

Name	*No*	*Builder*	*Type*	*Built*
Alpha	—	Bagnall (2472)	0-6-2T	1932
Triumph	—	Bagnall (2511)	0-6-2T	1934
Superb	—	Bagnall (2624)	0-6-2T	1940
Unique	—	Bagnall (2216)	2-4-0F	1924
Premier	—	K/Stuart (886)	0-4-2ST	1905
Leader	—	K/Stuart (926)	0-4-2ST	1905
Melior	—	K/Stuart (4219)	0-4-2ST	1924
Edward Lloyd	—	R/Hornsby (435403)	4wDM	1961
Victor	—	Hunslet (4182)	4wDM	1953

Industrial standard gauge locomotives

Name	*No*	*Builder*	*Type*	*Built*
—	4	H/Leslie (3718)	0-4-0ST	1928
Bear	—	Peckett (614)	0-4-0ST	1896
—	1	Barclay (1876)	0-4-0F	1925

Locomotive notes: In service: *Superb, Melior*. Under repair: *Leader, Triumph, Premier*. On static display *Alpha, Unique* and standard gauge exhibits

Stock
10 bogie coaches (4 ex-Chattenden & Upnor Railway); 2 open coaches; various wagons

Souvenir shop: Kemsley Down
Small Exhibits Museum: Kemsley Down
Depot: Kemsley Down (access by rail only)
Length of line: 2 miles, 2ft 6in gauge
Passenger trains: Ex-industrial line Sittingbourne-Kemsley Down
Journey time: 15min each way
Period of public operation: Good Friday, Easter Monday and Bank Holidays; Saturdays 11 April and during August; Sundays 12 April-mid-October; Wednesdays in August. Santa Specials, contact for details
Special events: Friends of Thomas the Tank Engine — 21 June;
Special notes: There is no public access to Kemsley Down other than by the railway on operating dates. When the line is closed all stock is stored in security compounds, on the mill premises. Family ticket available, special rates for parties and senior citizens. Picnic area at Kemsley Down
Membership details: Mr & Mrs K. Widdowson, 60 Doveney Close, St Paul's Cray, Orpington, Kent BR5 3WT
Marketing name: Sittingbourne Steam Railway

Museum

Snibston Discovery Park

Leicestershire

Members: TT
Location: Snibston Discovery Park, Ashby Road, Coalville, Leicestershire LE67 3LN
Telephone: (01530) 510851
Fax: (01530) 813301
Operating group: Leicestershire County Council, Museums, Arts & Records Service
Museum contact: Mr S. Mastoris, Snibston Discovery Park, Ashby Road, Coalville, Leicestershire LE67 3LN
Public opening: Daily 10.00-18.00 (during British Summer Time); 10.00-17.00 at other times. Closed Christmas Day & Boxing Day
Car & coach parking: On site, free
Access by public transport: Midland Fox from Loughborough and Nottingham (route 99); from Leicester (route 117); from Ashby de la Zouch (route 118), Mon-Sat; route 217/8 Sun & Bank Holiday Mondays. Further information, tel: (01533) 511411.
Stevensons Bus Services from Hinckley (route 179); limited service from Tamworth via Ashby (route 97). Connections at Ashby with Burton upon Trent. Further information, tel: (01283) 44662
On site facilities: Shop, toilets, car park, cafe. Conference facilities, tourist information centre (Tel: [01530] 813608). Family tickets, picnic areas, science play area, Sheepy Magna wheelwrights workshop. Special event days, nature reserve, golf driving range, colliery building tours
Railways on site: Approx 300yd of standard gauge track, aiming towards future operation of demonstration trains. Track to be extended when possible. No public riding on line.

Narrow gauge railway about 350yd in length. Colliery man-riding underground train to operate in future, subject to availability of equipment

Locomotives

Name	*No*	*Builder*	*Type*	*Built*
Mars II†	—	RSH (7493)	0-4-0ST	1948
—	2	Barclay (1815)	0-4-0F	1924
—†*	—	Brush (314)	0-4-0ST	1906
—††	2416	E/Electric	0-4-0	1978
—††	—	Huwood	0-6-0DM	1980
—	—	Hunslet (3851)	0-6-0ST	1962
—†	—	Hunslet	0-6-0DM	1966
—††	—	Hunslet (8973)	4WDM	1964

†Locomotives are stored
*Originally Powlesland & Mason No 6 taken over by GWR in 1924 and numbered 921
††2ft 6in gauge
Plus 2ft 6in gauge English Electric battery-operated electric man-riding locomotives — ex-NCB

Museum

Somerset & Dorset Railway Trust

Somerset

Member: AIRPS
Situated at Washford on the West Somerset Railway, the Trust Museum houses Somerset & Dorset memorabilia and artefacts to stir memories of cross-country travel in the era of steam. The sidings and restoration shed give the visitor a chance to see locomotives, wagons and carriages in close up
Headquarters: Washford Station, Minehead Road, Washford, Somerset TA21 0PP
Telephone: (01984) 640869 (opening hours); (01278) 683574 (otherwise)
Car park: small car park by main road
Access by public transport: West Somerset Railway trains on operating days, March to end October. Nearest main line station: Taunton. Southern National Omnibus Co service 28 (Taunton-Minehead) passes the station
On site facilities: Souvenir counter at the station. No refreshments on station but adjacent Inn offers food

Locomotive

Name	*No*	*Origin*	*Class*	*Type*	*Built*
—*	53808	S&DJR	7F	2-8-0	1925

*Undergoing heavy overhaul at Minehead

Industrial locomotives

Name	*No*	*Builder*	*Type*	*Built*
*Isabel**	—	H/Leslie (3437)	0-6-0ST	1919
Kilmersdon	—	Peckett (1788)	0-4-0ST	1929

*Undergoing restoration at Washford

Stock

3 Somerset & Dorset 6-wheeled coaches undergoing restoration. Large wagon collection. Display of narrow gauge equipment from Sedgemoor peat railways

and children are welcome
Public opening: 10.30-16.30 on WSR operating days. Other times by arrangement, Tel: (01278) 683574

Special events: 23/24 August, special weekend with reunion of ex-Somerset & Dorset Railway staff on 24th
Membership details: S&DJR Trust, 21 Greenhaven, Yateley, Hampshire GU17 7NA
Membership journal: *Pines Express* (6 issues/year)

Timetable Service

South Devon Railway - 'The Primrose Line'

Devon

Member: AIRPS, TT
A typical West Country branch line meandering up the Dart Valley to Buckfastleigh which is home to the railway's workshops, a butterfly and otter farm and several other attractions. After many years of isolation the line is now accessible from Totnes (BR) via a new footbridge (4min walk)
General Manager: R. Elliott
Headquarters: South Devon Railway, Buckfastleigh Station, Buckfastleigh, Devon TQ11 0D2
Telephone: Buckfastleigh (01364) 642338
Main station: Buckfastleigh
Other public stations: Staverton, Totnes (Littlehempston)
OS reference: Buckfastleigh SX 747663, Staverton SX 785638
Car park: Buckfastleigh (free), Staverton (free). Totnes — use BR pay & display or council car parks
Access by public transport: Bus, X38/9 Exeter-Plymouth; 188 Newton Abbot-Buckfastleigh; X80 Plymouth-Torquay. Main line trains to Totnes
Refreshment facilities: Buckfastleigh
Souvenir shop: On the train
Museum: Buckfastleigh
Depot: Buckfastleigh
Length of line: 7 miles
Passenger trains: Buckfastleigh-Totnes (Littlehempston) alongside the River Dart
Period of public operation: Telephone above for details
Facilities for disabled: Good
Membership details: South Devon Railway Association, c/o above address
Membership journal: *Bulliver* — quarterly
Marketing name: The Primrose Line

Locomotives and multiple-units

Name	*No*	*Origin*	*Class*	*Type*	*Built*
—	0298	LSWR	0298	2-4-0WT	1874
—	1420	GWR	1400	0-4-2T	1933
—	1369	GWR	1366	0-6-0PT	1934
—	3803*	GWR	2884	2-8-0	1939
Dumbleton Hall	4920**	GWR	'Hall'	4-6-0	1929
—	5526	GWR	4500	2-6-2T	1929
—	5786	GWR	5700	0-6-0PT	1930
—	D3666	BR	09	0-6-0DE	1959
—	D8110	BR	20	Bo-Bo	1960
—	51592	BR	127	DMBS	1959
—	51604	BR	127	DMBS	1959
—	59659	BR	115	TS	1960
—	59719	BR	115	TCL	1960
—	59740	BR	115	TS	1960
Broad gauge — 7ft 0.25in					
Tiny†	—	SDR	—	0-4-0VBT	1868

*Undergoing restoration at the Birmingham Railway Museum, Tyseley
**Will be away on loan during 1998

Industrial locomotives

Name	*No*	*Builder*	*Type*	*Built*
Ashley	1	Peckett (2031)	0-4-0ST	1942
Lady Angela	1690	Peckett (1690)	0-4-0ST	1926
—	1738	Peckett (1690)	0-4-0ST	1937
Sapper	WD132	Hunslet (3163)	0-6-0ST	1943
Glendower	—	Hunslet (3810)	0-6-0ST	1954
Carnarvon	47	Kitson (5474)	0-6-0ST	1935
—	—	Fowler (421014)	0-4-0DM	1958
Errol Lonsdale	68011	Hunslet (3796)	0-6-0ST	1953
Meteor	31	RSH (7609)	0-6-0T	1950

Stock
13 ex-BR Mk 1 coaches; 7 ex-GWR coaches; 3 ex-GWR auto trailers; 25 wagons

Owners
0298 on loan from the National Railway Museum
Tiny, 7ft 0.25in gauge, part of the National Collection
3803 the South Devon Railway Trust
Glendower is privately owned
Errol Lonsdale the South Devon Railway Trust
1420 the South Devon Railway Association
5526 the 5526 Ltd
D8110 the Class 20 Group
5786 the Worcester Locomotive Society
Sapper & 4920 the South Devon Railway Trust
1369 the South Devon Railway Association

Timetable Service

South Tynedale Railway

Cumbria

Member: AIRPS, TT
A narrow gauge line passing through the attractive scenery of the South Tyne valley, in the North Pennine area of outstanding natural beauty
Location: Approximately 0.75-mile north of Alston town centre, on A686 Hexham road
OS reference: NY 717467
Operating society: South Tynedale Railway Preservation Society, The Railway Station, Alston, Cumbria CA9 3JB
Telephone: Alston (01434) 382828 (timetable information); (01434) 381696 (other enquiries)
Car park: Alston station
Access by public transport: Wright Bros buses, Haltwhistle-Alston and Newcastle-Alston-Keswick. Also summer buses from Durham and Stanhope. Bus links from Langwathby in connection with Settle-Carlisle line trains on certain dates (Details of all buses: [01228] 606000.)
On site facilities: Book and souvenir shop, tourist information centre, picnic area, toilets (including disabled persons), parking, lineside footpath
Catering facilities: Tea room at Alston, serving selection of snacks (not operated by Society). Confectionery, ice cream and soft drinks on sale in railway shop
Length of line: 1.5 miles (2.25 to Kirkhaugh), 2ft gauge
Public opening: 1998 passenger train service: Weekends & Bank Holidays — April-October; daily — Easter week, Spring Bank Holiday week, July and August; Thursdays in June and September
Steam haulage scheduled at weekends from Spring Bank Holiday until September, also Easter and May Day Weekends, daily 25 July to 31 August, and most special event days
Special events: STRPS 25th Anniversary Weekend — 4/5 April; Friends of Thomas the Tank Engine — 2-4 May and 24/25 October; Teddy Bear Day — 27 May; Steam Gala — 19/20 September; Santa Specials — 6, 12/13, 19/20 December; Mince Pie Specials — 27 December
Special notes: The line has been constructed on the trackbed of the former BR Haltwhistle-Alston branch. Extension of the line from Gilderdale towards Slaggyford, a further 3 miles, is in progress. It is expected to open another three-quarter-mile, from Gilderdale to Kirkhaugh, during 1998
Membership details: Membership Secretary, c/o above address
Membership journal: *Tynedalesman* — quarterly
Marketing name: England's Highest Narrow Gauge Railway

Locomotives

Name	*No*	*Builder*	*Type*	*Built*
Phoenix	1	Hibberd (2325)	4wDM	1941
Sao Domingos	3	O/K (11784)	0-6-0WT	1928
Naworth	4	H/Clarke (DM819)	0-6-0DM	1952
Thomas Edmondson	6	Henschel (16047)	0-4-0T	1918
—	9	Hunslet (4109)	0-4-0DM	1952
Naklo	10	Chrzanow (3459)	0-6-0WTT	1957
Cumbria	11	Hunslet (6646)	0-4-0DM	1967
Chaka's Kraal No 6	12	Hunslet (2075)	0-4-2T	1940
—	13	Hunslet (5222)	0-4-0T	1958
Helen Kathryn	14	Henschel (28035)	0-4-0T	1948
—	—	Hunslet (4110)	0-4-0DM	1952
—	—	H/Clarke (DM1167)	0-6-0DM	1960
—	15	H/Clarke (DM1366)	0-6-0DM	1965
—	—	EE/Baguley (2519/3500)	4wBE	1958
Permanent Way	DB965062			
Trolley		Wickham	4WDM	?

Owners
1, 6, 9 & 10 the South Tynedale Railway Preservation Society
4, 11, 4110, DM1107, 2519/3500) & DB965082 the Durham Narrow Gauge Group
12 the North Gloucestershire Narrow Gauge Co
13 the Ayle Colliery Co
3, 14 & 15 Privately owned

Stock
6 bogie coaches; 2 brake van; 1 bogie open wagon; 3 4-wheel open wagons; 1 4-wheel box van; 4 4-wheel flat wagons; 1 4-wheel fuel tank wagon; 2 bogie well wagons, 4 4-wheel skip wagons; 6 bogie flat wagons; 6 bogie hopper wagons; 1 4-wheel hopper wagon; 1 4-wheel weed-killer wagon; 1 bogie compressor wagon

Museum

South Yorkshire Railway

South Yorkshire

Member: AIRPS
Location: Barrow Road Railway Sidings, Barrow Road, Meadowhall, Wincobank, Sheffield S9 1HN
OS Reference: SK 391914
General Manager: John Wade
Operating society: South Yorkshire Railway
Telephone: (0114) 2424405
Car park: Car parking facilities available; more facilities being developed nearby
Access by public transport: From Sheffield: By bus, No 93 Firth Park, alight at the top of Barrow Road, and follow the signposts. From Rotherham, Doncaster and Sheffield No X77 bus alighting on Barrow Road.
By rail: Meadowhall, 100yd
By Supertram: From city centre to Meadowhall Interchange
On site facilities: Small shop
Length of line: 3.5 miles in total, although only three quarters of a mile is currently occupied
Period of public operation: Not operating a service as yet
Journey time: See above
Membership Secretary: G. Barnes
Membership details: c/o above address
Membership journal: *41Z* — quarterly

Locomotives and multiple-unit

Name	*No*	*Origin*	*Class*	*Type*	*Built*
—	D2953	BR	01	0-4-0DM	1956
—	02003	BR	02	0-4-0DH	1960
—	D2854	BR	02	0-4-0DH	1960
—	D2866	BR	02	0-4-0DH	1961
—	D2867	BR	02	0-4-0DH	1961
—	D2868	BR	02	0-4-0DH	1961
—	03020	BR	03	0-6-0DM	1958
—	03037	BR	03	0-6-0DM	1959
—	03066	BR	03	0-6-0DM	1959
—	03094	BR	03	0-6-0DM	1960
—	03099	BR	03	0-6-0DM	1960
—	D2118	BR	03	0-6-0DM	1959
—	D2134	BR	03	0-6-0DM	1960
—	D2139	BR	03	0-6-0DM	1960
—	03180	BR	03	0-6-0DM	1962
—	03197	BR	03	0-6-0DM	1961
—	D2199	BR	03	0-6-0DM	1961
—	D2229	BR	04	0-6-0DM	1955
—	D2246	BR	04	0-6-0DM	1956
—	D2272	BR	04	0-6-0DM	1960
—	D2284	BR	04	0-6-0DM	1960
—	D2302	BR	04	0-6-0DM	1960
—	D2310	BR	04	0-6-0DM	1960
—	D2324	BR	04	0-6-0DM	1961
Dorothy	D2337	BR	04	0-6-0DM	1961
—	D2587	BR	05	0-6-0DM	1959
—	06003	BR	06	0-4-0DM	1958
—	07001	BR	07	0-6-0DE	1962
—	07012	BR	07	0-6-0DE	1962
—	07013	BR	07	0-6-0DE	1962
—	D3000	BR	08	0-6-0DE	1952
Gwyneth	D3019	BR	08	0-6-0DE	1953
—	D3023	BR	08	0-6-0DE	1953
—	08133	BR	08	0-6-0DE	1955
—	08216	BR	08	0-6-0DE	1956
—	08308	BR	08	0-6-0DE	1957
—	08390	BR	08	0-6-0DE	1958
—	08436	BR	08	0-6-0DE	1958
—	08507	BR	08	0-6-0DE	1960
—	08647	BR	08	0-6-0DE	1960
—	08668	BR	08	0-6-0DE	1960
—	08707	BR	08	0-6-0DE	1960
—	08818	BR	08	0-6-0DE	1960
—	08936	BR	08	0-6-0DE	1962
—	D3476	BR	10	0-6-0DE	1957
Christine	D4092	BR	10	0-6-0DE	1962
—	12074	BR	11	0-6-0DE	1950
—	D9500	BR	14	0-6-0DM	1964
—	D9502	BR	14	0-6-0DM	1964
—	20096	BR	20	Bo-Bo	1961
—	D8056	BR	20	Bo-Bo	1961
—	26038	BR	26	Bo-Bo	1959
Sea King	33002	BR	33	Bo-Bo	1960
Earl Mountbatten of Burma	33203	BR	33	Bo-Bo	1962

Rolling stock
2 diesel-electric cranes; 4 BR Mk 1 coaches; 6 BR Mk 1 General Utility Vehicles; 1 BR Mk 1 bogie van; 2 Covered Carriage TruckS; 2 LNER brake vans; Several other wagons

Name	No	Origin	Class	Type	Built
Andania	40013	BR	40	1Co-Co1	1959
—	53556	BR	104	DMCL	1958

Industrial locomotives

Name	No	Builder	Type	Built
WD75133	2	Hunslet (3183)	0-6-0ST	1944
—	7	H/Clarke (1689)	0-4-0ST	1937
Cathyrn	—	H/Clarke (1884)	0-4-0ST	1955
George	—	Sentinel (9596)	4wVBT	1955
William	—	Sentinel (9656)	4wVBT	1956
Ken	67	Sentinel (10180)	0-6-0DH	1964
Courtaulds	67	Sentinel/T. Hill (138C)	0-6-0DH	1964
Bigga	—	Fowler (4200019)	0-4-0DH	1947
Rotherham	2	YEC (2480)	0-4-0DE	1950
—	—	Hibbard (3817)	0-4-0DM	1956
—	44	Hunslet (6684)	0-6-0DH	1968
—	47	T/Hill (249V)	0-6-0DH	1974
—	8	T/Hill (288V)	0-6-0DH	1980
—	—	Barclay (335)	0-4-0DM	1939
Speedy	—	Barclay (361)	0-4-0DM	1942
Hotwheels	—	Barclay (422)	0-6-0DM	1958
Toffo	2	R/Hornsby (432479)	4wDM	1959
—	20	YEC (2688)	0-4-0DE	1959
—	220	Barclay (359)	0-4-0DM	1941

Timetable Service

Spa Valley Railway

Kent

Member: AIRPS
The shed at Tunbridge Wells West is an original LBSCR design dating from 1891 and consists of four roads which house various items of rolling stock and motive power
Location: Tunbridge Wells West station
Operating society/organisation: Spa Valley Railway, Tunbridge Wells West Station, Nevill Terrace, Tunbridge Wells, Kent
Telephone: (01892) 537715
Internet address: http//www.uel.ac.uk/pers/1278/rly-pres/spa. html
Access by public transport: Buses to Tunbridge Wells, direct services from London and Hastings. All services stop at Sainsbury's, 15min walk away
Refreshment facilities: Buffet car at Tunbridge Wells West
Souvenir shop: Tunbridge Wells West (within engine shed)
Museum: Tunbridge Wells West (within engine shed)
Length of line: 3 miles Tunbridge Wells-Groombridge

Locomotives and multiple-units

Name	No	Origin	Class	Type	Built
Ramillies	50019	BR	50	Co-Co	1968

Industrial locomotives

Name	No	Builder	Type	Built
Scottie	1	R/Hornsby (412427)	4wDM	1957
North Downs	3	RSH (7846)	0-6-0T	1955
Perkie	4	Fowler (4220008)	0-4-0DH	1957
Princess Margaret	6	Barclay (376)	0-4-0DM	1947
Pinkie	8	YEC (2686)	0-4-0DE	1960
Telemon	9	Drewry/Vulcan (D295)	0-4-0DM	1955
Topham	10	Bagnall (2193)	0-6-0ST	1922
Fonmon	—	Peckett (1936)	0-6-0ST	1924
Paxman	11	Sentinel (10007)	0-4-0DE	1959
—	—	Chrzanow (3135)	0-6-0T	1954
—	—	Chrzanow	0-6-0T	1950s

Stock
5 BR Mk 1 coaches; 1 BR Mk 2 coaches; 2 ex-London Transport T stock coaches; Various freight wagons

Passenger trains: Weekends from March and Tuesdays, Wednesdays and Thursdays in July and August
Special events: Please contact for details

Membership details: C/o Tunbridge Wells West Station

No 3 stands at Tunbridge Wells station on the Spa Valley Railway. ***Alan P. Barnes***

Steam Centre

Stephenson Railway Museum & North Tyneside Railway

Northumberland

Member: AIRPS
A display in buildings which began life as the Tyne & Wear Metro Test Centre now features locomotives and exhibitions which illustrate railway development from waggonways to the present day
Location: Middle Engine Lane, West Chirton
OS reference: NZ 396576
Operating society/organisation: Tyne & Wear Museums operates the Stephenson Railway Museum and the North Tyneside Steam Railway Association operates the North Tyneside Railway for North Tyneside Council, address c/o Stephenson Railway Museum, Middle Engine Lane, West Chirton, North Shields NE29 8DX
Car park: On site
Length of line: North Tyneside Steam Railway, 3 miles, Stephenson Railway Museum to California Siding (for Royal Quays)
Access by public transport: Tyne

Locomotive and multiple-unit

Name	*No*	*Origin*	*Class*	*Type*	*Built*
—	03078	BR	03	0-6-0DM	1959
—	3267	NER	—	DMLV	1904

Industrial locomotives

Name	*No*	*Builder*	*Type*	*Built*
Billy	—	Killingworth or RS & Co (1)	0-4-0	1816-26
—	A No 5	Kitson (2509)	0-6-0PT	1883
Ashington No 5	5	Peckett (1970)	0-6-0ST	1939
MEA No 1	1	RSH (7683)	0-6-0T	1951
—	E4	Siemens-Schuckert (457)	Bo-BoWE	1909
Thomas Burt MP 1837-1902	401	Bagnall (2994)	0-6-0ST	1950
—	10	Consett Iron Co	0-6-0DM	1958

Stock
1 LNER Gresley BFK; 3 BR Mk 1 non-gangwayed coaches, 2 BR Mk 2 coaches, 1 LNER Gresley BGP

Owners
NER van National Railway Museum

& Wear Metro to Percy Main when North Tyneside Railway is in operation
Public opening: Weekends and Bank Holidays only — Easter to September. Write or phone (0191) 262 2627 for details, including early/late season variations and special events
Special notes: Stephenson Railway Museum and North Tyneside Railway share facilities in buildings. North Tyneside Steam Railway Association operates and maintains exhibits from the Museum Collection
Facilities for disabled: Access for wheelchairs to Museum building at Middle Engine Lane. Access to stations; also wheelchair ramp onto train

Timetable Service

Swanage Railway — 'The Purbeck Line'

Dorset

Member: AIRPS
Overlooked by the historic ruins of Corfe Castle, this railway is slowly extending towards Wareham and a connection to the Railtrack network
Location: Swanage station
Operations Manager: Paul McDonald
Passenger Services Manager: David Green
Operating society/organisation: Swanage Railway Co Ltd, Station House, Swanage, Dorset BH19 1HB
Telephone: Swanage (01929) 425800. Talking Timetable — (01929) 425800
Fax: (01929) 426680
Main station: Swanage
Other public stations: Herston Halt, Harman's Cross, Corfe Castle and Norden
OS reference: SZ 026789
Car park: Norden park & ride signposted off A351 Wareham-Swanage road on the approach to Corfe Castle. Limited parking available at Swanage station
Access by public transport: Regular bus services operated by Wilts & Dorset from Bournemouth, Poole and Wareham to Swanage and Norden park & ride
On site facilities: Souvenir shop at Swanage and Corfe Castle. Buffet car on most trains. Picnic areas at Swanage, Harman's Cross and Norden. Exhibition and cinema coach at Norden. 5in gauge railway at Swanage on some weekends. Travel Agency at Swanage station
Length of line: 6 miles, Swanage-Herston Halt-Harman's Cross-Corfe Castle-Norden
Public opening: Swanage station open every day except Christmas Day. Trains operate during 1998 every weekend and daily from 8 April until 1 November
Special events: Please contact for details
Facilities for disabled: Access to shop and toilets; specially adapted coach on most trains
Membership details: Sue Payne, c/o Southern Steam Trust at above address
Membership journal: *Swanage Railway News* — quarterly
Marketing name: The Purbeck Line

Locomotives and multiple-units

Name	*No*	*Origin*	*Class*	*Type*	*Built*
—	6695	GWR	5600	0-6-2T	1928
—	30053	LSWR	M7	0-4-4T	1905
257 Squadron	34072	SR	BB	4-6-2	1948
—	80078	BR	4MT	2-6-4T	1954
—	80104	BR	4MT	2-6-4T	1955
—	1708	MR	IF	0-6-0T	1880
—	30075	JZ	USA	0-6-0T	1950s
—	D3591	BR	08	0-6-0DE	1958
—	D9521	BR	14	0-6-0DH	1964
—	52048	BR	108	DMCL	1960
—	51919	BR	108	DMBS	1956

Industrial locomotives

Name	*No*	*Builder*	*Type*	*Built*
Cunarder	47160	Hunslet (1690)	0-6-0T	1931
May	2	Fowler (4210132)	0-4-0DM	1957
Beryl	—	Planet (2054)	4wPM	1937
—	2150	Peckett (2150)	0-6-0T	1954
Rosedale	110070		0-4-0DE	—

Locomotive notes: 30053 and 34072 will be away periodically on short-term loan. *Cunarder* is on loan to the Lavender Line. 35022's frames are at Sellinge for shot blasting

Stock
3 ex-LSWR coach bodies; 4 ex-SR vans; 9 ex-SR coaches; 18 ex-BR Mk 1 coaches; 15 various types of wagons; 1 ex-BR Mk 3 Sleeping coach; 1 ex-SR 15ton diesel-electric crane; 1 ex-London Transport Plasser & Theurer ballast tamper; 1 ex-BR Corridor 2nd converted to disabled persons coach. Brake vans from SR, LMS, LSWR, GWR; 3 ex-BR Met-Camm Pullmans (2 restored for 'Wessex Belle', 1 under restoration)

Owners
6695 the Great Western Railway Preservation Group
Cunarder the 1708 Locomotive Preservation Trust Ltd
1708 the 1708 Locomotive Preservation Trust Ltd
34072 and 80104 the Southern Locomotives Ltd
30053 the Drummond Locomotive Society
30075 the Project 62 Group
80078 the Project 78 Group
Pullmans by Flying Scotsman Railways

Above: **Ex-LSWR 'M7' class 0-4-4T No 30053 stands on the turntable at Swanage in August 1997.** *Alan P. Barnes*

Below: Wellington **enters Andrews House station on the Tanfield Railway.** *John East*

Steam Centre

Swindon & Cricklade Railway

Wiltshire

Member: AIRPS, TT
This is the only preserved section of the former Midland & South Western Junction Railway, the society having had to re-lay track and associated works. The line is being extended to a new station, Hayes Knoll, and is expected to open 1998 to serve the planned engine shed complex
Location: Tadpole Lane, Blunsdon (approximately midway between Blunsdon St Andrew and Purton)
Chairman: J. Larkin
Operating society/organisation: Swindon & Cricklade Railway, Blunsdon Station, Blunsdon, Swindon, Wiltshire SN2 4DZ
Telephone: Swindon (01793) 771615 (weekends only)
Station: Blunsdon
OS reference: SU 110897
Length of line: 1-mile
Car park: Tadpole Lane, Blunsdon
Refreshment facilities: Blunsdon station amenities building
Toilet: Blunsdon station amenities building
Souvenir shop: Blunsdon station amenities building. Various sales stands on Open Days around station area. Museum in converted coach
Depot: Blunsdon
Public opening: Saturdays and Sundays throughout the year.

Locomotives and multiple-units

Name	*No*	*Origin*	*Class*	*Type*	*Built*
Foremarke Hall	7903	GWR	'Hall'	4-6-0	1949
—*	5637	GWR	56xx	0-6-2T	1924
—	3845	GWR	2884	2-8-0	1942
—	D2152	BR	03	0-6-0DM	1960
—	D5222	BR	25	Bo-Bo	1963
—	56317	BR	100	MBS	1958
—	51434	Met/Cam	101	MBS	1958
—	52005	BR	107	DMBS	1960
—	52025	BR	107	DMBS	1960
—	59117	Met/Cam	101	TC	1958

*Expected to return to service during 1998 for the first time since 1964

Industrial locomotives

Name	*No*	*Builder*	*Type*	*Built*
—	—	Fowler (4210137)	0-4-0DM	1958
Woodbine	—	Fowler (21442)	0-4-0DM	1936
Richard Trevithick	—	Barclay (2354)	0-4-0ST	1955
Merlin/Myrddin	1371	Peckett (1967)	0-4-0ST	1939

Stock
6 BR Mk 1 coaches; 2 GWR coaches; Selection of goods rolling stock; Wickham railcar

Owners
7903 the Foremarke Hall Locomotive Group
5637 the 5637 Locomotive Group

Passenger trains: Details from Public Relations Manager, c/o above address
Special events: No information supplied
Facilities for disabled: Access to shop and refreshments
Membership details: Membership Secretary c/o above address
Membership journal: Quarterly
Marketing name: Tiddlydyke

Museum

Swindon GWR Museum

Wiltshire

Member: AIRPS
The Great Western Railway Museum began life as a lodging house for railway workers, and was then a Wesleyan Methodist Chapel for 90 years before being acquired by Swindon Borough Council and converted into a museum. Alongside the museum, in the heart of the railway village, visitors can glimpse the living conditions of the railworkers at the turn of the century, in the carefully restored workman's house.

Plans are well advanced for a new enlarged Railway Heritage Centre

Locomotives

Name	*No*	*Origin*	*Class*	*Type*	*Built*
—	2516	GWR	2301	0-6-0	1897
Kings George V	6000	GWR	'King'	4-6-0	1927
—	9400	GWR	9400	0-6-0PT	1947
*North Star**	—	GWR	—	2-2-2	1837
—	4	GWR	Diesel railcar	Bo-Bo	1934

*Broad gauge (7ft 0.25in) replica

Owners
All locomotives are part of the National Railway Museum Collection

on the old Swindon Works site to replace the existing GWR Museum collection. This may well involve the closure of the Faringdon Road building in 1998, and readers are advised to telephone the museum before travelling. It is hoped that the new museum will open in spring 2000 after the award of a Lottery Grant in February 1997
Keeper: T. Bryan
Location: Faringdon Road, Swindon, Wiltshire
OS reference: SU 145846
Operating society/organisation: Borough of Thamesdown, GWR Museum, Faringdon Road, Swindon, Wiltshire SN1 5BJ
Telephone: Swindon (01793) 466555
Car park: Swindon BR station and street parking
Access by public transport: Swindon main line station (10 minutes walk)
On site facilities: A selection of souvenirs is available
Public opening: Weekdays 10.00-17.00, Sundays 14.00-17.00. Closed Good Friday, Christmas Eve, Christmas Day, Boxing Day, New Year's Day
Special notes: The Museum also houses a considerable number of photographs depicting scenes of the GWR, along with nameplates, models, posters, tickets, etc. 1998: Return to Swindon Exhibition continues this year
Membership details: The Friends of Swindon Railway Museum, c/o The GWR Museum
Membership journal: *North Star* — quarterly

Timetable Service

Tanfield Railway

County Durham

Member: AIRPS
The oldest railway in the world, featuring 1725 route, 1725 Causey embankment, 1727 Causey arch, 1766 Gibraltar bridge and 1854 Marley Hill engine shed. Also collection of local engines, Victorian carriages and vintage workshop
Location: Off the A6076 Sunniside to Stanley road
OS reference: NZ 207573
Operating society/organisation: The Tanfield Railway, Marley Hill Engine Shed, Sunniside, Gateshead. Postal address: 33 Stocksfield Avenue, Newcastle upon Tyne NE5 2DX
Telephone: (0191) 274 2002
Main stations: Andrews House, Sunniside, Causey, East Tanfield
Car park: Marley Hill, Causey picnic area
Access by public transport: X30 (weekdays) stops outside main entrance; 706, 708, 722 Sundays to Sunniside only, near to Sunniside station
Catering facilities: Light refreshment available on operating days
On site facilities: Shop and toilets
Length of line: 3 miles
Public opening: Trains run every Sunday and bank holiday weekend January to November. Also Thursdays and Saturdays from 24 July-30 August. Santa trains in December. Marley Hill engine shed open daily for viewing

Locomotives

Name	*No*	*Origin*	*Class*	*Type*	*Built*
—	M2*	TGR	M	4-6-2	1951

*3ft 6in gauge, Tasmanian Government Railways (RSH 7630)

Industrial locomotives

Name	*No*	*Builder*	*Type*	*Built*
—	9	AEG (1565)	4w-4wE	1913
Gamma	—	Bagnall (2779)	0-6-0ST	1945
Horden	—	Barclay (1015)	0-6-0ST	1904
—	6	Barclay (1193)	0-4-2ST	1910
—	17	Barclay (1338)	0-6-0T	1913
—	32	Barclay (1659)	0-4-0ST	1920
—	3	E. Borrows (37)	0-4-0WT	1898
—	6	Fowler (4240010)	0-6-0DH	1960
Wellington	—	B/Hawthorn (266)	0-4-0ST	1873
Enterprise	—	R&W Hawthorn (2009)	0-4-0ST	1884
Cyclops	112	H/Leslie (2711)	0-4-0ST	1907
—	2	H/Leslie (2859)	0-4-0ST	1911
Stagshaw	—	H/Leslie (3513)	0-6-0ST	1923
—	3	H/Leslie (3575)	0-6-0ST	1923
—	13	H/Leslie (3732)	0-4-0ST	1928
—	3	H/Leslie (3746)	0-6-0F	1929
Irwell	—	H/Clarke (1672)	0-4-0ST	1937
—	38	H/Clarke (1823)	0-6-0T	1949
—	501	Hunslet (6612)	0-6-0DH	1965
—	4	Sentinel (9559)	0-4-0T	1953
—	L2	R/Hornsby (312989)	0-4-0DE	1952
—	35	R/Hornsby (418600)	0-4-0DE	1958
—	158	RSH (6980)	0-4-0DM	1940
Hendon	—	RSH (7007)	0-4-0CT	1940
—	62	RSH (7035)	0-6-0ST	1940
—	3	RSH (7078)	4w-4wE	1940
—	49	RSH (7098)	0-6-0ST	1943
Progress	—	RSH (7298)	0-6-0ST	1946
Cochrane	—	RSH (7409)	0-4-0ST	1948
—	44	RSH (7760)	0-6-0ST	1953
—	38	RSH (7763)	0-6-0ST	1954
—	21	RSH (7796)	0-4-0ST	1954
—	47	RSH (7800)	0-6-0ST	1954
—	1	RSH (7901)	0-4-0DM	1958
—	16	RSH (7944)	0-6-0ST	1957

Special events: Teddy Bear Weekends — 19/20 April, 20/21 September; Children's Weekends — 14/15 June, 9/10 August; Two Train Days — 4/5, 25/26 May, 24/25 August; Santa Steamings — 6/7, 13/14. 20/21-24 December; Mince Pie Specials — 26 December
Family tickets: Available
Facilities for disabled: Access to Andrews House station and Marley Hill engine shed. Toilets at Causey car park
Membership details: Miss E. Martin, 33 Stocksfield Avenue, Fenham, Newcastle upon Tyne NE5 2DX
Membership journal: *Tanfield Railway News* — 4 times/year
Special notes: Families can alight at Causey station for 2 miles of walks through the picturesque Causey Woods; picnic facilities and toilet available in car park

Name	*No*	*Builder*	*Type*	*Built*
FGF	—	Barclay (D592)	0-4-0DH	1969
—	2	A/Whitworth (D22)	0-4-0DE	1933
2ft gauge				
Escucha	11	B/Hawthorn (748)	0-4-0ST	1883
—	—	Clayton (133141)	4wBE	1984
—	—	Hunslet(7332	4wDM	1973
—	—	L/Blackstone (53162)	4wDM	1962
—	—	L/Blackstone (54781)	4wDM	1962
—	—	R/Harnsby (323587)	4wDM	1952
—	—	R/Hornsby (244487)	4wDM	1946
—	25	RSH (8201)	4wBE	1960
—	—	W/Rogers	4wBE	—

Stock
19 4-wheel carriages; 3 6-wheel carriages; 1 6-wheel van; 14 hopper wagons; 9 contractors bogies; 3 brake vans; 3 steam cranes; 8 covered wagons; 4 open wagons; 4 black wagons; 3 flat wagons

Steam Centre | Shropshire

Telford Horsehay Steam Trust

Member: AIRPS
Location: Horsehay, Telford, Shropshire
OS reference: SJ 675073
Operating society/organisation: Telford Horsehay Steam Trust, The Old Loco Shed, Horsehay, Telford, Shropshire TF4 2LT
On site facilities: Model railway, picnic area, narrow gauge steam tramway, miniature railway (separate charge); ticket gives unlimited travel (except miniature railway)
Public opening: Easter until 27 September including Bank Holidays 11.00-16.00 (-17.00 on Bank Holiday weekends). Last Sundays in month usually steam-hauled, but steam tram every Sunday

Locomotives

Name	*No*	*Origin*	*Class*	*Type*	*Built*
—	5619	GWR	5600	0-6-2T	1925

Industrial locomotives

Name	*No*	*Builder*	*Type*	*Built*
—	MP1	Barclay (1944)	0-4-0F	1944
Tom	27414	N/British (27414)	0-4-0DH	1954
Ironbridge No 3	—	Peckett (1990)	0-4-0ST	1940
—	9535	Sentinel (9535)	4wVBT	1952
—	D2959	R/Hornsby (382824)	4wDM	1955
—	—	R/Hornsby	0-4-0DH	1968
—	—	R/Hornsby	0-4-0DE	1959
—	—	R/Hornsby	0-4-0DE	1969
Thomas	—*	Kierstead	4wVBT	1979
—	—	Sentinel	0-4-0DH	1968
—	—	Sentinel	0-4-0DH	1969

*2ft gauge

Stock
1 ex-BR Mk 1 coach; 1 ex-GWR auto-trailer; 1 ex-GWR Toad brake van; 1 ex-GWR 3-ton hand crane; 1 Wickham trolley; Various wagons

Museum | Devon

Tiverton Museum

The Museum, dominated by No 1442, affectionately known as the 'Tivvy Bumper', houses a large collection of railway relics
Location: Tiverton, Devon
OS reference: SS 955124

Locomotives

Name	*No*	*Origin*	*Class*	*Type*	*Built*
(Tivvy Bumper)	1442	GWR	1400	0-4-2T	1935

Operating society/organisation: Tiverton & Mid Devon Museum Trust, St Andrew Street, Tiverton, Devon EX16 6PH
Telephone: Tiverton (01884) 256295
Car park: Adjoining access by public transport: Rail to Tiverton Parkway, then by bus, or bus from Exeter
On site facilities: Museum, shop and toilets
Public opening: Daily 10.30-16.30; except Sundays February to Christmas
Special notes: Limited facilities for disabled

The centrepiece of Tiverton Museum is GWR No 1442 which is surrounded by railway artefacts. ***Tiverton Museum***

Museum

Transperience — West Yorkshire Transport Discovery Park

West Yorkshire

Member: AIRPS
The Transperience vehicle collection consists of some 26 items, of which six are rail or tramway vehicles. It is hoped to progressively reopen the Spen Valley Railway commencing at Low Moor.

Transperience looks at the history of public transport in a fun and educational way from 1830 to the present day. It covers the railway revolution and looks at the evolution of the tram, trolleybus, motorbus and supertram.

The five exhibition halls are linked with 700m of tram track. Motorbuses, trams and trolleybuses are run between the halls offering visitors a mix of vehicle ride experience. Over 90 hands-on activities and four hi-tech theatres keep all age groups entertained for a full day.
Location: Transperience Way, Bradford BD12 7HQ, at junction 2 on M606 Bradford or via bus 268 from Bradford Interchange
Chief Executive: Vacant
Operating society/organisation: West Yorkshire Transport Trust Ltd, Transperience Way, Bradford BD12 7HW
Telephone: (01274) 690909
Public opening: Not advised, please contact for opening times

Industrial locomotives (all electric)

Name	*No*	*Builder*	*Type*	*Built*
—	10	Siemens	Bo	1913
—	1	E/Electric	Bo	1935

Stock
Derby 'Lightweight' Battery Electric unit Sc79998/9 (on loan to East Lancashire Railway); 2 Budapest trams 2576/2577; Graz 210 tram

and admission prices
Membership details: West Yorkshire Transport Museum Society, c/o above address. The Society provides volunteers who support Transperience through the restoration of Trust-owned exhibits and driving the vehicles. Telephone Transperience for details

Museum

Vintage Carriages Trust Museum

West Yorkshire

Member: AIRPS, TT
A fascinating collection of elderly railway carriages and small locomotives, interestingly presented. Sit in a fully restored, prize winning 1876-built Manchester, Sheffield & Lincolnshire Railway carriage or relive the dark days of wartime travel in one of the three Metropolitan Railway carriages. Listen to the 'Travellers' Tales' and view the collection of railway posters and other items. Two hour video presentation. The carriages and locomotives have appeared in over 30 cinema and television productions including *The Unknown Soldier*, *The Woman in White*, *One Golden Afternoon*, *The Secret Agent* and *The Railway Children*.
Location: Vintage Carriages Trust Museum, Ingrow Station Yard, Halifax Road, Keighley, West Yorkshire BD21 5AZ. On the A629 road
Operations Manager: Michael Cope, Hon Secretary, VCT
Operating society/organisation: Vintage Carriages Trust (a Registered Charity No 510776)
Telephone: Keighley (01535) 680425 during opening hours, or (01535) 646472 when closed
Car Park: Yes. Also coach parking at Ingrow station
Access by public transport: Regional Railways North East through trains from Carlisle, Settle, Morecambe, Lancaster to Keighley (one mile). Fast and frequent Metro Train services from Bradford Forster Square, Leeds, Shipley, and Skipton to Keighley. Then either KWVR train to Ingrow West (adjacent) or Keighley & District buses 663, 664, 665 from Keighley railway station. Calderline bus 500 (limited winter service) from Hebden Bridge. Calderline bus 502 from Huddersfield and Halifax. Keighley & District buses 663, 664, 665 from Bradford, via Bingley, Saltaire and Keighley rail and bus stations. Keighley & District buses 696 and 697 from Bradford via Thornton and Denholme. Numerous buses from Keighley bus station. Tel: (0113) 245 7676 for bus and Metro Train information
On site facilities: Transport relics shop specialising in out of print magazines, lamps and hardware. Soft drinks, ice cream and chocolate available. Toilets with full disabled access. A determined effort has been made to provide a museum which will interest the casual visitor who is not knowledgeable about railways
Public opening: Daily 11.30-17.00 except 25/26 December. Special openings outside these times can be arranged for groups
Facilities for disabled: The museum building is level with easy access for wheelchair users. A stairlift has been provided to allow wheelchair users to view carriage interiors, and enter guards' brake areas, though naturally wheelchairs are too wide to enter individual passenger compartments. Toilets with full access for wheelchair users. Braille leaflet, guidebook and audio tape for loan during visit. Special facilities for visitors with hearing difficulties
Special notes: Visitors are welcome to either browse in the shop or visit the museum. During 1997 work was completed on a £300,000 extension and improvements were made to access in the museum area. *Bellerophon* and *Sir Berkeley* are both operational and may be visiting a

Stock

Railway	*BR or previous owner Number*	*Date type*	*built*	*Seats*	*Weight*	*Length*
MS&LR	176	4-wheel 1st/2nd/3rd/ luggage	1876	34	12T	28ft 0in
ECJS	143	6-wheel 3rd brake	1888	40	14T	34ft 11in
MR	358	6-wheel 1st/3rd/ luggage	1886	32	15T	34ft 0in
Met	427	BS	1910	84	30T	54ft 0in
Met	465	S	1919	108	30T	54ft 0in
Met	509	F	1923	84	30T	54ft 0in
SR (SECR)	S3554S	BSK	1924	42	33T	65ft 3in
BR (SR)	S1469S	TSO	1951	64	32T	67ft 1in
GN	2856	Non vestibule composite, lav brake	1898	34	?	45ft 0in

(also two oil tank wagons: MR, c1890, and Esso, 1939)

Industrial locomotives

Name	*No*	*Builder*	*Type*	*Built*
Bellerophon	—	Haydock Foundry (C)	0-6-0WT	1874
Sir Berkeley	—	M/Wardle (1210)	0-6-0ST	1891
Lord Mayor	—	H/Clarke (402)	0-4-0ST	1893

number of other railways during the year. Please telephone for details
Membership details: Membership Secretary, c/o above address
Marketing names: Vintage Carriages Trust or VCT

Timetable Service

Wells & Walsingham Light Railway

Norfolk

Member: AIRPS, TT
One man's railway, the life and love of retired naval commander, Roy Francis, this delightful line which is totally uncommercialised runs along the old Wells branch to Walsingham where the old station has been transformed into a Russian Orthodox Church by the addition of an onion-shaped dome to its roof. A must if you find yourself nearby
Location: On A149, Stiffkey Road, Wells next the Sea, Norfolk
General Manager: Lt-Cdr R. W. Francis
Operating organisation: Wells & Walsingham Light Railway, Wells Next The Sea, Norfolk NR23 1RB
Car park: Yes
Access by public transport: Eastern Counties buses
On site facilities: Souvenir shop, toilets and tea shop
Length of line: 4 miles, 10.25in gauge
Public opening: Daily Easter to the end September
Special notes: Journey may be commenced at either end. Believed to be the world's longest 10.25in gauge line. Built on the old Wells & Fakenham Railway trackbed. Old Swainsthorpe signalbox on site at Wells. Motive power is provided by a Garratt locomotive.
Life passes in the form of a gilt edged enamel medallion now available, please enquire for details
Membership details: Membership Secretary, Wells & Walsingham Light Railway Support Group, c/o above address
Membership journal: Newsletter — quarterly

Steam Centre

West Lancashire Light Railway

Lancashire

Location: Alty's Brickworks. Station Road, Hesketh Bank, near Preston, Lancashire
OS reference: SD 448229
Operating society/organisation: The West Lancashire Light Railway Association, Secretary, 8 Croft Avenue, Orrell, Wigan, Lancs WN5 5TW
Telephone: (01772) 815881 or (01645) 622654 (Secretary)
Car parks: On site
Access by public transport: Main line rail to Preston or Southport. Bus route 100 and 102, between Preston and Southport
On site facilities: Gift shop, light refreshments, picnic tables, 2ft gauge line
Public opening: Easter weekend (not Saturday); May Day Bank Holiday Sunday and Monday; Spring Bank Holiday, then every Sunday until end of October. Opening times 12.30-17.00
Special events: Friendly Engine Day — 17 May, Family Fun Day — 5 July; Gala Day — 9 August, Industrial Day — 5 October; Santa Specials — 13, 19/20 December

Industrial locomotives

Name	*No*	*Builder*	*Type*	*Built*
Clwyd	1	R/Hornsby (264251)	4wDM	1951
Tawd	2	R/Hornsby (222074)	4wDM	1943
Irish Mail	3	Hunslet (823)	0-4-0ST	1903
—	4	Hibberd (1777)	4wPM	1931
—	5	R/Hornsby (200478)	4wDM	1940
—	7	M/Rail (8992)	4wDM	1946
—	8	H/Hunslet (4480)	4wDM	1953
Joffre	9	K/Stuart (2405)	0-6-0T	1915
—	10	Hibberd (2555)	4wDM	1946
—	16	R/Hornsby (202036)	4wDM	1941
—	19	Lister (10805)	4wPM	1939
—	20	Baguley (3002)	4wPM	1937
—	21	H/Hunslet (1963)	4wDM	1939
—	25	R/Hornsby (297054)	4wDM	1950
Mill Reef	27	M/Rail (7371)	4wDM	1939
—	30	M/Rail (11258)	4wDM	1964
—	32	M/Rail (11246)	4wDM	1963
Montalban	34	O&K (6641)	0-4-0WT	1913
Utrillas	35	O&K (2378)	0-4-0WT	1907
—	36	R/Hornsby (339105)	4wDM	1953
Jonathan	37	Hunslet (678)	0-4-0ST	1898
—	38	Hudswell (D750)	0-4-0DM	1949
—	39	Hibberd (3916)	4wDM	1959
—	40	R/Hornsby (381705)	4wDM	1959
—	41	Lister (29890)	4wPM	1946
—	42	Hunslet (8917)	4wDM	1980

Stock

Toastrack coach built 1986 by WLLR
Semi-open coach built 1993 by WLLR
Brake van built 1987 by WLLR
Large collection various wagons

Timetable Service

West Somerset Railway

Somerset

Member: AIRPS, TT
Running for 20 miles, this is Britain's longest preserved railway and evokes all the atmosphere of a country railway from a more leisured age. The line is host to several societies and groups, and several stations have their own museum, such as the Somerset & Dorset Trust at Washford. There are some idyllic country stations in the Quantock Hills, and Dunster station serves as the model for Hornby Dublo's branch line station
Managing Director: Mark L. Smith
Headquarters: West Somerset Railway, The Railway Station, Minehead, Somerset
Telephone: Minehead (01643) 704996. Talking timetable: (01643) 707650
Main station: Minehead
Other public stations: Dunster, Blue Anchor, Washford, Watchet, Williton, Doniford Beach Halt, Stogumber, Crowcombe, Bishops Lydeard
OS reference: Minehead SS 975463, Williton ST 085416, Bishops Lydeard ST 164290
Car parks: Minehead, Williton, Bishops Lydeard. Some parking at all stations except Doniford Beach
Access by public transport: Nearest main line station, Taunton. Southern National Omnibus Co (01823) 272033
Refreshment facilities: Minehead, Bishops Lydeard (limited opening). Wine and Dine trains, contact (01984) 623873. Buffet car on most steam trains
Souvenir shops: Minehead, Bishops Lydeard
Museum: Somerset & Dorset Railway Museum Trust, Washford (open WSR operating days March-end October). GWR Museum at Blue Anchor (open Sundays & Bank Holidays WSR operating season)

Locomotives and multiple-units

Name	*No*	*Origin*	*Class*	*Type*	*Built*
—	53808	S&DJR	7F	2-8-0	1925
—	3205	GWR	2251	0-6-0	1946
—	3850	GWR	2884	2-8-0	1942
—	4160	GWR	5101	2-6-2T	1948
—	4561	GWR	4500	2-6-2T	1924
Dumbleton Hall	4920	GWR	'Hall'	4-6-0	1929
—	5542*	GWR	4575	2-6-2T	1928
—	6412	GWR	6400	0-6-0PT	1934
Dinmore Manor	7820	GWR	'Manor'	4-6-0	1950
Ditcheat Manor	7821	GWR	'Manor'	4-6-0	1950
Odney Manor	7828	GWR	'Manor'	4-6-0	1950
Braunton	34046	SR	WC	4-6-2	1946
Sir Keith Park	34053	SR	BB	4-6-2	1947
—	D2119	BR	03	0-6-0DM	1959
—	D2133	BR	03	0-6-0DM	1959
—	D2271	BR	04	0-6-0DM	1952
—	D3462	BR	08	0-6-0DE	1957
—	08850	BR	08	0-6-0DE	1961
—	D9526	BR	14	0-6-0DH	1964
—	D9551	BR	14	0-6-0DH	1965
—	33048	BR	33	Bo-Bo	1961
—	D7017	BR	35	B-B	1962
—	D7018	BR	35	B-B	1964
—	D7523	BR	25	Bo-Bo	1963
Royal Oak	50017	BR	50	Co-Co	1967
Defiance	50149	BR	50	Co-Co	1967
Western Campaigner	D1010	BR	52	C-C	1962
—	50413	P/Royal	103	DMBS	1957
—	51663	BR	115	DMBS	1960
—	51852	BR	115	DMBS	1960
—	51887	BR	115	DMBS	1960
—	56097	M/Cam	101	DTC	1957
—	56169	P/Royal	103	DTCL	1957
—	59678	BR	115	TC	1960

*Undergoing restoration at Bridgnorth, Severn Valley Railway

Industrial locomotives

Name	*No*	*Builder*	*Type*	*Built*
Isabel	—	H/Leslie (3437)	0-6-0ST	1919
Kilmersdon	—	Peckett (1788)	0-4-0ST	1929
—	24	Ruston (210479)	4wDM	1941
—	—	Ruston (183062)	4wDM	1937
—	57	Sentinel (10214)	0-6-0DM	1964
—	501	Brush/Bagnall (3066)	0-4-0DE	1954
—	512	Brush/Bagnall (3102)	0-4-0DE	1954

Stock

22 ex-BR Mk 1 coaches; 1 ex-BR Mk 2 coach; 2 ex-BR Restaurant cars; 1 ex-BR Sleeping Car; 3 ex-S&DJR 6-wheel coaches, 7 ex-GWR camping coaches; 1 ex-GWR Sleeping Coach; 1 ex-SR 'Ironclad' coach; 1 ex-GWR

Depots: Bishops Lydeard, Williton, Washford, Minehead
Length of line: 20 miles
Passenger trains: Steam and diesel trains to Bishops Lydeard
Period of public operation: SAE for details
Special events: Diesel Gala Weekend — 28/29 March; Easter Steam Weekend — 12/13 April; Steam in the West Country Gala — 8-10 May; Friends of Thomas the Tank Engine — 4/5 July; Vintage Transport Fayre at Bishops Lydeard — 1/2 August; Autumn Steam Weekend — 11-13 September
Facilities for disabled: Parking space level with entrance. No steps to shop or booking office, level access to toilets (disabled toilets at Minehead 100yd from station). Special saloon *Lorna Doone* accommodates 14 wheelchairs and has disabled toilet. Advanced booking essential. Catering facilities can be reached without difficulties. Groups can be catered for.
Membership details: West Somerset Railway Association, The Railway Station, Bishops Lydeard, Taunton TA4 3BX
Membership journal: *WSR Journal* — quarterly

Hawksworth coach; 1 ex-GWR 5-ton hand crane; more than 40 freight vehicles

Owners
53808, *Isabel, Kilmersdon* the Somerset & Dorset Museum Trust
D1010, D7017, D7018, D9526 & 08850 the Diesel and Electric Preservation Group
D2119, D3462, D7523 and 50017 Dr John F. Kennedy
5542 the 5542 Fund
3205 the 2251 Class Fund
3850 and 7820 the 3850 Preservation Society
4160 the 4160 Ltd
D2271 & D9551 the WSR plc
4920 the South Devon Railway Trust

GWR 'Manor' class 4-6-0 No 7828 *Odney Manor* is seen leaving Blue Anchor bound for Minehead on the West Somerset Railway. ***Alan P. Barnes***

Museum

Winchcombe Railway Museum

Glos

One mile from Winchcombe station on the Gloucestershire-Warwickshire railway, the diverse collection includes signalling equipment, lineside fixtures, horse-drawn road vehicles, tickets, lamps, etc. Indoor and outdoor displays set in half an acre of traditional Victorian Cotswold garden. Visitors are encouraged to touch and operate exhibits
Location: 23 Gloucester Street, Winchcombe, Gloucestershire
OS reference: SP 023283
Operating society/organisation: Winchcombe Railway Museum Association, 23 Gloucester Street, Winchcombe, Gloucestershire
Telephone: Winchcombe (01242) 620641
Car Park: On street at entrance
Access by public transport: Bus service from Cheltenham operated by Castleways Ltd
On site facilities: Relic, refreshments and souvenir shop
Public opening: Weekends — Easter to end October 13.30-17.30; daily 10-19 April, 23-31 May, 1-31 August 13.30-17.30. Also during school half-terms, Wednesdays, Thursdays and Fridays 10.00-14.00
Facilities for disabled: Access to all parts except toilets
Special notes: Many visitor-operated exhibits, picnic area, pet animals

Scotland

Steam Centre | Alford Valley Railway | Aberdeenshire

The Alford Valley Railway operates from the restored station yard which once marked the terminus of the branch line linking the villages of upper Donside with Kintore Junction, thence to Aberdeen
Location: On A944, 25 miles west of Aberdeen, adjacent to Grampian Transport Museum
Headquarters: Alford Valley Railway Co Ltd, Alford Station, Alford, Aberdeenshire
Main station: Alford
Car park: On site
Length of line: 3km, 2ft gauge
Museum: Grampian Transport Museum adjacent
Depot: Alford station
Period of public operation: Railway operates: April, May September — weekends only (13.00-17.00); June, July and August — daily 13.00-17.00. Trains depart at 30min intervals. Alford Heritage Centre is open daily (10.00-17.00)
Special notes: Steam-operated on first Sunday of each month from April to September. Special bookings available, tel: (01975) 562811
Membership details: Membership Secretary, AVR, Association, Creagmoor, Main Street, Alford, Aberdeenshire AB33 8AD

Industrial locomotives

Name	*No*	*Builder*	*Type*	*Built*
Saccharine	—	Fowler (13355)	0-4-2T	1914
Hamewith	—	Lister (3198	4wDM	c1930
—	—	M/Rail (9215)	4wDM	1946
—	—	M/Rail (9381	4wDM	1948
—	—	M/Rail (22129)	4wDM	1962
—	—	M/Rail (2221)	4wDM	1964

Rolling stock
Two 24-seat coaches, 50-seat coach, 24-seat ex-Aberdeen tramcar, various wagons

Timetable Service | Bo'ness & Kinneil Railway | West Lothian

Member: AIRPS, TT
Historic railway buildings, including the station and train shed, have been relocated from sites all over Scotland. In a purpose-built exhibition hall, the Scottish Railway Exhibition tells the story of the development of the railways in Scotland, and their impact on the people. The rich geology of the area, with its 300 million year old fossils, is explained during a conducted tour of the caverns of the former Birkhill Fireclay Mine
Operating society/location: Scottish Railway Preservation Society, Bo'ness Station, Union Street, Bo'ness, West Lothian, EH51 9AQ
Access by public transport:

Locomotives

Name	*No*	*Origin*	*Class*	*Type*	*Built*
Sovereign	44871	LMS	5MT	4-6-0	1945
—	419	CR	439	0-4-4T	1908
Morayshire	246	LNER	D49	4-4-0	1928
Glen Douglas	256	NBR	D34	4-4-0	1913
—	42	NBR	Y9	0-4-0ST	1887
Maude	673	NBR	J36	0-6-0	1891
—	80105	BR	4MT	2-6-4T	1955
—	08443 (D3558)	BR	08	0-6-0DE	1958
—	14901 (D9524)	BR	14	0-6-0DH	1964
—	D8020	BR	20	Bo-Bo	1959
—	25235 (D7585)	BR	25	Bo-Bo	1965
—	26004 (D5303)	BR	26	B0-Bo	1958
—	26024 (D5323)	BR	26	Bo-Bo	1959
—	27001 (D5347)	BR	27	Bo-Bo	1961
—	D5351	BR	27	Bo-Bo	1961
—	47643	BR	47	Co-Co	1968
Rodney	50021	BR	50	Co-Co	1968

Nearest ScotRail station — Linlithgow. Bus services from Linlithgow, Falkirk, Stirling, Edinburgh and Glasgow
OS reference: NT 003817
Telephone: Bo'ness (01506) 822298
Main station: Bo'ness
Other station: Birkhill
Car parks: At Bo'ness and Birkhill (free)
Refreshment facilities: Unlicensed buffets at Bo'ness and Birkhill. Buffet car on some trains. Picnic tables at both stations
Souvenir shop: Bo'ness
Depot: Bo'ness
Length of line: 3.5 miles
Period of public operation: Weekends 4 April-18 October; Easter 10-13 April; Mondays 4, 25 May, 31 August; daily (except Mondays) 3 July-30 August
Special events: Easter Egg Specials — 10-14 April; Friends of Thomas the Tank Engine — 16/17 May, 8/9 August; Vintage Vehicle Rally/Father's Day — 21 June; Model Railway Exhibition — 4/5 July; Diesel Gala Weekend— 5/6 September; Caley 150 Celebrations — October/November; Santa Specials — weekends 28 November-20 December
Facilities for disabled: Disabled access to platform and a specially adapted carriage for wheelchair users. Toilets at Bo'ness station

Owners
80105 and (*Denis*) owned by Scottish Locomotive Owners Group
246 and 24 owned by Royal Museum of Scotland
256 the Glasgow Museum of Transport
44871 the Sovereign Preservation Group
27001 the Class 27 Preservation Group
26004 and 26024 the 6LDA Group

Industrial locomotives

Name	*No*	*Builder*	*Type*	*Built*
Clydesmill	3	Barclay (1937)	0-4-0ST	1928
—	3	Barclay (2046)	0-4-0ST	1937
—	24	Barclay (2335)	0-6-0T	1953
Texaco	—	Fowler (4210140)	0-4-0DM	1958
(Lord King)	—	H/Leslie (3640)	0-4-0ST	1926
—	19	Hunslet (3818)	0-6-0ST	1954
DS3	—	R/Hornsby (275883)	4wDM	1949
DS4	P6687	R/Hornsby (312984)	0-4-0DE	1951
(Ranald)	—	Sentinel (9627)	4wVBT	1957
—	970214	Wickham (6050)	2w-2PMR	c1951
—	—	Matisa (48626)	—	—
—	5	Hunslet (3837)	0-6-0ST	1955
—	(7)	Bagnall (2777)	0-6-0ST	1945
Borrowstounness	—*	Barclay (840)	0-4-0T	1899
—	—*	M/Rail (110U082)	4wDH	1970
—	—	Wickham (10482)	2w-2PMR	1970
—	(17)	Hunslet (2880)	0-6-0ST	1943
—	970213	Wickham (6049)	2w-2PMR	c1951
—	17	Barclay (2296)	0-4-0ST	1952
Lady Victoria	3	Barclay (1458)	0-6-0ST	1916
The Wemyss Coal Co Ltd	20	Barclay (2068)	0-6-0T	1939
—	(6)	Barclay (2127)	0-4-0CT	1942
No 1	—	Barclay (343)	0-6-0DM	1941
City of Aberdeen	—	B/Hawthorn (912)	0-4-0ST	1887
F82 (Fairfield)	—	E/Electric (1131) (244)	4wBE	1940
Kelton Fell	13	Neilson (2203)	0-4-0ST	1876
Lord Roberts	1	N/Reid (5710)	0-6-0T	1902
(Tiger)	—	N/British (27415)	0-4-0DH	1954
Kilbagie	DS2	R/Hornsby (262998)	4wDM	1949
—	—	R/Hornsby (321733)	4wDM	1952
DS6	(1)	R/Hornsby (421439)	0-4-0DE	1958
St Mirren	(3)	R/Hornsby (423658)	0-4-0DE	1958
—	D88/003	R/Hornsby (506500)	4wDM	1965
—	(DS5)	R/Hornsby (423662)	0-4-0DE	1958
(Denis)	—	Sentinel (9631)	4wVBT	1958
—	—	Arrols (Glasgow)	2w-2DM	c1966

*3ft 0in gauge

Stock
A large selection of coaching stock, many built by Scottish pre-Grouping companies, ex-BR Class 126 dmu, and an appropriate collection of early freight vehicles

Timetable Service

Caledonian Railway (Brechin)

Angus

Member: AIRPS
Travellers can also visit the nearby House of Dun, a National Trust for Scotland property built by William Adam in 1730. Bridge of Dun station is also very close to one of the nation's finest bird sanctuaries, the two square mile Montrose Basin. Volunteers for the Caledonian Railway are provided exclusively by members of the Brechin Railway Preservation Society
Information enquiries: Iain A. H. Smith, Publicity Director, c/o 14

Moathill East, Cupar, Fife KY15 4DT
Headquarters: Caledonian Railway (Brechin) Ltd, The Station, 2 Park Road, Brechin, Angus DD9 7AF
Telephone: (01334) 655965, after 4.30pm Mon-Fri or (01674) 81318
Talking timetable: (01356) 622992
Main station: Brechin
Other public station: Bridge of Dun
OS reference: NO 603603
Car park: Brechin, Bridge of Dun
Access by public transport: Nearest BR station — Montrose, 9 miles. Local bus operator, Strathtay Scottish — Dundee (01382) 228054/227201, Arbroath (01241) 870646, or Montrose (01674) 672805
Refreshment facilities: Light refreshments available during steamdays at Brechin
Picnic area: Bridge of Dun
Souvenir shop: Brechin
Museum: Brechin
Length of line: 4 miles
Depot: Brechin
Passenger trains: Steam trains between Brechin and Bridge of Dun
Period of public operation: Easter and Sundays only, May to September
Special events: Easter Sunday and Santa Specials, please contact for further details
Facilities for disabled: Ramp access to both stations, disabled toilets at Brechin only. Passengers can be assisted on and off trains by railway staff
Family tickets: Available
Disclaimer: The Caledonian Railway (Brechin) Ltd reserves the right to amend, cancel or add to these events. And whilst every effort will be made to maintain the above services, the company does not guarantee that trains will depart or arrive at the time stated and reserves the right to suspend or alter any train without notice and will not accept any liability for loss, inconvenience or delay thereby caused
Membership details: Murray D. Duncan, 2 Binghill Crescent, Milltimber, Aberdeen

Locomotives and multiple-units

Name	*No*	*Origin*	*Class*	*Type*	*Built*
—	46464	LMS	2MT	2-6-0	1950
—	D2866	BR	02	0-4-0DM	1961
Brechin City	D3059	BR	08	0-6-0DE	1954
—	26014	BR	26	Bo-Bo	1959
—	26035	BR	26	Bo-Bo	1959
—	27024	BR	27	Bo-Bo	1962
—	51993	BR	107	DMBS	1960
—	52012	BR	107	DMSL	1960

Industrial locomotives

Name	*No*	*Builder*	*Type*	*Built*
—	16	Bagnall (2759)	0-6-0ST	1944
—	6	Bagnall (2749)	0-6-0ST	1944
Bon Accord	2	Barclay (807)	0-4-0ST	1897
—	1	Barclay (1863)	0-4-0ST	1926
Diana	1	Hunslet (2879)	0-6-0ST	1943
BAC Ltd	1	Peckett (1376)	0-4-0ST	1915
Yard No DY326	—	Hibberd (3743)	4wDM	1955
Yard No 5198	—	Hibberd (3747)	4wDM	1955
—	—	R/Hornsby (421700)	4wDM	1959
Dewar Highlander	—	R/Hornsby (458957)	4wDM	1961

Stock
4 ex-BR Mk 1 TSOs; 1 ex-BR Mk 1 BSK; 1 ex-BR Suburban; 1 ex-BR Mk 1 SO; 1 ex-BR Engineers Inspection Saloon; 1 ex-BR Full Kitchen Car; 3 ex-BR Mk 2s; 1 ex—BR diesel crane. Various items of freight stock

Museum

Glasgow Museum of Transport

Glasgow

Glasgow's magnificent railway collection represents one of the best efforts by a municipal authority to preserve a representative collection of items appropriate to the 'locomotive builders of the Empire'. In 1989 the collection opened to view once again in its new setting at the former Kelvin Hall
Access by public transport: Strathclyde PTE Underground. Kelvinhall: Strathclyde Buses 6, 6A, 8, 8A, 9, 9A, 16, 42, 42A, 44A, 57, 57A, 62, 62A, 62B, 64; Kelvin Scottish Buses 5, 5A; Clydeside

Locomotives

Name	*No*	*Origin*	*Class*	*Type*	*Built*
—	123	CR	123	4-2-2	1886
—	9	G&SWR	5	0-6-0T	1917
—	103	HR	—	4-6-0	1894
Gordon Highlander	49	GNSR	F	4-4-0	1920

Industrial locomotives

Name	*No*	*Builder*	*Type*	*Built*
—	1	Barclay (1571)	0-6-0F	1917
—	—	Chaplin (2368)	0-4-0TG	1888
—	—	BEV (583)	B	1927

Stock
Glasgow District Subway car 39T; Glasgow Corporation Underground cars 1 and 4; LMS King George VI's saloon 498 of 1941

Scottish Buses 17
Operating society/organisation: Glasgow Museums
Location: Museum of Transport, Kelvin Hall, 1 Bunhouse Road, Glasgow G3 8DP
Telephone: (0141) 287 2623 or (0141) 287 2721
Fax: (0141) 287 2692
Car park: Opposite Museum entrance
On site facilities: Toilets, cafeteria, shop and public telephone, cloaking facility
Public opening: Monday-Saturday (except Tuesdays) 10.00-17.00; Sunday 11.00-17.00. Closed 1/2 January and 25/26 December only. There are proposals before the Council to close the Museum from April until September 1998 as a budget saving. Visitors are advised to contact the Museum before visiting
Facilities for disabled: Both single-sex and uni-sex disabled facilities now available. A passenger lift to allow disabled access at the front entrance will be completed early in 1998

Steam Centre

Leadhills & Wanlockhead Railway

Strathclyde

Member: AIRPS
Situated in the Lowther Hills between Abington and Sanquhar the society was formed in 1983 to construct and operate a 2ft gauge tourist railway between the villages of Leadhills and Wanlockhead,. The track now extends to the old county boundary between Lanarkshire and Dumfries
Operating society/organisation: Leadhills & Wanlockhead Railway c/o Douglas Boyd, The Saltings, Battlehill, Annan DG12 6SN
Main station: Leadhills
Access by public transport: ScotRail trains stop at Sanquhar on Nith Valley Line (approx 10 miles) every 1hr 30min-2 hours. Bus service (Western Scottish Stagecoach) to Leadhills (please check for times). Nearest motorway — M74 — J14 from south/J15 from north. From A76 take B797 to Leadhills

Industrial locomotives

Name	*No*	*Builder*	*Type*	*Built*
—	—	O&K	0-4-0T	1913
The Gulliver	1	Fowler (18892)	4wDM	1931
Elvan	2	M/Rail (9792)	4wDM	1955
Luce	4	R/Hornsby (7002/0467/2)	4wDM	1966
Little Clyde	5	R/Hornsby (7002/0467/6)	4wDM	1966
Clyde	6	Hunslet (6347)	4wDH	1975
Nith	7	H/Clarke (DM1002)	0-4-0DMF	1956

Rolling stock
2 air braked passenger coaches and guard's van built at Leadhills. 1 air-braked coach chassis built by Talyllyn Railway, with the L&WR completing the bodywork. Assorted permanent way wagons

Length of line: 1-mile
Journey time: Approx 40min
On site facilities: Shop, ticket office, small museum and picnic tables. Extensive country walks. Also on 'Southern Uplands Way'. Scottish Lead Mining Museum at Wanlockhead (1-mile)
Period of public operation: Easter weekend; weekends May-October. Saturdays 12.00-17.00, Sundays 11.00-17.00 — later if passenger numbers justify. Schools charter trains planned for Saturdays during May and June by prior booking
Society journal: Quarterly

Timetable Service

Mull Rail

Isle of Mull

Member: AIRPS, TT
General Manager: Graham E. Ellis
Operations Manager: Peter Gush
Operating society/organisation: Mull & West Highland (NG) Railway Co Ltd, Old Pier Station, Craignure, Isle of Mull PA65 6AY
Telephone: (01680) 812494 (during operating period); (01680) 300389 (out of season);
Fax: (01680) 300595
OS reference: **NM** 725369
Car park: At Craignure, free
Access by public transport: Caledonian Macbrayne ferry from Oban (40min sail)
On site facilities: Gift shop, car park (free)
Family ticket: Available (2 Adults & 2 children under 14)
Length of line: 1.25 miles/10.25 in gauge
Public opening: Easter to mid-October
Facilities for disabled: No steps on railway, two compartments for wheelchairs
Membership details: Friends of Mull Rail, David Crombie, 1 Mulberry Drive, Dunfermline, Fife KY11 5BZ. Tel: (01383) 728652
Membership journal: *Crankpin Journal* — annual
Special notes: First island

passenger railway in Scotland, runs to Torosay Castle and 12 acres of gardens, superb panoramic views of mountains and sea. Joint discounted sail/rail tickets only from Caledonian MacBrayne, Oban. Group discount available for 20+ pre-booked passengers. Special trains can be chartered within and outside timetable hours. Visit Torosay and Duart Castles, Ride the Railway by the Mull Experience. Tel: (0168) 812421 for details

Locomotives

Name	*No*	*Builder*	*Type*	*Built*
Lady of the Isles	—	Marsh	2-6-4T	1981
Waverley	—	Curwen	4-4-2	1948
—	—	Alcock	4w-4PM	1973
Glen Auldyn	—	Davies	8wDH	1986
*Victoria**	—	Vere	2-6-2T	1993

*Largest tank engine built for 10.25in gauge

Rolling stock

12 coaches (two with wheelchair accommodation); 3 bogie wagons; 1 4-wheel wagon

Timetable Sailings

Paddle Steamer Preservation Society

Coastal & Inshore Waters

Member: AIRPS

Paddle steamers: *Waverley* & *Kingswear Castle*. Pleasure cruise ship: *Balmoral*

The Paddle Steamer *Waverley* was built for the London & North Eastern Railway in 1946, and replaced a vessel of the same name which was sunk off Dunkirk during May 1940. Sold to the PSPS – a Registered Charity – in 1974, *Waverley* sails on day trips and afternoon cruises from ports and piers in most coastal areas and river estuaries of the United Kingdom, from Easter until October each year. Also in the 'fleet' is the traditional motor cruiser *Balmoral* and the river paddle steamer *Kingswear Castle* which sails from Chatham Historic Dockyard on the River Medway

General Manager: David Duncanson

Headquarters: Waverley Excursions Ltd, Waverley Terminal, Anderston Quay, Glasgow G3 8HA

On ship facilities: Self service restaurants, bars, toilets (disabled toilets on *Waverley*)

Membership details: Paddle Steamer Preservation Society, PO Box 385, Hazlemere, High Wycombe HP11 1AE

Membership journal: *Paddlewheels* — quarterly

Details of the full programme of cruises operated by the three ships can be obtained from the National Booking Office, Waverley Excursions Ltd, Gwalia Buildings, Barry Docks CF62 5QR. Telephone: (01446) 720656.

PS *Waverley* is due to undergo a major overhaul following the awarding of Lottery money. *PSPS*

Steam Centre

Prestongrange Industrial Heritage Museum

East Lothian

Location: On the B1348 between Musselburgh and Prestonpans.

OS reference: NT 734737

Operating society/organisation: East Lothian Museum Service, Library & Museum Headquarters, Dunbar Road, Haddington, East Lothian EH41 3PJ

Telephone: (0131) 653 2904 (Prestongrange Visitor Centre), (01620) 82 8203 (Museum Service)

Car park: On site

On site facilities: Once part of the Scottish Mining Museum, Prestongrange is being developed as a museum which tells the story of people and industries in East Lothian — local coal deposits encouraged the growth of numerous other industries; such as pottery, pipe making, soap, glycerine, brewing and weaving

Visitor centre: Changing exhibitions of local industries.

Displays of local art and crafts — one-off events, demonstrations, workshops. Cornish beam engine, installed 1874 to pump water from the mine. Colliery locomotives restored by Prestongrange Railway Society are housed here
Toilets: Visitor Centre
Refreshment facilities: Available at Visitor Centre
Public opening: 30 March to 26 October, 11.00-16.00, last tour at 15.00
Length of line: 400m (standard gauge), extension in progress
Facilities for disabled: Access and toilet at Visitor Centre. Access to powerhouse exhibition, and footpaths along the site
Special events: Steam days are held on the first Sunday of each month April to September and the last Sunday in September.

Industrial locomotives

Name	*No*	*Builder*	*Type*	*Built*
—	6	A/Barclay (2043)	0-4-0ST	1937
—	17	A/Barclay (2219)	0-4-0ST	1946
Prestongrange	7	G/Ritchie (536)	0-4-2ST	1914
Tomatin	1	M/Rail (9925)	4wDM	1963
—	—*	Hunslet (4440)	4wDM	1952
—	32	R/Hornsby (458960)	4wDM	1962
George Edwards	33	R/Hornsby (221647)	4wDM	1943
—	—	E/Electric (D908)	4wDM	1964

*2ft gauge

Rolling stock
Steam crane, Whittaker No 30, c1890, occasionally in steam

Passenger rides available.
Advanced notice for larger parties
Membership details: Friends of Prestongrange. Contact Peter Gray, Museums Officer — c/o operating organisation
Contact: For Prestongrange Railway Society — Charles Young, The Smiddy, Middleton, Midlothian

Scottish Industrial Railway Centre

Steam Centre — Ayrshire

Member: AIRPS, TT
The Scottish Industrial Railway Centre is based on part of the former Dalmellington Iron Co railway system which was one of the best known industrial railway networks in Britain. Steam worked up until 1978 when the system closed and it is the aim of the centre to recreate part of the railway. The Ayrshire Railway Preservation Group also owns the former G&SWR station at Waterside, 2 miles from the Centre, and has access to the former NCB locomotive shed and wagon workshops at Waterside. These locations are not yet open to the general public. Working in conjunction with the Dalmellington & District Conservation Trust it is hoped to create an industrial heritage centre at Waterside based on the iron, coal and brick making industries. A passenger train service may operate between the two stations on certain Sundays
Location: Scottish Industrial Railway Centre, Minnivey Colliery, Dalmellington, Ayrshire
OS reference: NS 476074

Locomotives

Name	*No*	*Origin*	*Class*	*Type*	*Built*
—	MP228 (12052)	BR	11	0-6-0DE	1949
—	MP229 (12093)	BR	11	0-6-0DE	1951

Industrial locomotives

Name	*No*	*Builder*	*Type*	*Built*
—	16	A/Barclay (1116)	0-4-0ST	1910
—	8	A/Barclay (1296)	0-6-0T	1912
—	19	A/Barclay (1614)	0-4-0ST	1918
Aberdeen Corporation Gas Works	3	A/Barclay (1889)	0-4-0ST	1926
—	8	A/Barclay (1952)	0-4-0F	1928
Harlaxton	—	A/Barclay (2107)	0-6-0ST	1941
—	10	A/Barclay (2244)	0-4-0ST	1947
NCB No 23	—	A/Barclay (2260)	0-4-0ST	1949
—	25	A/Barclay (2358)	0-6-0ST	1954
—	1	A/Barclay (2368)	0-4-0ST	1955
—	118	A/Barclay (366)	0-4-0DM	1940
—	7	A/Barclay (399)	0-4-0DM	1956
Lily of the Valley	—	Fowler (22888)	0-4-0DM	1943
Tees Storage	—	N/British (27644)	0-4-0DH	1959
—	—	R/Hornsby (224352)	4wDM	1943
Blinkin Bess	—	R/Hornsby (284839)	4wDM	1950
Johnnie Walker	—	R/Hornsby (417890)	4wDM	1959
—	—	R/Hornsby (421697)	0-4-0DM	1959
—	107	Hunslet (3132)	0-4-0DM	1944
—	—	Sentinel (10012)	4wDM	1959
—	—	Donnelli (163)	4wDMR	1979
3ft gauge				
—	—	R/Hornsby (256273)	4wDM	1949
—	—	Hunslet (8816)	4wDH	1981

Operating society/organisation: Ayrshire Railway Preservation Group
Telephone: Doon Valley Heritage Office (01292) 531144. The Secretary (01292) 313579 (evening & weekends)
Length of line: 2.25 miles
Access by public transport: Nearest rail station, Ayr (14 miles). Stagecoach bus service from Ayr. Tel: (01292) 263382
On site facilities: Steam-hauled brake van rides (over 0.25-mile section). Guided tours of centre, museum of railway relics and photographs, souvenir shop, buffet, locomotive shed, narrow gauge demonstration line
Public opening: Open for static display with limited facilities every Saturday, June to end September
Passenger service: A steam-hauled passenger service may operate over the 2.25-mile long Scottish coal line to Dunaskin (Waterside) on certain Sundays in July and August
Special events: Steam days (with at least one engine in steam) will be held on: 30 May, 28 June, 5, 12, 19, 26 July, 2, 9, 16, 23, 30 August, 27 September
Membership details: Mr Frank Beattie, 1 McKnight Avenue, Waterside, Fenwick, Kilmarnock, Ayrshire
Special notes: For further information and details of special events, telephone the Doon Valley Heritage Office (01292) 531144 daytime, (01292) 313579 evenings and weekends, or write to Gordon Thomson, 8 Burnside Place, Troon, Ayrshire KA10 6LZ (SAE

	Name	*No*	*Builder*	*Type*	*Built*
2ft 6in gauge					
	—	2	R/Hornsby (183749)	4wDM	1937
	—	3	R/Hornsby (210959)	4wDM	1941
	—	1	R/Hornsby (211681)	4wDM	1942

Note: Not all vehicles on public display

Stock
1 BR Mk 1 TSO, 1 BR Mk 1 BSK, 2 Wickham trolleys; 1 steam crane; various other items

Timetable Service

Strathspey Railway

Inverness-shire

Member: AIRPS, TT
Scotland's steam railway in the Highlands connects the busy tourist resort at Aviemore to the more traditional highland village of Boat of Garten, famed as one of the few nesting places of the osprey (viewing site 3 miles from station). The bridge at Bridge of Garten has been replaced and three of the four miles of track between Bridge of Garten and Broomhill has been laid. A great deal of work still needs to be done but, subject to labour and finance being available, the railway would like to open to Broomhill for Easter 1999. 1998 is the centenary of the opening of Aviemore station
Commercial Manager: Laurence Grant
Enquiries: Aviemore Speyside Station, Dalfaber Road, Aviemore, Inverness-shire PH22 1PY (SAE for copy of timetable brochure)
Telephone: 01479 810725. For details of locomotives in operation (01479) 831692
Fax: (01479) 811022
Main station: Aviemore. The railway hopes to be operating from

Locomotives and multiple-units

Name	*No*	*Origin*	*Class*	*Type*	*Built*
—	5025	LMS	5MT	4-6-0	1934
—	46512	LMS	2MT	2-6-0	1952
—	828	CR	812	0-6-0	1899
—	08490	BR	08	0-6-0DE	1958
—	D5302	BR	26	Bo-Bo	1958
—	26025	BR	26	Bo-Bo	1959
—	D5394	BR	27	Bo-Bo	1962
—	51990	BR	107	DMBS	1960
—	52008	BR	107	DMBS	1960
—	52030	BR	107	DMC	1960
—	54047	BR	114	DTC	1960

Industrial locomotives

Name	*No*	*Builder*	*Type*	*Built*
—	48	Hunslet (2864)	0-6-0ST	1943
Cairngorm	9	RSH (7097)	0-6-0ST	1943
—	60	Hunslet (3686)	0-6-0ST	1948
Niddrie	6	Barclay (1833)	0-6-0ST	1924
*Forth**	10	Barclay (1890)	0-4-0ST	1926
Balmenach	2	Barclay (2020)	0-4-0ST	1936
—	17	Barclay (2017)	0-6-0T	1935
Inveresk	14	R/Hornsby (260756)	0-4-0DM	1950
Inverdon	15	Simplex (5763)	4wDM	1957
—	16	North British (27549)	0-4-0DM	1951
Queen Anne	20	R/Hornsby (265618)	4wDM	1948

*Not on site

Locomotive notes: In service 9, 828, 08490, D5265, 54047 & 52008. Under restoration 60, 46512 (possibly in traffic late 1999)

the original station from 29 March (subject to completion of work)
Other public station: Boat of Garten
OS reference: Aviemore NH 898131, Boat of Garten NH 943789
Car parks: Aviemore and Boat of Garten
Access by public transport: ScotRail services and express bus to Aviemore. Local service to Boat of Garten
Refreshment facilities: On-train buffet car or facilities on many trains. Picnic tables at Boat of Garten (for use of ticket purchasers). No refreshment facilities on DMU services
Souvenir shop: Boat of Garten and Aviemore
Museum: Small relics display at Boat of Garten. Extension progress display at Aviemore (Speyside)
Depot: Aviemore (not open to public), sidings at both stations are not open to the public
Length of line: 5.5 miles
Journey time: 17min, return within the hour possible on most services
Passenger trains: Steam-hauled services. Boat of Garten-Aviemore. DMU on Saturdays
Period of public operation: 19 March; 1/2, 4-12, 15/16, 18/19, 22/23, 25/26, 29/30 April; 2-4, 6/7, 9/10, 13/14, 16/17, 20/21, 23-25, 27/28, 30/31 May; Daily 1 June-1 October; 1, 3-5, 7/8, 10/11, 14-25, 28/29, 31 October; Saturday services operated by DMU except for special events
Special events: Confirm by telephone, send SAE for details. Enthusiasts' Day — 23 May (steam, diesel, DMU) (members & shareholders free travel plus access to restricted areas, workshops, extension); Friends of Thomas the Tank Engine — 2-4 May, 5/6 September
Facilities for disabled: Access possible at Boat of Garten and Aviemore. Please contact in advance for directions and if a party involved
Special notes: First and third class travel available on most trains. Family fares available for third class travel. Special rates/arrangements for parties. Luncheon on the train — Wednesdays in July and August. Bicycles carried free — groups must give prior notice
Membership details: Strathspey Railway Association at above address
Membership journal: *Strathspey Express* — quarterly

Stock
18 ex-BR coaches; 4 ex-LMS coaches; 1 Pullman coach; 3 ex-LMS sleeping cars; 1 ex-LNER sleeping car; 1 ex-HR coach; 1 ex-NBR coach; 1 ex-GNSR coach; Numerous examples of rolling stock

Owners
17 and 46512 the Highland Locomotive Co Ltd
828 the Scottish Locomotive Preservation Trust Fund
D5302 and 26025 the Highland Diesel Locomotive Co Ltd

Museum — Summerlee Heritage Park — Lanarkshire

Social and industrial history museum, interprets the communities in the west of Scotland in the 19th and 20th centuries. Working machinery in reconstructed workshops; miners' rows, reconstructed coal mine, art gallery, working tram
Manager: Vacant
Operating society/organisation: Summerlee Heritage Park, Heritage Way, Coatbridge, ML5 1QD (operated by North Lanarkshire Council)
Telephone: (01236) 431261
Fax: (01236) 440429
Public opening: Daily 10.00-17.00, except 25/26 December and 1/2 January
Access by public transport: BR Coatbridge Central and Coatbridge Sunnyside. Local buses
Car park: Opposite site
On site facilities: Tearoom, gift shop. Working electric tramway with cars from Motherwell, Brussels and Graz; underground mine tour and miners' cottages
Special events: Organised events from April-October, details on request
Facilities for disabled: Toilets, wheelchair available

Locomotives

Name	*No*	*Origin*	*Class*	*Type*	*Built*
Springbok	4112	SAR	GMAM	4-8-2+2-8-4	1956

(3ft 6in gauge/built by North British Loco Co)

Industrial locomotives

Name	*No*	*Builder*	*Type*	*Built*
—	—	Barclay (472)	0-4-0DH	1966
—	—	H/Clarke (895)	0-6-0T	1909
—	—	G/Hogg	0-4-0T	1898
Robin	—	Sentinel (9628)	4wTG	1957

Owner
Springbok Springburn Museum

Stock
2 rail-mounted steam cranes

Wales

Bala Lake Railway (Rheilfordd Llyn Tegid)

Timetable Service

Caernarfonshire

Member: AIRPS, TT
This delightful narrow gauge railway follows the route of the former Bala-Dolgellau Railway, along the shore of Wales' largest natural lake. The railway's headquarters are to be found in the fine old station building at Llanuwchllyn at the south-western end of the line. Do not be deterred by the fact that the railway runs down the opposite shore of the lake to the main road — it is well worth the detour
General Manager: Roy Hardiman
Headquarters: Rheilfford Llyn Tegid (Bala Lake Railway) Llanuwchllyn, Bala, Gwynedd LL23 7DD
Telephone: Llanuwchllyn (01678) 540666
Main station: Llanuwchllyn
Other public stations: Llangower, Bala. Request halts at Pentrepiod, Glanllyn (Flag Station) and Bryn Hynod
OS reference: Llanuwchllyn SH 880300, Bala SH 929350
Car parks: Llanuwchllyn, Llangower and Bala town centre
Access by public transport: Bus Gwynedd service No 94 to both Bala and Llanuwchllyn (from Wrexham or Barmouth)
Road access: Off the A494 Bala-Dolgellau road

Industrial locomotives

Name	*No*	*Builder*	*Type*	*Built*
Holy War	3	Hunslet (779)	0-4-0ST	1902
Maid Marian	5	Hunslet (822)	0-4-0ST	1903
Triassic	—	Peckett (1270)	0-6-0ST	1911
Meirionydd	11	Severn Lamb (7322)	Bo-Bo	1973
Chilmark	12	R/Hornsby (194771)	4wDM	1939
Bob Davies	—	YEC (L125)	4wDM	1983
Indian Runner	—	R/Hornsby (200744)	4wDM	1940
—	—	Lister (34025)	4wDM	1949
—	—	Motorail (5821)	4wDM	1934
—	—	R/Hornsby (189972)	4wDM	1938
—	—	Hibberd (FH2544)	4wDM	1941
—	—	Hunslet (1974)	4wDM	1939
Cernyw	—	R/Hornsby (200748)	4wDM	1940
Lady Madcap	—	R/Hornsby (283512)	4wDM	1949

Locomotive notes: *Holy War* and *Maid Marian* are in regular use, *Triassic* in steam for special weekends and other peak periods, remainder are on static display

Refreshment facilities: Llanuwchllyn. Large picnic site with toilet facilities by lake at Llangower
Souvenir shop: Llanuwchllyn
Depot: Llanuwchllyn
Length of line: 4.5 miles, 1ft 11.625in gauge
Passenger trains: Llanuwchllyn-Bala. Journey takes 25min in each direction
Period of public operation: 10 April-4 October
Facilities for disabled: Facilities available on most trains
Special notes: Small parties (10/12) may just turn up, but a day's notice required for larger groups
Family tickets: Available for all round trip journeys
Membership details: A. V. Brassington, 39 The Crest, West Heath, Birmingham B31 3PZ
Membership journal: *Llanuwchllyn Express* — approx 4 times a year

Brecon Mountain Railway

Timetable Service

Merthyr Tydfil

A narrow gauge passenger-carrying railway close to Merthyr Tydfil built on part of the trackbed of the former Brecon & Merthyr Railway. Gradually being extended northward, the railway has some interesting narrow gauge steam locomotives imported from East and West Germany and South Africa
General Manager: A. J. Hills
Headquarters: Brecon Mountain Railway, Pant Station, Dowlais, Merthyr Tydfil CF48 2UP
Telephone: Merthyr Tydfil (01685) 722988
Fax: (01685) 384854
Main station: Pant
Car park: Pant station
OS reference: SO 063120
Access by public transport: Bus

to Pant Cemetery — half hour frequency from Merthyr bus station. BR rail service to Merthyr from Cardiff Central
Depot: Pant
Length of line: 3.5 miles, 1ft 11.75in gauge
Period of public operation: Daily 4-5 April, 10-19 April, 4 and 19 May-13 September; Tuesdays-Thursdays & Saturdays 21 April-21 May, 15 September-1 October; Sundays 26 April-17 May, 20 September-25 October; Tuesday-Thursday 6-29 October
Refreshment facilities: Cafe at Pant, snackbar at Pontsticill
Special events: Santa Specials — December
Facilities for disabled: Facilities for disabled include ramps, toilets and carriage designed to carry wheelchairs
Special notes: There is no road access to Pontsticill

Locomotives

Name	*No*	*Builder*	*Type*	*Built*
—	2	Baldwin (61269)	4-6-2	1930
Sybil	—	Hunslet (827)	0-4-0ST	1903
Graf Schwerin-Löwitz	—	Arn Jung (1261)	0-6-2WT	1908
—	—	O&K (12722)	0-4-0WT	1936
Pendyffryn	—	de Winton	0-4-0VBT	1894
Redstone	—	Redstone	0-4-0VBT	1905
Rhydychen	—	Simplex (11177)	4wDM	1961
—	77	Hanomag (10629)	2-6-2+2-6-2	1928
—	—	Brecon MR (001)	0-6-0DH	1987

Stock
Two balcony end 39-seat coaches; 2 balcony end 40-seat coaches; 1 19-seat Caboose; miscellaneous rail-carrying and ballast wagons; Wickham petrol trolley

Museum — Conwy Valley Railway Museum — Aberconwy

Member: AIRPS
Conveniently situated alongside Betws-y-coed' railway station, the Museum presents some well-displayed distractions to pass the time including model train layouts to delight both adult and child
Location: Adjacent to Betws-y-coed station
OS reference: SH 796565
General Manager: Mr C. M. Cartwright
Operating society/organisation: Conwy Valley Railway Museum, The Old Goods Yard, Betws-y-coed, Gwynedd
Telephone: (01690) 710568
Car park: On site
Access by public transport: Betws-y-coed BR station
On site facilities: Refreshments in buffet car. Bookshop and model/gift shop in museum foyer, operating train layouts, miniature railway (1.25-miles, 7.25in gauge) steam-hauled. Picnic area.

15in Tramway (operates daily) with 1989-built single-deck bogie tram
Public opening: Daily Easter-end of October, 10.00-17.30
Facilities for disabled: Access to museum and toilets

Locomotives

Name	*No*	*Builder*	*Type*	*Built*
Britannia	70000	TMA Engineering (1ft 3in gauge)	4-6-2	1988
*Old Rube**	—	Milner Eng	2-8-0	1983
*Siân**	—	Humphries	0-4-2T	1989
*Shoeshone**	—	Simkins/Milner	2-8-0	1975
*Union Pacific**	—	R. Greatrex	Bo-Bo	1991
*Crocodile**	—	Donfifer/B. Howarth	0-6-0+0-6-0	1985
*Princess Elizabeth**	—	Barton (Lewis Shaw)	4-6-2	1960

*7.25in gauge

Stock
Standard gauge: 1 GWR fitter's van; 1 LMS 6-wheel van; 1 LNER CCT van; 1 BR Mk 1 coach; 2 SR luggage vans; 1 Pullman coach; 15in bogie tramcar
7.25in gauge: 5 articulated sit-in coaches, 2 sets 3 articulated sit-in open coaches, 4 wagons plus 'self-drive' 0-4-0 'Toby Tram'
15in gauge: 1 wagon

Museum

Corris Railway Museum

Caernarfonshire

Member: AIRPS
In the heart of Wales' 'narrow gauge country', the Corris Railway Museum, situated in the remaining buildings of Corris station, displays relics and photographs of mid-Wales' first public narrow gauge railway
Location: In Corris village off A487 trunk road. Turn opposite Braichgoch Hotel, five miles north of Machynlleth and 11 miles south of Dolgellau
OS reference: SH 755078
Operating society: The Corris Railway Society, Corris Station Yard, Gwynedd (postal address: Corris, Machynlleth, Powys SY20 9SH)
Car park: Adjacent
Access by public transport: Central train services to Machynlleth. Bus Gwynedd services 2 (Aberystwyth-Dolgellau-Machynlleth), 30 (Machynlleth-Tywyn) and 34 (Machynlleth-Aberllefenni); Dyfi Valley service 530 (Tywyn-Machynlleth-Abergynolwyn)
Catering facilities: Snacks, teas and light refreshments
On site facilities: Souvenir shop, toilets and children's playground; close to Corris Craft Centre and King Arthur's Labyrinth; two miles from Centre for Alternative Technology
Length of line: Three-quarter-mile, 2ft 3in gauge track between Corris and Maespoeth has been reinstated, and, subject to legal process, passenger services will recommence in late 1999. Planning permission for a further two miles of track has been granted
Public opening: Easter, May Day and Spring Bank Holidays, June-September. Half term week in October, other times by prior arrangement. Times as advertised locally. Please write for full details
Special events: Model Railway Exhibition, Machynlleth — 31 August
Facilities for disabled: Access to display area of Museum and shop
Internet address:
http//www.apricot.co.uk/hosts/corris/corris.htm
Membership details: Membership Secretary, c/o above address

Locomotives

Name	*No*	*Builder*	*Type*	*Built*
Alan Meaden	5	M/rail (22258)	4wDM	1965
—	6	R/Hornsby (51849)	4wDM	1966
—	7	Winson	0-4-2ST	19—

Locomotive notes: 5 and 6 operational on works trains. 7 under construction at Winson Engineering, based on Corris No 4 (now Talyllyn No 4) *Edward Thomas*.

Stock
Two carriages, brake van, 17 works wagons and 4 historic wagons

Timetable Service

Fairbourne Railway

Caernarfonshire

Member: AIRPS
Since 1986 this railway has been regauged from 15in to 12.25in and has been transformed by the introduction of new locomotives and rolling stock, a tunnel through the sand dunes, signalboxes, new workshops, a cafe overlooking the Mawddach estuary. Under new ownership since April 1995, there has been a big investment in the rolling stock maintenance so that all four steam locomotives are now in service. During the main season a two-train service is in operation. A new indoor nature attraction is scheduled to open at Fairbourne in 1998
Headquarters: North Wales Coast Light Railway Co Ltd, Fairbourne

Locomotives

Name	*No*	*Builder*	*Type*	*Built*
Beddgelert	—	Curwen	0-6-4ST	1979
Yeo	—	Curwen	2-6-2T	1978
Sherpa	—	Milner	0-4-0STT	1978
*Russell**	—	Milner	2-6-4T	1985
Lilian Walter	—	FLW	A1-1AD	1985
Gwril	—	FLW	4wBE	1987

FLW — Fairbourne Locomotive Works
*Built as replica Leek & Manifold *Elaine*, rebuilt to present form 1985 at FLW

Stock
12.25in gauge — 24 coaches (1st, 2nd class); 15 freight. New 1st class wheelchair coach under construction, anticipated to enter service in 1998

Note: The railway offers a range of driver experience courses (when no public trains are running). Please write for details

The Fairbourne Railway's *Yeo* is based an an original Lynton & Barnstaple Railway prototype. ***NWNGR***

& Barmouth Steam Railway, Beach Road, Fairbourne, Gwynedd LL38 2PZ
Telephone: (01341) 250362
Fax: (01341) 250240
Main station: Gorsaf Newydd (Fairbourne)
Other public stations: Gorsafawddacha'qidraigddanhed-dogleddolonpenrhynareudraeth-ceredigion, Porth Penrhyn (Barmouth Ferry Station)
OS reference: SH 616128
Car parks: Gorsaf Newydd
Access by public transport: Fairbourne railway station. Bus Gwynedd service (No 28)
Refreshment facilities: Porth Penrhyn cafe, tea shop on platform at Gorsaf Newydd (Fairbourne)
Souvenir shop: Gorsaf Newydd (Fairbourne)
Depot: Fairbourne
Length of line: 2.5 miles, 12.25in gauge
Passenger trains: A 2.5-mile journey connecting with ferry at Porth Penrhyn to Barmouth. 20min single journey. Through tickets to Barmouth (including ferry) available
Period of public operation: Daily Good Friday and Easter week, then weekends only. Daily service 3 May to 28 September. Santa Specials operate 12/13 December
Membership details: Fairbourne Railway Supporters' Association, contact Hon Sec at above address
Special notes: During inclement weather the service may be restricted or cancelled. Extra trains and special parties by arrangement with the manager

Timetable Service

Ffestiniog Railway

Caernarfonshire

Member: AIRPS
In many ways, evocative of the early Swiss mountain railways as it climbs high above Porthmadog with some breathtaking views, the railway still operates an interesting variety of locomotives including some unusual Victorian survivors. Passengers have replaced slate as the principal traffic over this former quarry line
General Manager: Alan Heywood
Headquarters: Ffestiniog Railway Co, Harbour Station, Porthmadog, Gwynedd, LL49 9NF
Telephone: Porthmadog (01766) 512340
Web site: http://www.festrail.co.uk
Main stations: Porthmadog Harbour, Blaenau Ffestiniog
Other public stations: Boston Lodge, Minffordd, Penrhyn, Plas Halt, Tan-y-Bwlch, Dduallt, Tanygrisiau
OS reference: SH 571384
Car parks: Porthmadog, Tan-y-Bwlch, Tanygrisiau, Blaenau Ffestiniog
Access by public transport: Minffordd and Blaenau Ffestiniog

main line stations. Porthmadog, Minffordd, and Blaenau Ffestiniog served by local buses
Refreshment facilities: Licensed restaurant at Porthmadog, cafe at Tan-y-Bwlch (summer only), refreshments also on most trains
Souvenir shops: Porthmadog, Tan-y-Bwlch (summer only), Blaenau Ffestiniog
Museum: Porthmadog
Depot: Boston Lodge
Length of line: 13.5 miles, 1ft 11.5in gauge
Passenger trains: Porthmadog-Blaenau Ffestiniog
Period of public operation: Daily March-November, limited winter service
Special events: Mini Gala — 2-4 May; Friends of Thomas the Tank weekend — 19/20 September; Santa Specials — phone for details
Facilities for disabled: Porthmadog and Blaenau Ffestiniog easily accessible for wheelchairs. Facilities on trains for disabled in wheelchairs by prior arrangement
Special notes: Reduced return rates available for journeys beginning on diesel services, shown in timetable
Membership details: Ffestiniog Railway Society (see above address)
Membership journal: *Ffestiniog Railway Magazine* — quarterly

Locomotives

Name	*No*	*Builder*	*Type*	*Built*
Princess	1	G/England (199/200)	0-4-0STT	1863
Prince	2	G/England	0-4-0STT	1863
Palmerston	4	G/England	0-4-0STT	1863
Welsh Pony	—	G/England (234)	0-4-0STT	1867
Earl of Merioneth	—	FR	0-4-4-0T	1979
Merddin Emrys	10	FR	0-4-4-0T	1879
David Lloyd George	12	FR	0-4-0T	1992
*Moelwyn***	—	Baldwin (49604)	2-4-0DM	1918
Blanche	—	Hunslet (589)	2-4-0STT	1893
Linda	—	Hunslet (590)	2-4-0STT	1893
*Britomart**	—	Hunslet (707)	0-4-0ST	1899
Mountaineer	—	Alco (57156)	2-6-2T	1917
Livingston Thompson†	3	FR	0-4-4-0T	1886
Harlech Castle	—	Baguley-Drewry (3767)	0-6-0-DH	1983
Ashover	—	Hibberd (3307)	4wDM	1948
Conway Castle	—	Hibberd (3831)	4wDM	1958
Moel Hebog	—	Hunslet (4113)	0-4-0DM	1955
Mary Ann	—	M/Rail (596)	4wDM	1917
Criccieth Castle	—	FR	0-6-0DH	1995
*Monarch**	—	Bagnall (3024)	0-4-4-0T	1953
The Colonel	—	M/Rail (8788)	4wDM	1943
Diana	—	M/Rail (21579)	4wDM	1957
Stefcomatic	—	Matisa (48589)	2-2-0DH	1956
—	—	Funkey	Bo-Bo	1968

*Privately owned
** Not on site
†On loan to National Railway Museum

Stock
32 bogie coaches; 6 4-wheel coaches; 2 brake vans, plus numerous service vehicles

Timetable Service

Great Orme Tramway

Aberconwy

Member: AIRPS
A cable-hauled street tramway to the summit of the Great Orme is operated as two sections involving a change half-way. Opened throughout in July 1903, it involves gradients as steep as 1 in 3.9
Location: Great Orme Tramway, Victoria Station, Church Walks, Llandudno
OS reference: SH 7781
Operating society/organisation: Contract Services, Maesdu, Llandudno LL30 1HF
Telephone: Llandudno (01492) 574229
Car park: Approximately 100yd from Lower Terminal or adjacent to Summit Terminal
Access by public transport: Good
On site facilities: Shop
Period of public operation: Easter to end of October (daily) 10.00-18.00
Special notes: The only remaining cable-hauled street tramway in Britain. 1-mile long rising to 650ft (3ft 6in gauge)
Stock: 4 tramcars each seating 48, built 1902/3
Family tickets: Available, along with joint tickets for Great Orme Mine — Bronze Age Heritage Centre

Timetable Service

Gwili Railway (Rheilffordd Gwili)

Carmarthenshire

Member: AIRPS, TT
Runs alongside the River Gwili on part of the former Carmarthen-Aberystwyth line. Attractions include a fully restored signalbox and historic station building. Extension towards Conwil Elfed in progress. A 7.25in gauge miniature railway operates at Llwyfan Cerrig.
Headquarters: Gwili Railway Co Ltd, Bronwydd Arms Station, Bronwydd Arms, Carmarthen, SA33 6HT
Telephone: Carmarthen (01267) 230666
OS reference: Bronwydd Arms SN 417239
Llwyfan Cerrig SN 405258,
Main station: Bronwydd Arms
Other public station: Llwyfan Cerrig,
Car park: Bronwydd Arms (free) (not 16-19 April when Park & Ride from Carmarthen must be used)
Access by public transport: Carmarthen railway station, then Bus Dyfed services No 460, 461 (not Sundays)
Refreshment facilities: Bronwydd Arms, Llwyfan Cerrig (picnic site). Bar on train
Souvenir shop: Bronwydd Arms
Depot: Llwyfan Cerrig, stock also kept at Bronwydd Arms and Conwil
Length of line: 1.5 miles
Passenger trains: Bronwydd Arms-Llwyfan Cerrig, approximately hourly service
Period of public operation: 10-13, 16-19 April; 3/4, 6, 10, 13, 17, 20, 23-29 May; 3, 7, 10, 14, 17, 21, 24, 28 June; 1, 4/5, 8, 11/12, 15, 18/19, 22, 25-31 July; Daily – August; 1, 6, 13, 20, 27 September; 25, 28/29 October; 12/13, 19-24 December
Public opening: Trains leave Bronwydd Arms at 11.30, 12.30, 14.00, 15.00 and 16.00 on most operating days. A more frequent service operates on 13 April, 25 May and 31 August

Locomotives

Name	*No*	*Origin*	*Class*	*Type*	*Built*
—†	12061	BR	11	0-6-0DE	1949
—**	D2178	BR	03	0-6-0DM	1962

Industrial locomotives

Name	*No*	*Builder*	*Type*	*Built*
—	1	H/Clarke (1885)	0-6-0ST	1955
Idris	—	R/Hornsby (207103)	4wDM	1941
Trecatty	—	R/Hornsby (421702)	0-6-0DM	1959
Olwen	—	RSH (7058)	0-4-0ST	1942
Welsh Guardsman	71516	RSH (7170)	0-6-0ST	1944
Nellie	02101	YEC(2779)	0-4-0DE	1960
Rosyth No 1•	—	A/Barclay (1385)	0-4-0ST	1914
Victory••	—	A/Barclay (2201)	0-4-0ST	1945
Sir John†	—	Avonside (1680)	0-6-0ST	1914
—†	3	H/Clarke (D1246)	0-4-0DM	1961
Gunby	—	Hunslet (2413)	0-6-0ST	1941
*Swansea Vale No 1**	—	Sentinel (9622)	4wVBTG	1958
*Swansea Jack**	—	R/Hornsby (393302)	4wDM	1955
*Dylan Thomas**	—	N/British (27654)	0-4-0DH	1956
Folly	—	R/Hornsby (183062)	4wDM	1937
—	114	N/British (27878)	0-4-0DH	1962
—	21	H/Leslie (3931)	0-6-0ST	1938
Haulwen†*	—	V/Foundry (5272)	0-6-0ST	1945

Stock
8 ex-BR Mk 1 coaches; 1 ex-BR griddle car; 1 ex-BR Mk 3 sleeper; 1 ex-TVR coach (built 1891); Coles diesel rail crane; 1 Stothert & Pitt diesel rail crane; 2 ex-GWR Mink vans; 2 ex-GWR Fruit D; 1 ex-GWR Crocodile; 1 GWR Bloater; 2 ex-GWR Loriot D; 3 GWR Toad brake vans; 2 GWR bogie bolster wagons; 1 SECR Parcels Van; 2 SR Parcels vans; 1 SR bogie parcel van; 1 LMS 20ton brake van; 1 LNER open wagon; 5 LNER vans; 2 Army vans; 6 BR open wagons; 2 BP tank wagons; 2 tar tankers; 3 open wagons

Owners
*The Railway Club of Wales
** Caerphilly Railway Society
†Vale of Neath Railway Society
†*National Museum of Wales Industrial & Maritime Museum in care of Caerphilly Railway Society

Special events: Friends of Thomas the Tank Weekend — 16-19 April. Santa Specials in December — details: Booking Officer, Bronwydd Arms Station, Carmarthen SA33 6HT (Tel: [01276] 230666)
Special notes: Family tickets available. Disabled access to stations and trains

Timetable Service

Llanberis Lake Railway (Rheilffordd Llyn Padarn)

Caernarfonshire

Member: AIRPS
A narrow gauge passenger-carrying railway starting at the historic Dinorwic Quarry workshops (now part of the National Museum of Wales) and running along the shores of the Llanberis lake using the trackbed of the former slate railway line to Port Dinorwic. Excellent views of Snowdonia and good picnic spots along the line
General Manager: Mr B. Yarborough
Headquarters: Llanberis Lake Railway, Gilfach Ddu, Llanberis, Gwynedd LL55 4TY
Telephone: Llanberis (01286) 870549
Main station: Llanberis (Padarn station/Gilfachddu)
Other public stations: Cei Llydan
OS reference: SH 586603
Car park: Llanberis (Padarn station)
Refreshment facilities: Padarn station
Souvenir shop: Padarn station
Length of line: 2 miles, 1ft 11.5in gauge
Passenger trains: Llanberis-Penllyn-Llanberis

Industrial locomotives

Name	*No*	*Builder*	*Type*	*Built*
Elidir	1	Hunslet (493)	0-4-0ST	1889
Thomas Bach/Wild Aster	2	Hunslet (849)	0-4-0ST	1904
Dolbadarn	3	Hunslet (1430)	0-4-0ST	1922
—	7	R/Hornsby (441427)	4wDM	1961
Twll Coed	8	R/Hornsby (268878)	4wDM	1956
Dolgarrog	9	M/Rail (22154)	4wDM	1962
—	—	R/Hornsby (425796)	4wDM	1958
Garrett	11	R/Hornsby (198286)	4wDM	1939
Braich	10	R/Hornsby (203031)	4wDM	1942
—	18	M/Rail (7927)	4wDM	1941
Llanelli	19	R/Hornsby (451901)	4wDM	1961
*Una**	—	Hunslet (873)	0-4-0ST	1905

*Not part of the railway's motive power stock. Housed at the adjacent slate museum and can sometimes be seen working demonstration freight trains

Stock
13 bogie coaches; 20 wagons

Journey time: 40min round trip
Period of public operation: Mondays to Thursdays in March and October. Mondays to Fridays in April. Sundays to Fridays, May through September. Saturdays July and August. Family tickets available, under 5s free
Facilities for disabled: Level approaches throughout shop, café and to train. Special toilet facilities provided. Specially adapted carriage for wheelchair users
Marketing names: Rheilffordd Llyn Padarn Cyfyngedig (Padarn Lake Railway Ltd); Llanberis Lake Railway

Timetable Service

Llangollen Railway

Denbighshire

Member: AIRPS, TT
The line, which is presently 7.5 miles long, is the only preserved standard gauge line in North Wales. Situated in the Dee Valley, it follows the course of the River Dee for much of its route, and affords good views of the surrounding countryside between Llangollen and Carrog. It is the eventual aim to reach Corwen, some 10 miles from Llangollen, where a new terminus will be built. The most recent extension to Carrog opened on 2 May 1996. The railway was the winner of the Ian Allan Independent Railway of the Year Award in 1996. There are many

Locomotives and multiple-units

Name	*No*	*Origin*	*Class*	*Type*	*Built*
—	2859	GWR	2800	2-8-0	1918
*Kinlet Hall**	4936	GWR	'Hall'	4-6-0	1929
—	4141	GWR	4101	2-6-2T	1946
—	5199	GWR	5101	2-6-2T	1934
—	5532	GWR	4575	2-6-2T	1928
—	6430	GWR	6400'	0-6-0PT	1937
—	7754	GWR	5700	0-6-0PT	1930
Foxcote Manor	7822	GWR	'Manor'	4-6-0	1950
—	7298	LMS	3F	0-6-0T	1924
Magpie	4806	LMS	5MT	4-6-0	1944
—	5197	USATC	S160	2-8-0	1942
Castell Dinas Bran	76079	BR	4MT	2-6-0	1957
—	80072	BR	4MT	2-6-4T	1954
—	80072	BR	4MT	2-6-4T	1954
—	03162	BR	03	0-6-0DM	1960
—	D3265	BR	08	0-6-0DE	1956

pleasant walks beginning and ending at the railway's stations. Picnic facilities are available at all stations and camping can be arranged at Carrog station
Location: Llangollen station, A542 from Ruthin, A539 from Ruabon, A5 from Shrewsbury/Betws y coed
Commercial Manager: Mr C. Keyse
Operating organisation: Llangollen Railway plc
Supporting organisation: Llangollen Railway Trust Ltd, The Station, Abbey Road, Llangollen, Denbighshire LL20 8SN (both organisations)
Telephone: Talking timetable (24hr): Llangollen (01978) 860951. Other enquiries: (01978) 860979 (office hours only). Llangollen Railway Trust Ltd (24hr answerphone) (01978) 861143
Main station: Llangollen
Other stations: Berwyn, Deeside Halt (by request), Glyndyfrdwy, Carrog
OS reference: SJ 214422
Car park: Llangollen (Market St) and Mill St (Lower Dee Mill), also at Carrog station on B5437 off the A5 west of Llangollen
Access by public transport: Nearest station: Ruabon (2hr service), then hourly Bryn Melyn bus (Wrexham-Llangollen) or Crosville 94 Wrexham-Barmouth service (3 a day)
Refreshment facilities: Llangollen, Berwyn, Glyndyfrdwy and Carrog
Souvenir shop: Llangollen
Length of line: 7.5 miles
Passenger trains: Llangollen-Carrog
Period of public operation: Most weekends throughout the year plus school holidays, including half-term. Daily services 2 May-end of October
Special events: Spring Steam Gala, BR at 50 — 23-25 May; Vintage Military Weekend — 6/7 June; Friends of Thomas the Tank Engine — 1/2 August, 24 October- 1 November; Transport Extravaganza — 19/20 September; Diesel Gala — 17/18 October; Santa Specials — 5/6, 12/13, 19-24 December
Special notes: The 'Berwyn Belle' operates midday Sunday and Saturday evening dining train, tel: (01978) 860583 for details. Driver experience courses are offered on both diesel and steam locomotives.

Locomotives and multiple-units *(continued)*

Name	*No*	*Origin*	*Class*	*Type*	*Built*
—	D8142	BR	20	Bo-Bo	1966
Chirk Castle	25313	BR	25	Bo-Bo	1966
—	46010	BR	46	1Co-Co1	1961
—	47449	BR	47	Co-Co	1962
—	50454	BRCW	104	DMBS	1957
—	50528	BRCW	104	DMC	1957
—	51618	BR	127	DMBS	1959
—	51907	BR	108	DMBS	1960
—	53447	BRCW	104	DMBS	1957
—	53454	BRCW	104	DMBS	1958
—	54456	Cravens	105	DMBS	1958
—	54490	BR	108	DTC	1960
—	50416†	Wickham	108	MBS	1958

No 76079 is moving to the Churnet Valley Railway in May
*Undergoing restoration at Birmingham Railway Museum, Tyseley
†Undergoing restoration at the Midland Railway Centre, Butterley

Industrial locomotives

Name	*No*	*Builder*	*Type*	*Built*
*Darfield No 1**	—	Hunslet (3783)	0-6-0ST	1953
Eliseg	—	Fowler (22753)	0-4-0DM	1939
Richboro†	—	H/Clarke (1243)	0-6-0T	1917
*Burtonwood Brewer**	—	Kitson (5459)	0-6-0ST	1932
—	14	H/Clarke (D1012)	0-4-0DM	1956
—	1	YEC/BTH	0-4-0D	c1950

*Undergoing overhaul at Bury
†On display at the Dr Who Exhibition at Lower Dee Mill, Llangollen

Stock: *coaches* — 17 BR Mk 1 coaches; 5 BR Mk 1 sleepers (3 ex-'Queen of Scots'); 1 BR BG (converted to generator van); 1 BR Mk 3 sleeper; 4 GWR coaches;

Stock: *wagons* — 4 wagons; 1 Bolster wagon; 1 LNWR tool van; 2 GWR brake vans; 1 GWR Mink D wagon; 1 SR 'BY' parcels van; 3 tank wagons; 1 LNER parcels van; 2 BR Fruit vans; 1 ex-LNWR brake van; 1 Matisa track tamper; 1 BR ballast wagon; 1 Coles diesel/electric 5-ton crane; 1 BR generator van; 1 LMS Inspection saloon; 1 GWR Siphon G coach; 1 LMS box van; 1 GWR Mink A van; 1 BR Presflow bulk cement wagon; 1 BR CCT; 2 LMS Sole ballast wagons

Stock: *maintenance* — ARD96718 45ton Cowans breakdown crane, 1 Matisa Track Recording Machine; 1 BR Bridge/Viaduct Inspection Unit, Unimog road-rail vehicle, Permaquip Permaclipper

Owners
2859, 5532 and 5952 the Llangollen Railway GW Locomotive Group
5199 the 5199 Project
7822 the Foxcote Manor Society
7754 the Llangollen Railway Trust Ltd
80072 the 80072 Steam Locomotive Co Ltd
Richboro the National Coal Board
Burtonwood Brewer the Burtonwood Brewery
03162 the Wirral Borough Council

Party rates available for groups of more than 10
Facilities for disabled: Special passenger coach for wheelchairs. During 1998 extensive restoration work is expected to be undertaken at Llangollen and Berwyn stations. Access to shop at Llangollen. Toilets available at Glyndyfrdwy and Carrog stations. Advance notice required for special coach
Membership details: Mr David Short, Llangollen Railway Trust Ltd, c/o above address
Membership journal: *Steam at Llangollen* — quarterly

Stanier Class 5MT No 4806 tries to hide behind a smoke and steam screen at Llangollen in August 1997.
Alan C. Butcher

Museum

Penrhyn Castle Industrial Railway Museum

Aberconwy

Member: AIRPS
A collection of historic industrial steam locomotives, both standard and narrow gauge, displayed in Penrhyn Castle, a well known National Trust property in the area regularly open to visitors
Location: Llandegai, near Bangor. One mile east of Bangor on the A5
OS reference: SH 603720
Operating society/organisation: National Trust, Penrhyn Castle, Industrial Railway Museum, Llandegai, near Bangor LL57 4HN
Telephone: Bangor (01248) 353084
Car park: Within castle grounds
Access by public transport: By rail: Bangor (3 miles). Bus: Crosville Cymru 5, Purple 6/7 and D&E 65/6
On site facilities: The castle is open to the public, and contains a gift shop. Light refreshments are available
Public opening: Daily 25 March-1 November (except Tuesdays), 11.00-17.00 (last admission 30min before closing
Facilities for disabled: Access to castle and museum
Special notes: For those interested in stately homes the castle is well worth a visit. The entrance fee covers both the castle and the railway exhibits housed in the castle courtyard. All the roof repairs are now completed. *Acorn* can be seen operating on some occasions during opening times

Industrial locomotives

Name	No	Builder	Type	Built
Kettering Furnaces No 3	—	B/Hawthorn (859)	0-4-0ST	1885*
Watkin	—	de Winton	0-4-0VBT	1893*
Fire Queen	—	Horlock	0-4-0	1848†
Hawarden	—	H/Clarke (526)	0-4-0ST	1899
Vesta	—	H/Clarke (1223)	0-6-0T	1916
Charles	—	Hunslet (283)	0-4-0ST	1882§
Hugh Napier	—	Hunslet (855)	0-4-0ST	1904§
—	1	Neilson (1561)	0-4-0WT	1870
Haydock	—	Stephenson (2309)	0-6-0T	1879
Acorn	—	R/Hornsby (327904)	0-4-0DM	1948

*3ft gauge
†4ft gauge
§1ft 10.75in gauge

Stock
10 narrow gauge rolling stock exhibits from the Padarn/Penrhyn system. The small relics section includes a comprehensive display of railway signs and model locomotives

Steam Centre

Pontypool & Blaenavon Railway

Monmouthshire

Member: AIRPS
The historic Blaenavon site, complete with its railway installations and locomotives, can easily be included in a visit to Big Pit Mining Museum
Location: Near Big Pit, Blaenavon
OS reference: SO 237093
Operating society/organisation: Pontypool & Blaenavon Railway Co (1983) Ltd, Council Offices, High Street, Blaenavon NP4 9PT
Telephone/Fax: (01495) 792263
Car park: Adjacent to railway terminus
On site facilities: Light refreshments and souvenir shop
Public opening: Sundays Easter-end of September, and Bank Holiday Mondays
Special events: Friends of Thomas the Tank Engine, Santa Special. Please contact for details
Special notes: The railway incorporates the former mineral/LNWR passenger lines running through Big Pit. Both north and southward extensions are being considered. Service currently operates between Furnace Sidings platform and Whistle Inn platform
Membership details: c/o above address, or phone (01873) 857539

Locomotives

Name	*No*	*Origin*	*Class*	*Type*	*Built*
—	2874	GWR	2800	2-8-0	1918
—	3855	GWR	2884	2-8-0	1942
—	4253	GWR	4200	2-8-0T	1917
—	5668	GWR	5600	0-6-2T	1926
Bickmarsh Hall	5967	GWR	'Hall'	4-6-0	1937
—	9629	GWR	5700	0-6-0PT	1946
Renown	50029	BR	50	Co-Co	1968
Repulse	50030	BR	50	Co-Co	1968
Eagle	50043	BR	50	Co-Co	1968
—	51074	GRCW	119	DMBC	1958
—	51104	GRCW	119	DMS	1958
—	51942	BR	108	DMCL	1960
—	52044	BR	108	DMCL	1960
—	54270	BR	108	DTCL	1960
—	53632	BR	108	DMCL	1960

Industrial locomotives

Name	*No*	*Builder*	*Type*	*Built*
Nora	5	Barclay (1680)	0-4-0ST	1920
Harry	—	Barclay (1823)	0-4-0ST	1926
—	8	RSH (7139)	0-6-0ST	1944
—	104	E/Electric (D1249)	0-6-0DH	1968
—	106	E/Electric (D1226)	0-6-0DH	1971
—	1	Fowler (22497)	0-6-0DM	1938
—	170	Hunslet (7063)	0-8-0DH	1971
—	10083	R/Royce (10083)	0-4-0DH	1961

Stock
7 ex-BR Mk 1 coaches, 5 ex-GWR coaches, 2 ex-LSWR coaches, 36 other vans, china clay, coke and tank wagons

Owners
50029 and 50030 Operation Collingwood

Timetable Service

Rheilffordd Eryri — Welsh Highland Railway (Caernarfon)

Caernarfonshire

The Welsh Highland Light Railway Ltd has been incorporated to reconstruct much of the original WHR line. The new northern terminus is at Caernarfon, with re-opening to Porthmadog in stages over the next 10 years.
General Manager: Alan Heywood
Headquarters: Ffestiniog Railway Co, Harbour Station, Porthmadog LL49 9NF
Telephone: Porthmadog (01766) 512340
Main station: Caernarfon
Other public station: Dinas
OS reference: SH 481625
Car parks: Caernarfon
Access by public transport: Caernarfon is served by local buses. The station at Bangor is served by Virgin and North Western Railways. There is a regular bus service between Bangor and Caernarfon
Depot: Dinas
Length of line: 3 miles, 1ft 11.5in gauge
Passenger trains: Caernarfon-Dinas
Future extensions: Dinas-Rhyd Ddu-Beddgelert-Porthmadog
Period of public operation: 4 April-8 November

Facilities for disabled, refreshments & souvenirs: Telephone for details
Membership details: Welsh Highland Railway Society (see above address)
Membership journal: *Snowdon Ranger* — quarterly

Locomotives

Name	No	Builder	Type	Built
—†	K1	B/Peacock (5292)	0-4-0+0-4-0	1909
—*	138	B/Peacock	2-6-2+2-6-2	1958
—*	140	B/Peacock	2-6-2+2-6-2	1958
—*	143	B/Peacock	2-6-2+2-6-2	1958
Castell Caernaron	—	Funkey	Bo-Bo	1968
Upnor Castle	—	Hibberd (3687)	4wDM	1954

*Former South African Railways NGG16 class locomotives
†Not on site
The above locomotives may not be on site. Ffestiniog Railway Co locomotives may operate some services

Stock
5 bogie coaches, 1 bogie coach under construction. Numerous service vehicles

Timetable Service

Snowdon Mountain Railway

Caernarfonshire

Member: AIRPS
The only public rack and pinion railway in the British Isles, opened in 1896, this bustling line climbs the slopes of Snowdon, often through the clouds, to the hotel at the top. The trip should not be missed
General Manager: A. P. Hopkins
Engineering Manager: M. Kressman
Headquarters: Snowdon Mountain Railway, Llanberis LL55 4TY
Telephone: Llanberis (01286) 870223
Fax: (01286) 872518
Main station: Llanberis
Other public stations: Summit, also Clogwyn/Rocky Valley when Summit is inaccessible
OS reference: SH 582597
Car park: Llanberis
Access by public transport: Bangor railway station then by bus to Caernarfon and there change to local bus to Llanberis. There is also a less frequent direct service between Bangor and Llanberis. Snowdon Sherpa Services to/from Beddgelert and Betws-y-coed stop outside the station
Refreshment facilities: Llanberis, Summit
Souvenir shops: Llanberis, Summit
Depot: Llanberis

Locomotives

Name	No	Builder	Type	Built
Enid	2	SLM (924)	0-4-2T	1895
Yr Wyddfa	3	SLM (925)	0-4-2T	1895
Snowdon	4	SLM (988)	0-4-2T	1896
Moel Siabod	5	SLM (989)	0-4-2T	1896
Padarn	6	SLM (2838)	0-4-2T	1922
*Ralph**	7	SLM (2869)	0-4-2T	1923
*Eryri**	8	SLM (2870)	0-4-2T	1923
Ninian	9	Hunslet (9249)	0-4-0DH	1986
Yeti	10	Hunslet (9250)	0-4-0DH	1986
Peris	11	Hunslet (9305)	0-4-0DH	1991
George	12	Hunslet (9312)	0-4-0DH	1992

All steam locomotives were built by Swiss Locomotive Works, Winterthur
All diesel locomotives were built by Hunslet Engine Co, Leeds
*Currently stored out of service (boilerless)

Stock
8 closed bogie coaches; 1 bogie works car; 1 4-wheel open wagon; a 3-car diesel-electric railcar set built 1995 by HPE Tredegar (fleet Nos 21, 22, 23 [Works Nos 1074/5/6])

Length of line: 7.5km, 800mm gauge
Passenger trains: Llanberis-Summit. Journey time approx 60min. Departures from Llanberis at 30min intervals during peak periods. Round trip approx 2hr 30min
Period of public operation: Daily 15 March-1 November
Special notes: All trains are subject to weather and traffic restrictions, especially before mid-May and during October. Parties welcome by prior arrangement in off-peak periods. Family ticket (2 adults, 2 Children) available to Summit only on early morning trains up to and including 09.30

Museum

Swansea Maritime & Industrial Museum

Swansea

Member: AIRPS
This Museum houses a number of relics from Swansea's industrial and maritime past, one of which is stationed outside the Museum. The Tramshed Annexe houses a restored Swansea City double-deck tram (Brush Electrical Engineering 1923/24 model), and a replica of the early Mumbles railway carriage, in addition to the sole surviving example of the Mumbles Railway rolling stock, the front section of the tramcar, manufactured by the Brush Electrical Engineering Co in 1928.

Artefacts from the Mumbles Railway are also displayed within a graphic presentation, as are examples of Brunel's 'GWR' broad gauge rail track.

Location: On the south side of the city between the shopping centre and the sea in the newly created Maritime Quarter
OS reference: SS 659927
Operating society/organisation: City & County of Swansea Museum Services, Maritime & Industrial Museum, Museum Square, Maritime Quarter, Swansea SA1 1SN
Telephone: Swansea (01792) 650351
Car park: Public car parks nearby
Access by public transport: Reached on foot from shopping centre, central bus depot, or by car
On site facilities: No refreshments in the Museum but several cafés close by. Museum shop selling souvenirs and produce of the Woollen Mill which operates in the Museum throughout the year. Education Service available on request to Education Officer
Public opening: 10.00-17.00 six days a week, closed Mondays and 25/26/27 December and New Year's Day. Last admission 16.45
Facilities for disabled: Available

Industrial locomotives

Name	*No*	*Builder*	*Type*	*Built*
*Sir Charles**	—	A/Barclay (1473)	0-4-0F	1919
—	—	Peckett (1426)	0-6-0ST	1916

Notes
*Not on public display

Timetable Service

Swansea Vale Railway

Swansea

Member: AIRPS
Location/headquarters: Swansea Vale Railway Upper Bank, Pentrechwyth, Swansea SA1 7DB
Telephone: (01792) 653615
Marketing Manager: Mike Meyrick
Main stations: Six Pit Junction, Nany-Y-Ffin Road, Llansamlet (Swansea)
Other stations: Cwm Halt (planning, to open May 1998), Upper Bank Junction (awaiting restoration)
OS reference: Six Pit Junction — SN 683969, Upper Bank Junction — SN 668953
Car parks: Six Pit Junction, Upper Bank Works
Access by public transport: To Six Pit Junction (ask for Llansamlet) — by train Llansamlet (1-mile); by bus South Wales Transport (from Quadrant Bus Stn) 30B/31/31B/32/33/34.

Locomotives and multiple-units

Name	*No*	*Origin*	*Class*	*Type*	*Built*
—	4270	GWR	4200	2-8-0T	1919
—	9642	GWR	5700	0-6-0PT	1946
—	51135	BR	116	DMBS	1958
—	51148	BR	116	DMS	1958
—	52061	BR	108	DMSL	1960
—	53982	BR	108	DMBS	1959
—	55026	P/Steel	121	DMBS	1960
—	59445	BR	116	TS	1959

Industrial locomotives

Name	*No*	*Builder*	*Type*	*Built*
Llantarnam Abbey	—	Barclay (2074)	0-6-0ST	1939
—	—	Hunslet (3829)	0-6-0ST	1955
—	1	Peckett (1345)	0-4-0ST	1914
—	12514	H/Clarke (D1254)	0-6-0DM	1962
—	2	N/British (27914)	0-4-0DM	1961
—	—	R/Hornsby (312433)	4wDM	1951

Owners
9642 the South Wales Pannier Group
51135, 51148 and 59445 the Llanelli & District Railway Society
Llantanam Abbey the Llantarnam Abbey Locomotive Association

Stock: *coaches;* 1 BR suburban SO; 1 BR Mk 2 BSK

To Upper Bank bus 34. Bus Info (01792) 580580
Refreshment facilities: On train on operating days only (snacks & drinks)
Souvenir shop: On train on operating days only
Depot: Upper Bank
Facilities for disabled: Six Pit platform will have wheelchair ramp
Period of public operation: Open all year for viewing. April-October 11.00-17.00; October-April 11.00-16.00
Operating days: Steam: 10-13 April; 3/4, 23-25 May; 7, 21 June; 5, 19 July; 2, 9, 16, 23, 29-31 August; 24/25 October; 12/13, 19/20, 27 December.
DMU services: 2 May, 14, 28 June, 12, 26 July; 1, 8, 15, 22 August; 5/6 December. Party bookings at any time by arrangement
Special events: Easter Bunny Specials — 10-13 April; Friends of Thomas the Tank Engine — 23-25 May, 29-31 August; Teddy Bear Specials — 5 July; Halloween Ghost Trains— 24/25 October; Santa Specials — 12/13, 19/20 December; Mince Pie Specials — 27 December
Membership details: G. Fuller, Swansea Vale Railway Society, 21 Elmhurst Crescent, St Thomas, Swansea SA1 8EA
Membership journal: *Vale News* — quarterly

Stock: *wagons:* 1 GWR brake van, 1 BR brake van, 3 4-wheel tar tanks (ex-NCB), 3 LMS 12ton mineral wagons, 1 BR 'Gane A' bogie bolster, 1 GWR 'Mink' 10ton van, 3 GWR 10ton vans, 1 10ton open, 2 GWR 'tunney' wagons, 1 LNER low-fit, GWR Pooley van, BR 13-ton single bolster wagon

Stock: *cranes:* Smith-Rodley 4-wheel steam crane, Cowans & Sheldon LMS rail-mounted hand crane, Jones 72ton rail-mounted diesel crane

Railway preservation is not just about locomotives and rolling stock; today a large number of structures have been relocated to ensure their survival. One of them is King Dock Junction Signalbox. Once owned by the Swansea Harbour Trust, it has been relocated at the Swansea Vale's Upper Bank station where it will form the centrepiece of the railway centre. ***SVR/City Photographic***

Timetable Service

Talyllyn Railway

Caernarfonshire

Member: AIRPS, TT
The very first railway in the country to be rescued and operated by enthusiasts, the line climbs from Tywyn through the wooded Welsh hills past Dolgoch Falls to Nant Gwernol. The trains are hauled by a variety of veteran tank engines, all immaculately maintained by the railway's own workshops at Tywyn Pendre
Managing Director: Maurice Wilson
Traffic manager: David Leech
Headquarters: Talyllyn Railway Co, Wharf Station, Tywyn, Gwynedd LL36 9EY
Telephone: Tywyn (01654) 710472
Fax: (01654) 711755
Main station: Tywyn Wharf
Other public stations: Tywyn Pendre, Rhydyronnen, Brynglas, Dolgoch Falls, Abergynolwyn, Nant Gwernol
OS reference: SH 586005 (Tywyn Wharf)
Car parks: Tywyn Wharf, Dolgoch, Abergynolwyn
Access by public transport: Tywyn BR station. Bus Gwynedd services to Tywyn
Refreshment facilities: Tywyn Wharf, Abergynolwyn hot and cold snacks available. Picnic areas at Dolgoch Falls and Abergynolwyn. Picnic site at Dolgoch Falls
Souvenir shops: Tywyn Wharf, Abergynolwyn
Museum: Tywyn Wharf
Depot: Tywyn Pendre
Length of line: 7.25 miles, 2ft 3in gauge
Passenger trains: Tywyn-Nant Gwernol
Period of public operation: Sundays 22 February-29 March. Daily 30 March to 31 October, 26

December-2 January 1999
Journey times: Tywyn-Nant Gwernol — single 55min, return 2hr 15min
Special events: Enthusiasts' Weekend — 2/3 May; Rolt Vehicle Rally — 24 May; Victorian Week— 2-8 August; Land Rover Rally — 30 August; Entertainment by Train — (Sundays only) 26 July-30 August; Peter Sam's Birthday — 31 August; Enthusiast Weekend — 26/27 September; Santa Specials — December
Family tickets: Available
Facilities for disabled: No problem for casual visitors, advance notice preferred for groups. Access to shop and cafeteria possible at Tywyn and Abergynolwyn. Disabled toilet facilities at Tywyn and Abergynolwyn. Access possible to lower floor of museum. Limited capacity for wheelchairs on trains. New vehicle for wheelchairs now in operation
Special notes: Parties and private charter trains by arrangement. Children under 5 years of age free. Narrow gauge 'Wanderer' four- and eight-day tickets accepted
Membership details: Mr A. Johnston, 9 Reynolds Way, Croydon, Surrey CR0 5JW
Membership journal: *Talyllyn News* — quarterly
Marketing names: One of the Great Little Trains. The first preserved railway in the world

Locomotives

Name	*No*	*Builder*	*Type*	*Built*
Talyllyn	1	F/Jennings (42)	0-4-2ST	1865
Dolgoch	2	F/Jennings (63)	0-4-0WT	1866
Sir Haydn	3	Hughes (323)	0-4-2ST	1878
Edward Thomas	4	K/Stuart (4047)	0-4-2ST	1921
Midlander	5	R/Hornsby (200792)	4wDM	1940
Douglas	6	Barclay (1431)	0-4-0WT	1918
*Tom Rolt**	7	Barclay (2263)	0-4-2T	1949
Merseysider	8	R/Hornsby (476108)	4wDH	1964
Alf	9	Hunslet (4136)	0-4-0DM	1950

Locomotive notes: In service — Nos 1, 3, 4 , 6 and 7; No 2 not currently in service
*Virtually a new locomotive rebuilt from the original at Pendre Works

Stock
13 4-wheel coaches/vans; 10 bogie coaches; 45 wagons

Narrow Gauge Museum, Tywyn

Name	*No*	*Builder*	*Type*	*Built*
Dot	—	B/Peacock (2817)	0-4-0ST	1887
Rough Pup	—	Hunslet (541)	0-4-0ST	1891
—	2	K/Stuart (721)	0-4-0WT	1902
Jubilee 1897	—	M/Wardle (1382)	0-4-0ST	1897
George Henry	—	de Winton	0-4-0T	1877
—	13	Spence	0-4-0T	1895
*Nutty**	—	Sentinel (7701)	0-4-0VB	1929

*Not currently on site

Stock
Various wagons and miscellaneous equipment

Timetable Service

Teifi Valley Railway

Pembrokeshire

Member: AIRPS
Operating Society/organisation: Teifi Valley Railway, Henllan Station, Llandysul SA44 5TD
Manager: Mr R. Sanderson
Telephone: (01559) 371077
Main station: Henllan
Other public stations: Forest Halt, Pontprenshitw, Llandyfriog
Car park: Henllan
OS reference: SN 358407
Access by public transport: BR station — Carmarthen (14 miles). Bus service 461 to Henllan
Refreshments: Henllan
Souvenirs: Henllan

Industrial locomotives

Name	*No*	*Builder*	*Type*	*Built*
Alan George	—	Hunslet (606)	0-4-0ST	1894
Sgt Murphy	—	K/Stuart (3117)	0-6-2T	1918
Sholto	—	Hunslet (2433)	4wDM	1941
Simon	—	M/Rail (7126)	4wDM	1936
Sammy	—	M/Rail (605)	4wDM	1959

On site facilities: Children's play areas, woodland theatre and trails, crazy golf and crazy quoits, GWR library, plus quarter-mile 7.25in gauge miniature railway
Depot: Henllan, engine shed open to public

Facilities for disabled: All facilities including portable steps and wide door for wheelchairs in one coach
Period of public operation: Good Friday to 31 October
Special events: Easter Sunday fair,

Victorian Day (late August), Halloween, Santa Specials
Membership details: Teifi Valley Railway Society, c/o Henllan station
Membership journal: *Right Away* — quarterly

Steam Centre

Vale of Glamorgan Railway

Vale of Glamorgan

Member: AIRPS
Steam operations will start at Barry Island early in 1998. Rides will be available over a short distance of track within the station area. Meanwhile work will start on the extension of the line across the causeway towards Barry Town. For details please phone (01443) 432205
Location: Barry Island Station, Barry, Glamorgan
Operating society: Vale of Glamorgan Railway Company
Car park: Large public car park near site
Access by public transport: Frequent train services from Cardiff to Barry Island for same platform interchange (Cardiff Railway Co)
On site facilities: Museum, shop, light refreshments
Public opening: Please telephone (01446) 748816 (daytime) or (01443) 204627 (evenings)
Length of line: 600yd
Further inforation: Mr D. J. Morgan, 34 Bryn Gwyn Road, Cyncoed, Cardiff CF2 6PQ

Locomotives and multiple-unit

Name	*No*	*Origin*	*Class*	*Type*	*Built*
—	2861	GWR	2800	2-8-0	1918
—	4115	GWR	4101	2-6-2T	1936
—	5227	GWR	5205	2-8-0T	1924
—	5538	GWR	4575	2-6-2T	1928
—	5539	GWR	4575	2-6-2T	1928
—	6686	GWR	5600	0-6-2T	1928
Willington Hall	7927	BR	'Hall'	4-6-0	1950
—	44901	LMS	5MT	4-6-0	1945
—	48518	LMS	8F	2-8-0	1944
—	80150	BR	4MT	2-6-4T	1956
—	92245	BR	9F	2-10-0	1958
—	54279	BR	108	DTC	1959

Locomotive notes: In store, not on public view, except 5538 on site

Industrial locomotives

Name	*No*	*Builder*	*Type*	*Built*
Sir Gomer	—	Peckett (1859)	0-6-0ST	1932
Menalaus	—	Peckett (1889)	0-6-0ST	1935
Pamela	—	Hunslet (3840)	0-6-0ST	1956
—	52/001	Barclay (1966)	0-4-0F	1929
—	107	North British (27932)	0-6-0DM	1959
Bill Chaddick	—	H/Clarke (1168)	0-6-0DM	1959
—	—	Unilok (2183)		1964

Stock
BR Mk 1 coaches, TVR coach No 153, various freight vehicles

Timetable Service

Vale of Rheidol Railway

Cardiganshire

Member: AIRPS
This narrow gauge railway offers a 23-mile round trip from Aberystwyth to Devil's Bridge providing spectacular views which cannot be enjoyed by road. At Devil's Bridge there are walks to the Mynach Falls and Devil's Punch Bowl. Many artists have been inspired by the magnificence of Devil's Bridge and the Rheidol Valley
General Manager: N. Thompson

Locomotives

Name	*No*	*Origin*	*Ex-BR Class*	*Type*	*Built*
Owain Glyndŵr	7	GWR	98	2-6-2T	1923
Llywelyn	8	GWR	98	2-6-2T	1923
Prince of Wales	9	GWR	98	2-6-2T	1924
—	10	Brecon MR (002)	98/1	0-6-0DH	1987

Stock
16 bogie coaches including one Vista coach; 1 4-wheel guards van; 11 wagons for maintenance use; 1 inspection trolley

Headquarters: Vale of Rheidol Railway, The Locomotive Shed, Park Avenue, Aberystwyth SY23 1PG
Telephone: (01970) 625819
Main station: Aberystwyth (adjacent to main line station)
Other public stations: Devil's Bridge, Rhiwfron, Rheidol Falls, Aberffrwd, Nantyronen, Capel Bangor, Glanrafon, Llanbadarn
OS reference: SN 587812
Car parks: Aberystwyth, Devil's Bridge
Access by public transport: Aberystwyth BR station: and bus services to Aberystwyth
Refreshment facilities: Aberystwyth (not railway-owned), Devil's Bridge (not railway operated)
Souvenir shop: Aberystwyth
Depot: Aberystwyth (not open to the public)
Length of line: 11.75 miles, 1ft 11.75in gauge
Journey time: Single 1hr, return 3hr
Passenger trains: Aberystwyth-Devil's Bridge
Period of public operation: No details supplied, please see Timetable Supplement

Steam Centre

Welsh Highland Railway (Porthmadog)

Caernarfonshire

Member: AIRPS
The Welsh Highland Railway Ltd operates services at the south-western end of the old Welsh Highland line and has its base in the bustling holiday town of Porthmadog. The company is developing an exciting project to enhance visitor facilities at the Gelert's Farm site. The WHR is very much a family orientated attraction and adults have the opportunity to purchase a footplate pass
Location: Tremadog Road, Porthmadog, adjacent to Cambrian line station
OS reference: SH 571393
General Manager: Stuart Weatherby
Operating society/organisation: Welsh Highland Light Railway (1964) Ltd, Gelert's Farm Works, Madoc Street West, Porthmadog, LL49 9DY
Telephone: Porthmadog (01766) 513402 (weekends and operating days); this is a 24hr information line
Internet address: http:/www.roke.co.uk/WHR/WHR.html
Car park: Tremadog Road (free)
Catering facilities: 'Russells' supplying a range of adult/children's meals and light refreshments
Access by public transport: Central Trains to Porthmadog station. Bus Gwynedd service 1 and 3 to Porthmadog

Locomotives

Name	*No*	*Builder*	*Type*	*Built*
Moel Tryfan	—	Bagnall (3023)	0-4-2T	1953
Gelert	—	Bagnall (3050)	0-4-2T	1953
Russell	—	Hunslet (901)	2-6-2T	1906
Pedemoura	—	O&K (10808)	0-6-0WT	1924
Karen	—	Peckett (2024)	0-4-2T	1942
Glaslyn	1	R/Hornsby (297030)	4wDM	1952
Kinnerley	2	R/Hornsby (354068)	4wDM	1953
Cnicht	36	M/Rail (8703)	4wDM	1941
Katherine	9	M/Rail (605363)	4wDM	1968
—	4	M/Rail (605333)	4wDM	1963
—	5	Hunslet (6285)	4wDM	1968
—	3	R/Hornsby (370555)	4wDM	1953
Jonathon	6	M/Rail (11102)	4wDM	1959
—	7	Hunslet (7535)	4wDM	1977
—	10	R/Hornsby (481552)	4wDM	1962
—	11	Hunslet (3510)	4wDM	1947
Sezela No 4	—	Avonside (1738)	0-4-0T	1915
Beddgelert	NG120	S. F. Belge	2-8-2	1950
Edward Saunders	—	Bagnall (2287)	4-4-0T	1926
Snowdonia/Eryri†	—	Buch (23389)	0-6-0DM	1977
—†	—	Buch (2405)	0-6-0DH	1980
—	—	Barclay (554)	4wDH	1970
—	—	Barclay (555)	4wDH	1970
—	—	M/Rail (22237)	4wDM	1965

*Ex-South African Railways Class NG15
†Ex-Polish State Railways class LYD2

Locomotive notes: 1998 steam service will be worked by WHR veteran *Russell*, assisted by *Gelert* and possible guest locomotives

Stock
Passengers will have the opportunity to travel in the historic 'Gladstone' coach or the new 4-wheel coach due to enter service in 1998

On site facilities: Souvenir and railway book/video shop, disabled toilet facilities, information boards and extended shed tours
Length of line: To Pen-y-Mount, Tremadog. Three-quarter-mile, 1ft 11.5in gauge
Passenger trains: Porthmadog-Pen-y-Mount. Return journey approx 40min incorporating works

tours. Steam-hauled Bank Holidays, every weekend and every day (except Mondays and Fridays from early July to end of August). Adults may purchase a footplate pass
Family tickets: Available, 2 Adults + 2 children
Period of public operation: Easter, then May-October
Special events: See 1998 leaflet, contact for details
Facilities for disabled: Toilets. Disabled passengers can be accommodated without prior notice
Membership details: Membership Secretaries, R. & P. Hughes, Cil-y-nant, Gladestry, Kington, Herefordshire HR5 3NR. Instant membership available at the shop
Membership journal: *The Journal* — quarterly

Timetable Service

Welshpool & Llanfair Light Railway

Mid Wales

Locomotives

Name	No	Builder	Type	Built
The Earl	1	B/Peacock (3496)	0-6-0T	1902
The Countess	2	B/Peacock (3497)	0-6-0T	1902
Chattenden	7	Drewry (2263)	0-6-0DM	1949
Dougal	8	Barclay (2207)	0-4-0T	1946
Sir Drefaldwyn	10	Franco-Belge (2855)	0-8-0T	1944
Ferret	11	Hunslet (2251)	0-4-0DM	1940
Joan	12	K/Stuart (4404)	0-6-2T	1927
SLR 85	14	Hunslet (3815)	2-6-2T	1954
Orion	15	Tubize (2369)	2-6-2T	1948
Scooby	16	Hunslet (2400)	0-4-0DM	1941

Locomotive notes: Locomotives expected in service 1998 — *Countess, Sir Drefaldwyn,* SLR No 85. The remainder can be seen at Llanfair station, No 12 is displayed with access to the footplate.

Stock
1 Wickham trolley; 6 W&LLR wagons; 8 ex Admiralty wagons; 2 ex Bowater wagons; 5 ex Zillertalbahn coaches; 4 ex-Sierra Leone coaches

Member: AIRPS
There is a decidedly foreign atmosphere to the trains over this line. The steam locomotive collection embraces examples from three continents, and the coaches are turn-of-the-century balcony saloons from Austria or 1960s bogies from Africa. The line follows a steeply graded route (maximum 1 in 24) through very attractive rolling countryside, and is rather a gem in an area too often missed by the traveller heading for further shores
General Manager: Andy Carey
Headquarters: Welshpool & Llanfair Light Railway Preservation Co Ltd, The Station, Llanfair Caereinion SY21 0SF
Telephone: Llanfair Caereinion (01938) 810441
Fax: (01938) 810861
Main station: Welshpool (Raven Square)
Other public stations: Castle Caereinion, Sylfaen, Llanfair Caereinion
OS reference: SJ 107069
Car parks: Llanfair Caereinion, Welshpool (both free)
Access by public transport: Main line station at Welshpool, one mile from Raven Square. Cambrian Midland Red buses from Shrewsbury, Oswestry and Newtown to Welshpool
Refreshment facilities: Light refreshments at Llanfair Caereinion. Picnic areas at Welshpool & Llanfair
Souvenir shops: Welshpool, Llanfair Caereinion
Depot: Llanfair Caereinion
Length of line: 8 miles, 2ft 6in gauge
Passenger trains: Welshpool-Llanfair Caereinion
Period of public operation: Weekends and Bank Holidays 4 April to 27 September. Daily 12 July-7 September, 24-27 October
Special events: Santa trains on three weekends before Christmas; Friends of Thomas the Tank Engine — 4/5 July; Narrow Gauge Steam Gala — 5/6 September
Family tickets: Available
Facilities for disabled: Specially adapted coaches for wheelchairs now available. Easy access to shops. Disabled toilet facility at Welshpool
Membership details: John Parkinson, 124 London Road, Long Sutton, Spalding, Lincolnshire PE12 9EE
Membership journal: *The Journal* — quarterly
Marketing name: Llanfair Railway
Special notes: New buildings at Raven Square largely a reconstruction of the 1863 station from Eardisley in Herefordshire. Restored station at Llanfair. Access to No 12 at Llanfair, steps up to footplate. Children can see how an engine works. Open balcony coaches — travel right next to the engine at the front of the train. Or see the line rolling away behind the back end!

Channel Islands & Isle of Man

Steam Centre — Alderney Railway — Channel Islands

Last year the Alderney Railway was 150 years old, having opened on 14 July 1847. Queen Victoria was the only passenger until 1980
Location: Alderney, Channel Islands
Operating society/organisation: Alderney Railway Society, PO Box 75, Alderney, Channel Islands
Telephone: (01481) 823260
Car park: Yes
Access by public transport: Aurigny Air Services from Southampton
On site facilities: Station at Braye Road (tickets & souvenirs; teas [Sundays]) at Mannez Quarry
Public opening: Weekends and Bank Holidays, Easter to September
Special events: Alderney Week August. Easter Egg Specials on Easter Saturday. Santa Specials, Saturday before Christmas
On site facilities: Miniature railway (7.25in gauge), quarter-mile circuit operates at Mannez in connection with standard gauge line
Length of line: 2 miles
Facilities for disabled: Yes
President: Roger Warren
Chairman: Bruce Nightingale
Hon Sec: Mike Taylor
Membership journal: Issued infrequently.
Notes: New shed at Quarry. Three Wickham 'trains' to operate 1998 low season; *Elizabeth* and tube cars high season and Easter

Industrial locomotives

Name	*No*	*Builder*	*Type*	*Built*
Elizabeth	—	Vulcan (D2271)	0-4-0DM	1949
Molly 2	—	R/Hornsby	0-4-0DM	1958

Stock
4 Wickham trolleys
2 Goods wagons
2 ex-London Underground 1938 Stock tube cars, Nos 10177/11177 (locomotive-hauled)
2 Wickham Flats
NB: all Wickhams privately owned

Steam Centre — Groudle Glen Railway — Isle of Man

Location: Groudle Glen Railway, Isle of Man
Officer in charge: Tony Beard
Operating company: Groudle Glen Railway Ltd (managed by the Isle of Man Steam Railway Supporters' Association) of 29 Hawarden Avenue, Douglas, Isle of Man IM1 4BP
Telephone: (01624) 622138 (evenings); (01624) 670453 (weekends)
Car park: Yes

Locomotives

Name	*No*	*Builder*	*Type*	*Built*
Dolphin	1	H/Hunslet (4394)	4wDM	1952
Walrus	2	H/Hunslet (4395)	4wDM	1952
Sea Lion	—	Bagnall (1484)	2-4-0T	1896
Annie	—	GGR	0-4-2T	1987

Access by public transport: Manx Electric Railway (Groudle Hotel)
On site facilities: Sales shop
Length of line: 0.75-mile, 2ft gauge
Public opening: Easter Sunday and Monday, Sundays and Bank Holidays May to September (11.00-16.30), Wednesday evening services July/August (19.00-21.00); Santa Trains 13, 20 December (11.00-15.30); 26 December (12.00-15.30)
Facilities for disabled: Due to the line's location, those who are disabled will have some difficulty. It is suggested that they telephone for advice
Further information and membership details: From above address
Membership journal: *Manx Steam Railway News* — quarterly

Timetable Service

Isle of Man Railway

Isle of Man

The 3ft gauge Isle of Man Railway is a survivor of a system which covered the whole island. Almost continuous operation since 1873 makes it one of the oldest preserved railways in the British Isles. The railway has changed little since the turn of the century and retains much of its Edwardian atmosphere. It runs for over 15 miles between Douglas and Port Erin through the island's rolling southern countryside
Director of Public Transport: R. H. Smith
Operations Superintendent: M. G. Warhurst
Engineering Superintendent: G. F. Lawson
Headquarters: Isle of Man Railways, Strathallan Crescent, Douglas, Isle of Man IM2 4NR
Telephone: Douglas (01624) 663366
Fax: (01624) 663637
Main station: Douglas
Other public stations: Port Soderick, Santon, Castletown, Ballasalla, Port St Mary and Port Erin
Car parks: Douglas, Ballasalla, Castletown, Port Erin
Access by public transport: Isle of Man Transport bus to main centres
Special events: Enthusiasts' Week — 2-9 May; Gala Fortnight — 27 June -11 July; Summer Spectacular — 15-23 August
Refreshment facilities: Port Erin and Douglas
Souvenir shops: Douglas and Port Erin stations and Douglas – Lord Street Travel Shop
Museum: Port Erin
Depot: Douglas
Length of line: 15.5 miles, 3ft gauge
Passenger trains: Douglas-Port Erin
Period of public operation: Daily Easter-end September, and last week of October
Facilities for disabled: Level access throughout Douglas and Port Erin stations including refreshment area. Carriages able to carry wheelchairs, ramps provided.

Locomotives

Name	*No*	*Builder*	*Type*	*Built*
Sutherland	1**	B/Peacock (1253)	2-4-0T	1873
Loch	4	B/Peacock (1416)	2-4-0T	1874
Peveril	6	B/Peacock (1524)	2-4-0T	1875
G.H. Wood	10*	B/Peacock (4662)	2-4-0T	1905
Maitland	11*	B/Peacock (4663)	2-4-0T	1905
Hutchinson	12*	B/Peacock (5126)	2-4-0T	1908
Kissack	13	B/Peacock (5382)	2-4-0T	1910
Caledonia	15*	Dubs & Co (2178)	0-6-0T	1885
Viking	17*	Schottler (2175)	0-4-0DH	1958
—	19*†	Walker (GNR (I))	diesel railcar	1950
—	20*†	Walker (GNR (I))	diesel railcar	1951
—	—*	M/Rail (22021)	4wDM	1959
—	—*	M/Rail (485280)	4wDM	1966
—	—	Wickhams	4wPM	1956
—	—*	Wickhams	4wPM	1961

*Operational, Nos 4, 6 and 13 stored out of use
**Returning to service in 1998
†Undergoing restoration to full working order

On display in museum at Port Erin

Name	*No*	*Builder*	*Type*	*Built*
Mannin	16	B/Peacock (6296)	2-4-0T	1926

Owned by IoM Railway & Tramway Preservation Society Ltd (not on display)

Name	*No*	*Builder*	*Type*	*Built*
Mona	5	B/Peacock (1417)	2-4-0T	1874
*Tynwald**	7	B/Peacock (2038)	2-4-0T	1880
Fenella†	8	B/Peacock (3610)	2-4-0T	1894
Douglas	9	B/Peacock (3815)	2-4-0T	1896

*Chassis only
†Undergoing restoration to working order. Work temporarily suspended as boiler is being used in No 1 for three years

Rolling stock
Gibbons crane (on display at the former Union Mills station/owned by IoMR&TPS), 41 coaches, 3 vans, 2 'M' type wagons, 1 well wagon

Timetable Service

Manx Electric Railway

Isle of Man

The 3ft gauge Manx Electric Railway is a unique survivor of Victorian high technology. A mixture of railway and tramway practice, it was built in 1893 and was a pioneer in the use of electric traction. Two of the original cars are still in service making them the oldest tramcars still in operation in the British Isles. After leaving Douglas, the railway passes the Groudle Glen Railway before reaching the charming village of Laxey, home of the Snaefell Mountain Railway. The line continues over some of the most breathtaking coastal scenery in the island before reaching its terminus at Ramsey nearly 18 miles from Douglas

Director of Public Transport: R. H. Smith
Operations Superintendent: M. G. Warhurst
Engineering Superintendent: G. F. Lawson
Headquarters: Isle of Man Railways, Strathallan Crescent, Douglas, Isle of Man IM2 4NR
Telephone: Douglas (01624) 663366
Fax: (01624) 663637
Main station: Douglas (Derby Castle)
Other public stations: Laxey, Ramsey, Groudle, Dhoon Glen, Ballaglass and numerous wayside stops
Car parks: Douglas, Laxey, Ramsey (nearby)
Access by public transport: Isle of Man Transport buses to main centres

Motor Cars

Nos	*Type*	*Seats*	*Body*	*Built*
1, 2	Unvestibuled saloon	34	Milnes	1893
5, 6, 7, 9	Vestibuled saloon	32	Milnes	1894
14, 15, 17, 18	Cross-bench open	56	Milnes	1898
16	Cross-bench open	56	Milnes	1898
19-22*	Winter saloon	48	Milnes	1899
23†	Centre-cab locomotive	—	IOMT & EP6	1900
25-27	Cross-bench open	56	Milnes	1898
28-31	Cross-bench open	56	ERTCW	1904
32, 33	Cross-bench open	56	UEC	1906

*22 re-bodied 1991, McArd/MER
†owned by IoM Railway & Tramway Preservation Society Ltd

Trailers

Nos	*Type*	*Seats*	*Body*	*Built*
13	Cross-bench open	44	Milnes	1893
36, 37	Cross-bench open	44	Milnes	1894
40, 41, 44	Cross-bench open	44	EE Co	1930
42, 43	Cross-bench open	44	Milnes	1903
45-48	Cross-bench open	44	Milnes	1899
49-50, 53, 54	Cross-bench open	44	Milnes	1893
52	pw flatcar (ex trailer)	—	Milnes	1893
55, 56*	Cross-bench open	44	ERTCW	1904
57, 58	Saloon	32	ERTCW	1904
59	Special Saloon	18	Milnes	1895
60	Cross-bench open	44	Milnes	1896
61, 62	Cross-bench open	44	UEC	1906

*rebuilt as invalid carriage in 1993

Special events: Enthusiasts' Week — 2-9 May; Gala Fortnight — 27 June -11 July; Summer Spectacular — 15-23 August
Depots: Douglas, Laxey, Ramsey
Refreshment facilities: Laxey
Museum: Ramsey
Souvenir shops: Ramsey and Douglas – Lord Street Travel Shop
Length of line: 17.5 miles, 3ft gauge

Passenger service: Douglas-Ramsey
Period of public operations: Daily Easter-October. Limited service November-March
Special notes: Folded wheelchairs can be carried. Please notify in advance. One trailer (capable of carrying wheelchairs) with built-in lift. Please notify in advance

Timetable Service

Snaefell Mountain Railway

Isle of Man

The 3ft 6in gauge Snaefell Mountain Railway is unique. It is the only electrically-driven mountain railway in the British

Trams

Nos	*Type*	*Seats*	*Body*	*Built*
1-4, 6	Vestibuled saloon	48	Milnes	1895
5 (rebuild)	Vestibuled saloon	48	MER/	1971

Isles. Almost all the rolling stock is original and dates back to 1895. The railway begins its journey at the picturesque village of Laxey where its terminus is shared with the Manx Electric Railway. The climb to the summit of Snaefell (2,036ft) is a steep one and the cars travel unassisted up gradients as steep as 1 in 12. From the summit, the views extend to Wales, Scotland, England and Ireland.
Director of Public Transport: R. H. Smith
Operations Superintendent: M. G. Warhurst
Engineering Superintendent: G. F. Lawson
Headquarters: Isle of Man Railways, Strathallan Crescent, Douglas, Isle of Man IM2 4NR
Telephone: Douglas (01624) 663366
Fax: (01624) 663637
Main station: Laxey
Other public stations: Bungalow, Summit
Car parks: Laxey, Bungalow (nearby)
Access by public transport: Manx Electric Railway or Isle of Man Transport bus to Laxey
Special events: Enthusiasts' Week — 2-9 May; Gala Fortnight — 27 June -11 July; Summer Spectacular — 15-23 August
Depot: Laxey
Refreshment facilities: Laxey, Summit
Museum: Ramsey
Souvenirs shops: Summit and Douglas – Lord Street Travel Shop
Length of line: 5 miles, 3ft 6in gauge
Passenger service: Laxey-Snaefell summit
Period of public operation: Daily May-September
Special notes: No special facilities for disabled

Ireland

Steam Centre

Cavan & Leitrim Railway

County Leitrim

Restoration work commenced in June 1993 and to date some half-mile of line has been rebuilt, water tower and engine shed refurbished and new workshops and carriage shed constructed. The ultimate objective is to rebuild a further 5.75 miles of line to Mohill
Location/headquarters: The Narrow Gauge Station, Dromod, Co Leitrim, adjacent to the Irish Rail station
Telephone: 00353 78-38599 (from UK)
General Manager: David Parks
Running Superintendent: Michael Kennedy
Main station: Dromod
Other stations: Clooncolry Halt
Car park: At Dromod terminus
Access by public transport: Rail service to Dromod (Irish Rail) on the Dublin/Sligo line
Refreshment facilities: At nearby 'Railway Bar'
Souvenir shop: Dromod
Length of line: Half-mile (3ft gauge)
Museum: Large collection of Irish and British narrow gauge locomotives and rolling stock
Period of public operation: Daily all year round. Steam-hauled 1 May-31 October
Special events: Annual Vintage Rally — second weekend in May; Ghost Trains — 31 October; Santa Specials — weekends in December
Contact address for operating Co: Cavan & Leitrim Railway Co Ltd, Dromod, Co Leitrim, Republic of Ireland
Membership journal: *Cavan & Leitrim News* – quarterly, and an annual handbook

Locomotives

Name	*No*	*Builder*	*Type*	*Built*
Nancy	—	Avonside (3024)	0-6-0T	1908
Dromod	1	K/Stuart (3024)	0-4-2ST	1916
Dinmor	F511	Fowler (3900011)	4wDM	1947
–	LM87	R/Hornsby (329696)	4wDM	1952
–	–	H/Hunslet (2659)	4wDM	1942
–	9	Motorail (115U093)	4wDH	1970
–	LM350	Simplex (60SL748)	4wDM	1980

Railcars

Name	*No*	*Builder*	*Type*	*Built*
–	C11	Bord Na Mona	2w-2wPHR	–
–	C42	Wickham (7129)	2w-2wPHR	1955
–	C56	Wickham (7681)	2w-2wPHR	1957
–	C47	Bord Na Mona/ Southern Motors	4wPHR	1958
–	W6/11-4	Wickham (9673)	2w-2wPHR	1963

Rolling stock

Includes West Clare railway trailer 47c, Tralee & Dingle coaches 7 and 10, Isle of Man carriage F21, Alan Keef-built No 13

Steam Centre

Cumann Traenach Gaeltacht Lair

County Donegal

This stretch of track has been laid on the formation of the Fintown-Glenties line. The railway runs along the shore of Lough Finn and for 1998 it is planned to have a dual ride, out by rail and return by boat.
Location/headquarters: Fintown Railway Station, Fintown, Co Donegal, Eire
Telephone: 00 353 46280 (from UK)
Manager: Anne-Marie Bonner
Main station: Fintown Station
Car park: Located at station area
Access by public transport: Local buses
Refreshment facilities: Local cafe at top of station lane

Locomotives

Name	*No*	*Builder*	*Type*	*Built*
—	LM77	R/Hornsby (329680)	4wDM	1952
—	—	Simplex	4wDM	

Rolling stock
3 Belgian tramcars

Souvenir shop: Located at station area
Length of line: 2.5 miles (3ft gauge)
Museum: Not in operation but a collection of antiquated farm machinery is being restored
Period of public operation: June — Monday/Sunday 13.00-17.00; July-September 11.00-18.00

Special events: Easter Specials, Halloween Train, Santa Train
On site facilities: Toilet, it is also hoped to have a playground in operation
Membership details: Bernadette McGee, (Membership Secretary), c/o above address
Membership journal: *An Mhuc Dhubh* — annual

Timetable Service

Downpatrick Steam Railway

County Down

Members: AIRPS
Location: Downpatrick Station, Market Street, Downpatrick, Co Down BT30 6LZ
OS reference: J483444
Operating society/organisation: Downpatrick & Ardglass Railway Co Ltd, with the support of the Downpatrick Railway Society
Telephone: (01396) 615779
Car park: Available adjacent to station in Downpatrick
Access by public transport: A regular service is operated by Ulsterbus from Belfast Europa bus centre, tel: (01232) 320011
Refreshment facilities: Buffet carriage open on operating days
On site facilities: Souvenir shop, toilets
Length of line: 1.75-miles. King Magnus' Grove built. Track is extending southwards towards Ballydugan Mill and northwards to Inch Abbey
Public opening: St Patrick's Day (17 March); Easter Sunday, Monday; Sundays in July and August; First Sunday in September
Period of public operation: 14.00-17.00
Journey time: 30min return journey to Quoile marshes

Diesel locomotives

Name	*No*	*Origin*	*Class*	*Type*	*Built*
W. F. Gillespie OBE	E421	CIE	421	C	1962
—	E432	CIE	421	C	1962
—	G611	CIE	611	B	1962
—	G613	CIE	611	B	1962
—	G617	CIE	611	B	1962

Steam locomotives

Name	*No*	*Builder*	*Type*	*Built*
Guinness	3BG	H/Clarke (1152	0-4-0ST	1919
—	1	O&K (12475)	0-4-0T	1934
—	3	O&K (12662)	0-4-0T	1935

Rolling stock
2 CIE Brake open standards; 1 CIE Travelling Post Office; 1 CIE Brake open standard generating steam van; 1 CIE Buffet open standard; 4 NCC parcels vans; 1 NIR brake open standard; 1 NIR brake open standard driving trailer; 2 NCC open wagon; 1 LMS (NCC) brake van; 1 GNR(I) brake van; 1 CIE closed van; 1 GS&WR ballast hopper; 1 GSR ballast hopper; Belfast & County Down Railway 'Royal Saloon' No 153; 1 B&CDR 1st/2nd composite (No 152); 1 B&CDR 3rd open (ex-railmotor); 1 B&CDR 6 wheeled brake 3rd (No 39); 1 B&CDR 6 wheeled 2nd (No 154); 1 GS&WR 3rd open (No 836); 1 GS&WR ballast plough van (on loan from Westrail [Tuam] Ltd); 1 Ulster Railway Family Saloon (No 33, built 1862); 1 GSWR 6-wheeled full brake (No 69); selection of carriage and wagon underframes for internal use

Owners
1 and 3 the Irish Sugar Locomotive Group
3BG on loan from the Railway Preservation Society of Ireland
G611 and G617 the Irish Traction Group
G613 privately owned

Special events: Ghost Trains — October; Santa Specials — December
Facilities for disabled: All station facilities at Downpatrick accessible for disabled
Membership details: The Secretary, Downpatrick Railway Society, The Railway Station, Downpatrick, Co Down BT30 6LZ

Steam Centre | Foyle Valley Railway | County Londonderry

Members: AIRPS
The Foyle Valley Railway Centre is a museum of narrow gauge railways in the north-west of Ireland, adjoining, and associated with, an operating pleasure railway. The centre houses a number of items and rolling stock from the former County Donegal and Lough Swilly railways. The centre is housed in a modern building in an attractive, newly developing, riverside park. Plans exist for the line to run along the former Great Northern Railway (Ireland) formation to Carrigans, and then on towards St Johnston, a total distance of 8 miles.

Locomotives and railcars

Name	*No*	*Origin*	*Class*	*Type*	*Built*
Meenglas	4	CDRJC	5	2-6-4T	1907
Columbkille	6	CDRJC	5	2-6-4T	1907
—	12	CDRJC	—	Diesel Railcar	1934
—	18	CDRJC	—	Diesel Railcar	1940

Industrial locomotives

Name	*No*	*Origin*	*Type*	*Built*
—	—	Simplex	0-4-0DH	1974

Rolling stock
1 ex-CDRJC carriage No 12, 1 ex-Londonderry & Lough Swilly Railway carriage, 1 ex-Ballymena & Larne Railway carriage, 1 ex-Clogher Valley Railway Box wagon No 19, 2 ex-CDRJC goods wagons

Location: Foyle Valley Railway Centre, Foyle Road, Londonderry BT48 6AQ
Main station: Waterside Railway station
Car park: Adjacent to the station
Access by public transport: By NI Railways to Londonderry station (quarter-mile). By Ulsterbus from various centres (three-quarter-mile)
Souvenir shop: Operated by North West of Ireland Railway Society at railway museum
Operating group: A combined project operated by Derry City Council and the North West of Ireland Railway Society (responsible under Council control for the rail service)
Museum: At Foyle Valley Railway Centre
Facilities for disabled: Yes
Operating society: North West of Ireland Railway Society, 8 Letterkenny Road, Londonderry BT48 9XG
Telephone: (01504) 265358 or (01504) 264865
Membership details: Secretary, D. W. Mason, 7 Nicholson Terrace, Londonderry BT48 7LW
General Manager: R. Gallagher, telephone (01504) 265234
Society journal: *The Starter* published once a year
Refreshment facilities: None on site but city centre quarter-mile away
On site facilities: Souvenir shop, museum, toilets, and 3ft gauge railway
Period of public operation: April-September, Tuesday-Saturday and public holidays 10.00-17.00, Sunday 14.00-18.00. October-March, Tuesday-Saturday 10.00-17.00. Special opening times Easter and Christmas
Length of line: 2.5 miles operated by diesel railcars of the former County Donegal Railways

Steam Centre | Irish Steam Preservation Society | County Laois

Members: AIRPS
Steam operation resumes on this line in 1998 following boiler repairs to No 2
Location: Stradbally Hall, eight miles from Athy, six miles from Portlaoise (on N80 road).
Telephone: 00353 502 25444 (from UK)

Access by public transport: Irish Rail train to Athy or Portlaoise. Kavanagh's Bus Portlaoise-Stradbally-Athy also Portlaoise-Stradbally-Kilkenny (both routes twice daily Monday-Saturday)
On site facilities: 3ft gauge railway
Catering facilities: None on site but town centre quarter-mile away
Length of line: 1km
Public opening: Easter Sunday & Monday — 12/13 April; May Bank Hoilday — 3/4 May; June Bank Holiday Sunday & Monday — 1/2 June; Stradbally Flower Festival — 24 July; National Steam Rally, August Bank Holiday Sunday & Monday — 2/3 August; 19 September; October Bank Holiday — 25/26 October. Please contact for details of other dates
Special notes: This is the longest established steam railway in Ireland, now in its 30th year — please contact Secretary, ISPS, Bunnacrannagh, Timahoe Road, Stradbally, Co Laois

Industrial locomotives

Name	*No*	*Builder*	*Type*	*Built*
—	2	Barclay (2264)	0-4-0WT	1949
—	—	Hunslet (2281)	4wDM	1941
Nippy	—	Planet (2014)	4wDM	1936
—	4	R/Hornsby (326052)	4wDM	1952

Stock

1 Passenger coach; 2 Ballast wagons; 1 Brake van

Museum

Irish Traction Group

County Tipperary

Member: AIRPS
Location: The former goods store adjacent to Carrick-on-Suir railway station
Operating society/organisation: Irish Traction Group, 31 Hayfield Road, Bredbury, Stockport, Cheshire SK6 1DE, England
Telephone: (0161) 285 5836 (Mon-Fri 18.00-21.00 only)
Car park: Available in station goods yard
Access by public transport: Infrequent train service. Services operated by Bus Eireann from Dublin, Limerick and Waterford
Facilities: Toilets on EI station. Site is located quarter-mile from town centre

Locomotives/Railcar

Name	*No*	*Origin*	*Class*	*Manufacturer*	*Type*	*Built*
–	1	NIR	DH	E/Electric (D1266)	6wDH	1969
–	2	NIR	DH	E/Electric (D1267)	6wDH	1969
–	3	NIR	DH	E/Electric (D1268)	6wDH	1969
-	A3R	CIE	001/A	M/Vickers (889)	Co-Co	1955
-	A39	CIE	001/A	M/Vickers (925)	Co-Co	1956
-	B103	CIE	0101/B	BRCW (DEL22)	A1A-A1A	1956
–	226	CIE	201/C	M/Vickers (972)	Bo-Bo	1957
–	C231	CIE	201/C	M/Vickers (977)	Bo-Bo	1957
–	G601	CIE	601/G	Deutz (56119)	4wDH	1956
–	G611	CIE	601/G	Deutz (57225)	4wDH	1962
–	G616	CIE	601/G	Deutz (57227)	4wDH	1962
–	G617	CIE	601/G	Deutz (57229)	4wDH	1962
–	712	CIE	–	Wickham (8919)	4wDH	1962

The first main line run in preservation of the ITG's 'A' class locomotive No A39 was made whilst the locomotive was on hire to the RPSI for a filming contract set in the late 1950s. *Andrew Marshall/ITG*

Special events: Operation of railtours over EI/NIR systems
Opening times: Premises open most weekends throughout the year, although most locomotives are stabled outside. Please telephone above number before visiting

Notes: A3R is stored at EI depot, Limerick
A39 and C231 stored at EI, Inchicore Works
G611 and G617 on loan to Downpatick Steam Railway
712 currentle stored at the Cavan & Leitrim Railway, Dromod

Steam Centre

Railway Preservation Society of Ireland

County Antrim

Members: AIRPS, TT
The RPSI was formed in 1964, making it one of the older preservation societies in these islands. It has always specialised in main line steam operations, and runs an intensive summer programme of trips out of both Belfast and Dublin. The main maintenance base is situated at Whitehead, 15 miles north of Belfast on the NIR route to Larne Harbour. Here not only are the traffic locomotives shedded, but the locomotive shed is also used for heavy maintenance. Currently the society is completing the full rebuilding of its fifth boiler 'in-house'. A large engineering workshop has just been constructed for the Locomotive Department, with the 100-year-old overhead crane which was originally in the Belfast & County Down Railway Locomotive Erecting Shop at Queen's Quay in Belfast. This workshop which will undertake all heavy engineering for the Society, has still to be fitted out, and will be commissioned hopefully during the course of 1998. A large carriage shed is also on site where traffic vehicles are maintained and coaches are fully rebuilt. There are also heavy lifting facilities on site, and access may occasionally be limited for safety reasons when these are in use. Annual operations commence with 'Easter Bunny' trains out of Belfast, usually on Easter Monday. In May the 'International Railtour' is the main event, a three day steam extravaganza, which in 1998 will visit Waterford. During June there are main line trips out of both Belfast and Dublin, including a Midsummer Barbecue train and a Musical Special. July and August see the 'Portrush Flyers' from Belfast to Portrush and back, around 180 miles of main line steam, as well as the 'Sea Breeze' excursions from Dublin to Rosslare and back, covering 205 miles. During July and August there are often steam train rides on site at Whitehead on Sunday afternoons, and at the end of July will be staged an Open Day when not only will there be train rides but also at least two locomotives will be in steam and there will be access to the workshop areas. The season usually ends with further excursions in September, giving the Society a breather before the 'Santa Specials' out of both capitals. This coming year the likelihood is a run to Londonderry and hopefully at least one run to Dublin, possibly in early October, as it is hoped to re-introduce 'Steam Enterprise' trains
Location: Whitehead Excursion station, Co Antrim, Northern Ireland

Locomotives

Name	*No*	*Origin*	*Class*	*Type*	*Built*
Merlin	85*	GNR (I)	V	4-4-0	1932
Slieve Gullion	171	GNR (I)	S	4-4-0	1913
—	4††	LMS (NCC)	WT	2-6-4T	1947
—	184†	GS&WR	J15	0-6-0	1880
—	186†	GS&WR	J15	0-6-0	1879
—	461**	D&SER	K2	2-6-0	1922
Lough Erne	27	SL&NCR	Z	0-6-4T	1949

Industrial locomotives

Name	*No*	*Builder*	*Type*	*Built*
Guinness	3§	H/Clarke (1152)	0-4-0ST	1919
R. H. Smyth	3	Avonside (2021)	0-6-0ST	1928
—	23	Planet (3509)	0-4-0DM	1951
—	4	R/Hornsby	0-4-0DM	1954

* On loan from Ulster Folk & Transport Museum
** Currently based in Dublin for regular operations
† Awaiting restoration, hopefully to commence soon
§ On loan to Downpatrick & Ardglass Railway Society
†† Returning to the main line mid-1998

Stock
The Society also owns some 20 operational coaches, normally divided between Whitehead and Dublin. Further coaches are awaiting restoration and a small number of freight wagons are also preserved, as well as a steam crane. A serious fire due to vandalism a couple of years ago destroyed several vehicles, and any rebuilding is likely to be some years in the future at best. The Society plans to purchase Craven steel-bodied coaches from Irish Rail as soon as these become available. The Society's secondary maintenance base is at Mullingar, Co Westmeath, but there is **no** access to the public.

Operating society: Railway Preservation Society of Ireland, Castleview Road, Whitehead, Carrickfergus, Co Antrim BT38 9NA
Telephone/fax: Whitehead (01960) 353567
Car park: Public car parking is readily available adjacent to the Society premises, with a further large car park less than 5min walk away on the sea front. Both car parks are normally free
Access by public transport: Northern Ireland Railways or Ulsterbus to Whitehead
On site facilities: Souvenir shop (operating days only)
Public opening: Visitors welcome most weekends. Site not open during the week (except public holidays) or when main line trains are operating from Whitehead or Belfast. Special opening for parties, or in the evening, may be arranged by telephoning in advance
Special notes: The RPSI is noted for its main line excursions and traditional rolling stock. For details: RPSI Railtours, c/o 22 Town Lane, Islandmagee, Larne, Co Antrim BT20 3SZ (9x4 SAE please).
Facilities for disabled: Please note that wheelchair facilities can be provided on trains, with advance notice if possible. A dedicated coach for carrying wheelchairs operates out of Whitehead on Belfast-based trains. Wheelchair access around the workshops at Whitehead is possible, but difficult, and advanced warning is requested of any visitors who may need special facilities
Operations Officer: Heather Boomer
Membership details: Membership Secretary, 148 Church Road, Newtownabbey, Co Antrim BT36 6HJ
Future developments: Completion of new heavy engineering workshop is planned, as well as a projected extension to the Carriage Shed and additional stores and maintenance areas, and there are further developments in the pipeline which will hopefully improve access. Additional locomotive and coach restoration is proposed

Museum — South Donegal Railway Restoration Society — County Donegal

Members: AIRPS
Location/Headquarters: Old Station House, Donegal Town, Ireland
Telephone: (00353-73 [from UK]) (073 [from Ireland]) 22655
General Manager: Patrick Stewart
Public opening: Old Station House opened as a permanent Railway Museum & Heritage Centre from Easter 1995
Membership details: From above address
Membership journal: *The Phoenix*
Special notes: Unfortunately, the development of the track at Barnesmore had to be abandoned due to unforeseen and severe planning restrictions, but the group is now in the process of developing a very scenically attractive 3-mile section between Rossnowlagh and Ballintra

Locomotives

Name	*No*	*Origin*	*Class*	*Type*	*Built*
*Drumboe**	5	CDR	5	2-6-4T	1907

*On loan from the Foyle Valley Railway

Stock
1 CDR brake/third coach
1 CDR railcar No 14
1 CDR trailer No 5
1 CDR combined goods/cattle and horse van (247 of 1893)
1 goods van

Viewing of all rolling stock is by arrangement only

Museum — Ulster Folk & Transport Museum — County Down

Forty-five acres are devoted to the Transport Galleries. Permanent exhibitions include the earliest forms of transport, horse-drawn vehicles, bicycles, motor cars and the Museum's *Titanic* exhibition.

The Irish Railway Collection is displayed in an award-winning purpose-built gallery — the largest Transport Museum gallery in Ireland.

The collection features *Maedb* — the largest locomotive run in Ireland. The display includes narrow gauge and standard gauge rolling stock, locomotives, carriages, goods wagons, railcars and railbuses along with new,

previously undisplayed material and memorabilia
Location: Ulster Folk & Transport Museum, Cultra, Holywood
Operating organisation: Ulster Folk & Transport Museum, Cultra, Holywood BT18 0EU
Telephone: (01232) 428428
Fax: (01232) 428728
Access: By car or bus the museum is about 7 miles from Belfast city centre on the A2 Belfast-Bangor Road. You can also reach the museum by train
Car park: Extensive free parking
On site facilities: Shops, toilets, tea room, 7.25in line
Opening times: All year round; opening times vary with season check with the Museum for details

Locomotives (5ft 3in)

Name	*No*	*Origin*	*Class*	*Type*	*Built*
—	93	GNR(I)	JT	2-4-2T	1895
—	30	BCDR	I	4-4-2T	1901
Dunluce Castle	74	LMS(NCC)	U2	4-4-0	1924
Maedb	800	GSR	B1A	4-6-0	1939
—	1	R/Stephenson (2738)	—	0-6-0ST	1891
Merlin	85	GNR(I)	V	4-4-0	1932
—	1	GNR(I)	—	Railbus	1932

Locomotives (narrow gauge)

Name	*No*	*Origin*	*Class*	*Type*	*Built*
Blanche	2	CDRJC	5A	2-6-4T	1912
Kathleen	2	CLR	—	4-4-0T	1887
Phoenix	11	CVR	—	4wD	1928
—	20	Industrial	—	0-4-0	1905
—	2	Industrial	—	0-4-0	1907

Stock
1 Dublin, Wicklow & Wexford Railway coach; 1 Dundalk, Newry & Greenore Railway coach; 1 Midland & Great Western Railway director's saloon (ex-private vehicle); 1 Electric tramcar of Bessbrook-Newry Tramway; 2 trams from Giant's Causeway Tramway, Great Northern Railway Ireland Fintona tram, 1 Cavan-Leitrim Railway coach; 2 County Donegal Railway railcars; 1 County Donegal Railway director's coach; 1 County Donegal Railway trailer coach (bodywork ex-Dublin & Lucan Railway coach); 1 Giants Causeway (P&BVR) saloon trailer; 1 Castlederg & Victoria Bridge Tramway 1st/3rd coach; 1 County Donegal Railway 7ton open wagon, 3 Belfast trams, 1 Belfast trolleybus, 1 Belfast double-deck bus. Extensive collection of cars, motorcycles, bicycles, commercial vehicles, fire fighting equipment and industrial railway vehicles

Timetable Srvice

Westrail

County Galway

Location: Tuam, Co Galway, Ireland
OS Reference: Lat 42, Long 52
Operating society/organisation: Westrail (Tuam) Ltd, The Railway Station, Vicar Street, Tuam, Co Galway
Telephone: 00 353 (093) 25400, 00 353 (091) 91039, 00 353 (093) 49253.
Fax: 00 353 (091) 25111
Car park: On site
Catering facilities: On train, licensed snack bar. Platform shops at Athenry
Length of line: Athenry-Tuam, 15 miles or Galway-Athenry 13 miles
Period of public operation: At the time of writing it was uncertain what, if any, services would be operated during 1998. *If* services are operated they will be on Saturdays in July and August, departing Galway at 12.00 and 15.30, Athery at 14.00 and 17.05
Journey time: 1-3hr return (see timetable for details)
Membership details: Contact above address for details
Note: Prospective travellers are advised to check before visiting

Locomotives

Name	*No*	*Origin*	*Class*	*Type*	*Built*
—	90	GSWR	J30	0-6-0T	1875
—	E428	CIE	421	C	1962
—	3	CSET	—	0-4-0DM	1960

Rolling stock
3 ex-CIE coaches

Miniature Railways

Audley End Railway, Essex

Audley End, Saffron Walden, Essex. Tel: (01799) 541354 or 541956
General Manager: Donald Saggers
Opening details: Daily — Easter week, summer half-term, summer school holidays; Saturdays, Sundays and Bank Holidays April-October (from 14.00)
10.25in gauge; 1.5 miles long; 4 steam, 3 diesel locomotives
Public access: Rail to Audley End (1-mile), car park
Site facilities: Light refreshments on ex-London Transport RT-type double-deck bus, toilets, large picnic area
Note: (Postal address) Audley End Estate Office, Brunketts, Wendens Ambo, Saffron Walden, Essex CB11 4JL

Dobwalls Family Adventure Park

Dobwalls, Nr Liskeard, Cornwall PL14 6HD. Tel: (01579) 320325/321129. Infoline (01579) 320578. Fax: (01579) 21345
General Manager: J. B. Southern
Opening details: Daily Easter-30 September. 10.00-18.00 (last admissions 16.30)
7.25in gauge; two 1-mile long routes; 6 steam and 4 diesel locomotives
Public access: By train to Liskeard — 3 miles; by bus — National Express coaches to/from Cornwall via Plymouth stop in Dobwalls village; By car — signposted off A38
Site facilities: Refreshments, toilets inc disabled, mother & baby facilities, picnic area, souvenirs, radio-controlled boats and trucks, crazy golf, children's adventure playground, wildlife gallery
Facilities for disabled: Wheelchair access throughout (free loan, subject to availability), toilets

Great Cockcrow Railway, Surrey

Hardwick Lane, Lyne, Chertsey, Surrey. Tel: Mon-Fri (01932) 255500; Sun (01932) 565474
Opening details: Every Sunday May to October inclusive, 14.00-17.30
7.25in gauge; normal run 1.25-mile (including planned extension); 16 steam locomotives, 1 electric, 2 petrol (nine normally in service). Journey time about 15min
Public access: BR Chertsey (1.25 miles); London Buslines 561, 586 Holloway Hill (half-mile), free car park
Site facilities: Toilet, light refreshments
Special note: Sponsored by Ian Allan Group

Kerr's Miniature Railway

West Links Park, Arbroath, Angus. Tel: (01241) 879249
(Along the sea front to the west of town)
General Manager: Mathew B. Kerr
Opening details: Easter-end of September — weekends (14.00-17.00). All of July and first half of August — daily 11.30-13.00/14.00-17.00. All times weather permitting
10.25 in gauge; 400yd (alongside ScotRail line); 3 steam, 2 diesel, 2 petrol
Public access: ScotRail Arbroath station 1.5 miles; Strathtay Buses route A92
Site facilities: None, but park has toilets, snack bar, etc

Lightwater Valley Theme Park, North Yorkshire

North Stainley, Nr Ripon, North Yorkshire. Tel: (01765) 635368 (24 hours), 635321 (administration/party bookings)
Opening details: Easter-October (daily in June/July/August). Telephone for details
Chief Engineer: Chris Bulmer
15in gauge; 1-mile long; 6 steam, 1 diesel, 1 petrol locomotives
Public access: Main line station Harrogate (12 miles) and Thirsk (9 miles), free car park
Site facilities: 125 acres of country park featuring unique white knuckle rides including the world's biggest rollercoaster, live family entertainment, leisure pursuits, skill-testing activities. Wide range of catering facilities and themed shopping malls

Moors Valley Railway, Dorset

Moors Valley Country Park, Horton Road, Ashley Heath, Nr Ringwood, Dorset. Tel: (01425) 471415
General Manager: Mr J. A. W. Haylock
Opening details: Sundays all year; Saturdays March-October; daily all school holidays and Spring Bank Holiday to mid-September. Santa Specials in December. Steam Gala — 7/8 June
7.25 in gauge; 1-mile long; 10 steam locomotives
Public access: Wilts & Dorset bus X2, from Bournemouth/Ringwood to Ashley Heath
Site facilities: Picnic areas, lakeside walks, adventure playground, railway shop and refreshments all set in the beautiful Moors Valley Country Park. Car park and toilets (including disabled)

Association of Independent Railways & Preservation Societies Ltd

Company Secretary & General Administrator
Raymond Williams, 16 Woodbrook, Charing, Ashford, Kent TN27 0DN. Tel/Fax: (01233) 712130

Company Limited by Guarantee and not having a share capital.
Registered in England No 2226245
(Registered Office: 21 Market Place, Wednesbury, West Midlands WS10 7AY)
President: Dame Margaret Weston DBE
Vice Presidents: Ian Allan OBE, Allan Garraway MBE

Private Membership Secretary:
Arthur Harding, 6 Ullswater Grove, Alresford, Hants SO24 9NP. Tel/Fax: (01962) 733327.

Corporate Membership Secretary:
David Woodhouse MBE, 8 Ffordd Dyfrig, Tywyn LL36 9EH. Tel/Fax: (01654) 710344

Journal Editors:
Jackie and Michael Cope, 30 Gledhow Drive, Oxenhope, Keighley, West Yorkshire BD22 9SA

Members of the Association of Independent Railways & Preservation Societies Ltd

UK Affiliate Members

Britt Alcroft (Thomas) Ltd:
3 Grovenor Square, Southampton, Hampshire SO1 2BE

Friends of Tynemouth Station:
Ylana First, 20 Hotspur Street, Tynemouth NE30 4EL

Lloyd's Railway Society:
Mr P. Wood, 30 Beechwood Avenue, Caterham, Surrey CR3 6NA

Locomotive Club of Great Britain:
Mr R. L. Patrick, 8 Wolviston Ave, Bishopgate, York YO1 3DD

London Transport Museum Library: 39 Wellington Street, Covent Garden, London WC2E 7BB

Railworld: Oundle Road, Peterborough PE3 9NR

Transport Trust: Mr D. Muirhead, 202 Lambeth Road, London SE1 7JW

Westinghouse Signals: Mr J. Mills PO Box 79, Pew Hill, Chippenham, Wiltshire SN15 1ND

Winson Engineering: Miss Gill Watkins, Units 3 Faraday Close, Drayton Fields, Daventry, Northants NN11 5RD

Overseas Affiliate Members

AJECTA: M Phillippe Tomatis, Depot des Machines, Boite Postale No 1, F-77650, Longeville, France

APPEVA: Secretariat, BP 106-80001, Amiens Cedex 1, France

Berliner Eisenbahn Freunde E V: Herr Rudiger Reich, Wilhelmstrasse 80, D-10117, Berlin, Germany

Stoomscentrum Maldegem: Rik Degruyter, De Streep 19, B-8340 Damme-Sysele, Belgium

Stoompoorlijn Dendermonde-Puurs: Mr Jaak Serckx, Station Baasrode Noord, Fabrieksstraat 118, B-9200, Baasrode, Belgium

Association of Preservation Groups: Mr R. Jowett, Treasurer, New South Wales Inc, 43 Gara Drive, Mt Riverview, NSW 2774, Australia

Australian Railway Historical Society: Mr R. Jowett, New South Wales Division, 67 Renwick St, Redfern, NSW 2016, Australia

Mary Railway Heritage Railway: Mr K. Coulter, Old Cottage Gardens, 432 Ilkley, QW 4554, Australia

Association of Preservation Socs (NSW) Inc: Mr C. G. Wheaton, Gen Secretary, PO Box 31, Burwood, NSW 2134, Australia

National Museum of Science & Technology: The Librarian, PO Box 9724, Ottawa Terminus, Ottawa, Ontario, K1G 3A5, Canada

Additional Corporate Members not listed in the main part of the book

Aln Valley Railway Society:
Mr S. Manley, Alnwick Station, Alnwick, Northumberland NE66 2NP

Bahamas Locomotive Society:
Mr K. J. Tait, 73 Derby Road, Heaton Moor, Stockport, Cheshire SK4 4NG

Battle of Britain Locomotive Preservation Society:
Mr R. J. Tanner, 317 Cardington Road, Bedford MK42 0DU

Bredgar & Wormshill Light Railway: Mr B. Best, The Warren, Bredgar, Sittingbourne, Kent ME9 8AT

Britain's Great Little Railways:
M. Gaunt, 28 South View, Holton le Clay, Grimsby DN36 5BW

Britannia Locomotive Society:
Mr A. Sixsmith, 6 Vermont Grove, Peterborough PE3 6BN

Bulleid Society Ltd:
Mr D. A. Foale, Namron, South Chailey, Lewes, East Sussex BN8 4AD

Caerphilly Railway Society Ltd:
Mr A. Smith, 51 Worcester Crescent, Newport, NP9 7NX

Camelot Locomotive Society: Mr P. W. Gibbs, 54 Latimer Gardens, Pinner, Middx HA5 3RA

Class 45/1 Preservation Society:
P. Crumpton, 34 Alexander Road, Handsworth, Birmingham B21 0PL

Cornish Steam Locomotive Preservation Society Ltd:
Mr M. Orme, 3 Jubilee Terrace, Goonhavern, Truro, Cornwall TR4 9JY

Cotswold Steam Preservation Ltd:
Mr F. G. A. Leach, Kelso, Vicarage Lane, Brockworth, Glos GL4 3EZ

Devon Diesel Society Ltd: Mr D. Martin, 19 Knapp Park RoAd, Paignton, Devon TQ4 7LA

Diesel and Electric Group:
Mr R. Jones, 32 Ty Wern Road, Rhiwbina, Cardiff CF4 6EB

Diesel Units Preservation Associates Ltd: Mr M. Cornell, 24 Ashbury Drive, Marks Tey, Colchester, Essex SS6 9AR

Eden Valley Railway Society:
Mr C. Jones, 3A Murrayfield Terrace, Ravenglass, Cumbria CA18 1SR

Errol Station Museum Trust:
David Tough, 48 Moyness Park Drive, Blairgowrie, Perthshire PH10 6LX

Forest Pannier Tank Fund:
Mr J. S. Metherall, 15 Sudbrook Way, Gloucester GL4 4AP

Foxcote Manor Society:
Mr M. Whitton, Meadow Brook, Station Lane, Mickle Trafford, Chester CH2 4EH

Great Northern & East Lincolnshire Railway plc:
3 Barnsway, Kings Langley, Herts WD4 9PW

Grimsby & Louth Railway Society:
Mr W. B. Herbert, 41 Humberston Avenue, Humberston, Grimsby, Lincs

GWR 813 Preservation Fund:
Mr P. Goss, 23 Hatchmere, Thornbury, Bristol BS12 3EU

Hampshire & Sussex Units Preservation Society: Mr C. Dann, 48 Hollybrook, Bordon, Hants GU35 0DL

Hastings Diesels Ltd:
Mr G. Smith, 15 Orchard Glade, Headcorn, Nr Ashford, Kent TN27 9SS

Hull & Barnsley Railway Stock Fund: Mr A. Hallman, 6 Chequerfield Court, Chequerfield Avenue, Pontefract, West Yorkshire WP8 7TQ

Irchester Narrow Gauge Railway Trust: Mr R. Kingston, 'Lysander', 71 Bedford Road, Cranfield, Bedfordshire MK43 0EX

Keith & Dufftown Railway Association: Mrs M. H. Webster, 36 Low Shore, Whitehills, Banff AB45 2NN

Lambton No 29 Syndicate:
Mr J. M. Richardson, 5 Ravine Hill, Filey, North Yorkshire YO14 9EU

Lancashire & Yorkshire Railway Preservation Society: Mr E. Ring, 111 Huddersfield Road, Elland, West Yorks HX5 0EE

Lincolnshire Coast Light Railway Historical Vehicles Trust:
Mr H. L. Goy, 12 Giles Street, Cleethorpes DN35 8AE

Liverpool Locomotive Preservation Group: Mr K. Soper, 90 Brick Kiln Lane, Rufford, Lancs L40 1SY

Llangollen Great Western Locomotive Group:
Mr C. R. Cooksley, 21 Allanson Road, Colwyn Bay LL28 4HN

Locomotive Owners Group (Scotland) Ltd: Mr J. L. Stevenson, 4 Queens Road, Blackhall, Edinburgh EH4 2BY

London & North Western Society:
Mr J. C. James, c/o Westlands Hotel, 30 Trinity Ave, Llandudno LL15 2TQ

Lynton & Barnstaple Light Railway: Mr D. Tooke, 3 Torrs Walk Ave, Ilfracombe, Devon EX34 8AU

Maid Marian Locomotive Fund:
Mr R. Mason, Bodnolwyn Wen, Llantrisant, Anglesey LL65 4TW

Manston Locomotive Preservation Society: Mr J. Cleverdon, PO Box 169, Ramsgate, Kent CT12 6GG

Market Drayton Railway Preservation Society:
Mr M. Brinkman, The Old Smithy, Childs Ercall, Market Drayton, Shropshire TF9 2BZ

Maunsell Locomotive Society:
Mr J. S. Pilcher, 312 Riverside Mansions, Garnett Street, Wapping, London E1 9SZ

Merchant Navy Locomotive Preservation Society Ltd:
Mr R. Abercrombie, 12 Inglewood Avenue, Heatherside, Camberley, Surrey GU15 1RJ

Modern Railway Society of Ireland: Mr M. A. McFerran, 54 Prince's Drive, Newtownabbey, Northern Ireland BT37 0AZ

North Eastern Locomotive Preservation Group:
Mr C. Watton, 20 Sorrell Court, Marton, Middlesbrough TS7 8RZ

North Gloucestershire Railway Co Ltd: Mr R. H. Wales, 'Wellesbourne', Oakfield Street, Tivoli, Cheltenham, Gloucestershire GL33 8HR

North London Locomotive Preservation Society: Mr R. T. Moore, 7 Woodbine Grove, Enfield, Middlesex EN2 0EA

North Somerset Railway:
Mr D. J. Hill, 8 Long Lakes, Willington, Taunton, Somerset TA4 4SR

North West Ireland Rly Soc: D. W. Watson, 7 Nicholson Ter, Londonderry BT49 7LW

Ongar Railway Preservation Society: Mr B. Ayton, 75 Highland Road, Nazeing, Essex EN9 2PU

Rother Valley Railway (East Sussex) Ltd: Mr G. S. Crawley, Penny Cottage, Yelsted, Sittingbourne, Kent ME9 7UT

Salisbury Steam Locomotive Preservation Trust: Mr E. J. Roper, 33 Victoria Road, Wilton, Salisbury, Wiltshire SP2 0OZ

Scottish Locomotive Preservation Trust: Mr D. P. Roland, 24 Laswade Road, Dalkeith EH22 3EF

Somerset & Dorset Railway Trust: M. J. Palmer, The Haven, Chandlers Lane, Edington, Bridgwater, Somerset TA7 9JY

South Wales Pannier Group: Mr J. Melhuish, 74 Loychurch Road, Bridgend, Mid Glamorgan CF31 2AP

South West Main Line Steam Co: Mr P. Gould, 8 Parcroft Gardens, Yeovil, Somerset BA20 2BS

Southern Electric Group: Mr J. M. Cousins, 51 Primrose Walk, Shortcroft Road, Ewell, Surrey KT17 2EZ

Southern Locomotives Ltd: Mr S. Kerley, 369 Wimborne Road, Poole, Dorset BH15 3ED

Southwold Railway Society: Mr G. Crabb, 1 Barnby Green, Southwold, Suffolk IP18 6AP

Stanier 8F Locomotive Society Ltd: Mr D. R. McIntosh, 1 The Hawthornes, Comberton Road, Kidderminster, Worcs DY10 3DH

Steam Power Trust '65: Mr A. R. Thompson, The Station House, Penshaw, Houghton le Spring DK4 7PQ

Stephenson Locomotive Society: Mr B. F. Gilliam, 25 Regency Close, Chigwell, Essex IG7 5NY

The Gresley Society: Mr P. J. Coster, Pendoggett Farm, St Kew, Bodmin, Cornwall PL30 3HH

Underground Railway Rolling Stock Trust: Mr D. C. Alexander, 13 Irvine Drive, Stoke Mandeville, Aylesbury HP22 5UN

Urie Locomotive Society: Mr A. Ball, 'Lavenham', Adams Lane, Selborne, Alton, Hants GU34 3LJ

Wainwright 'C' Preservation Society: Mr I. DeMaid, 69 Bromley Gardens, Bromley, Kent BR2 0ES

Weardale Railway Society: Mr G. Chatsfield, Stanhope Station, Bondisle, Bishop Aukland, Co Durham DL13 2YS

Western Locomotive Association: Mr D. H. Tompkins, 23 Haytor Drive, Newton Abbot, Devon TQ12 4DR

Worcester Locomotive Society Ltd: Mr A. T. Dowling, 23 Belle Orchard Close, Ledbury, Herefordshire WR14 1HR

1708 Locomotive Preservation Trust Ltd: Mr G. W. Kingham, 106 Stanford Road, Luton, Beds LU2 0QA

1857 Society: Mr K. R. Bowen, 18 Lochmore Close, Hollycroft, Hinckley, Leicestershire

4247 Ltd: Mr N. Rowles, Station House, Station Road, Lower Heyford, Oxon OX6 3PD

48624 Locomotive Soc: G. Robb, 26 Old Gardens Close, Tunbridge Wells, Kent TN2 5ND

6024 Preservation Society Ltd: Mr C. K. Hargreaves, Spencer Lodge, Back Lane, Chapel Brampton, Northampton NN6 8AJ

6201 Princess Elizabeth Society Ltd: Mr A. Harries, 1 Ormerod Close, Sandbach, Cheshire CW11 4HA

71000 Duke of Gloucester Steam Locomotive Trust Ltd: Mr F. Reid, 2 Bodmin Avenue, Marthside, Soutport PR4 9TU

8E Association: Mr A. Ashurst, 149 St Mary Street, Latchford, Warrington, Cheshire WA4 1EL

A1 Steam Locomotive Trust Ltd: PO Box 282, Doncaster, Yorks DN8 7LF

A4 Locomotive Society Ltd: Mr G. R. Pope, Secretary, Keeper's Cottage, Muntham Farm, North End, Findon, Worthing BN14 0RQ

LM2MT 46464 Trust: Mr D Fraser, 6 Westbury Lodge Close, Pinner, Middx HA5 3FG

Applicant Organisations

Amman Valley Railway Society

Barrow Hill Engine Shed Society

Cumann Traenach Gaeltrachta Lair

Gloucestershire Railway Trust

Great Yorkshire Railway Preservation Society

Kingdon of Fife Railway Preservation Society

London & North Western Railway Society

Mersey & Tyneside Electric Preservationists

Port Road Railway Society

Almond Valley Heritage Trust

Princess Royal Class locomotive Trust Ltd

Red Rose Steam society

Rhondda Valley Railway Society

West Lancs Light Railway

INDEX

Association of Independent Railways & Preservation Societies Ltd

To a person actively interested in nationwide railway preservation as opposed to one particular preservation scheme, PRIVATE MEMBERSHIP of the ASSOCIATION OF INDEPENDENT RAILWAYS & PRESERVATION SOCIETIES LTD offers many advantages. Five major meetings are organised annually, some at the railway site of a leading Member Society. Here one can meet well-known personalities in the railway preservation world, and the host railway invariably lays on a full day's programme which is both stimulating and enjoyable.

The *Heritage Railway Journal* (published quarterly) is sent to members, containing information on Association activities from member organisations, book reviews and wants, etc.

Railways Restored is made available at a reduced price.

Private members receive Transport Trust Travel Back cards yearly enabling them to visit transport museums or travel on steam railways at reduced charges (and in some cases free). Some 120 sites are covered and are listed in Railways Restored and Steam Heritage Yearbook. In addition to annual membership, a two year Inter Rail and membership package is available which includes travel facilities on most member railways

Private Membership
Application Form (1998)

Send this form (or photostat of) to: Membership Secretary, AIRPS, 6 Ullswater Grove, Alresford, Hants SO24 9NP

Name

....

(*BLOCK LETTERS PLEASE*)

Address

....

....

....

Post Code

....

Telephone

....

Subscription enclosed

....

Donation enclosed

....

Private membership costs:

	UK	Overseas
Annual (1 April-31 March)	£15	£20
Life	£200	£250
Two year package	£40	N/A

HERITAGE RAILWAYS 1998

NATIONAL TIMETABLE OF SCHEDULED SERVICES

This timetable has been produced in collaboration with the Association of Independent Railways and Preservation Societies Ltd by *Railway World* and Ian Allan Ltd and was printed by Ian Allan (Printing) Ltd of Coombelands, Runnymede, England.

NOTES TO THE TIMETABLE

Throughout the Timetable, the 24 hour clock is used.

Days of operation are shown on the grid at the head of most entries. The letter, or in some cases number, contained in each square denotes the service pattern for that day, and the appropriate letter or number is shown against 'service' in the timetable columns below.

Many trains have refreshment facilities. These are not shown herein as availability may vary according to staffing conditions and seasons of the year.

For details of Wine and Dine, Thomas the Tank Engine, Santa Specials and other out-of-the-ordinary facilities, please enquire of the appropriate railway company for details. Operating days for these are shown by the letter X on the grids.

The telephone number and postal address of each railway operator is shown at the head of each entry so that specific enquiries can be made direct.

The entries are mostly in alphabetical order but in some cases there has been a slight variation to meet space requirements.

It would be helpful if this timetable was read in conjunction with the annual publication *Railways Restored,* obtained from booksellers or direct from Ian Allan Ltd.

DISCLAIMER

This timetable has been compiled from information received from operating companies and is believed to be accurate. However, neither the publisher nor AIRPS Ltd accept any responsibility for any loss, damage or delay which may be caused by variances between this brochure and actual operations or any other cause.

MARKS OF QUALITY

Some railways excel in certain fields, and in this timetable special merit markings are applied as has been thought appropriate. The symbols represent individual quality; a double symbol represents excellence. Winners in the 1997 Ian Allan Independent Railway of the Year Awards are highlighted.

 Award winner 1997

 Interesting Rolling Stock

 On-board catering

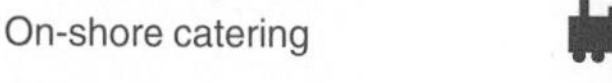 On-shore catering

 Interesting Engines

 Interesting Stations and Signals

 Big Engines

 Loos

 Views from the train

INDEX TO TIMETABLES

** Narrow Gauge Railway † 1997 Award Winners*

BALA LAKE RAILWAY

Rheilfford Llyn Tegid, Llanuwchllyn, Bala, Gwynedd LL33 7DD   01678 540666

1998	1	2	3	4	5	6	7	8	9	10	11	12	13	14	15	16	17	18	19	20	21	22	23	24	25	26	27	28	29	30	31
Apr										A	A	A	A	A	A	A	A	A	A		A	A	A		A	A		A	A	A	
May		A	A	A	A	A	A		A	A		A	A	A		A	A		A	A	A		A	A	A	A	A	A	A	A	A
June		A	A	A		A	A		A	A	A		A	A		A	A	A		A	A		A	A	A		A	A		A	
July	A	A	A	A	A	A	A	A	A	A	A	A	A	A	A	A	A	A	A	A	A	A	A	A	A	A	A	A	A	A	A
Aug	A	A	A	A	A	A	A	A	A	A	A	A	A	A	A	A	A	A	A	A	A	A	A	A	A	A	A	A	A	A	A
Sept	A	A	A	A	A	A		A	A	A		A	A		A	A	A		A	A		A	A	A		A	A		A	A	
Oct	A		A	A																											

Service A

No service in January, February, March, November and December.

Llanuwchllyn	dep	11.15	12.50	14.25	16.00
Bala	dep	11.50	13.25	15.00	16.35

Journey times:

Llanuwchllyn–Bala: Return trip 1 hour; single trip 25 minutes. Break of journey allowed at any station.

Bala–Llanuwchllyn: Return trip 1 hour 30 minutes as train stops at Llanuwchllyn to take on coal and water etc. Single journey 25 minutes.

All trains arrive at and depart from Llangower 10 minutes after leaving Llanuwchllyn and 15 minutes after leaving Bala. Trains also call by request at Pentrepiod, Glanllyn and Bryn Hynod halts. To join the train please signal clearly to the Driver.To alight, inform the Guard when you board the train.

BATTLEFIELD LINE (SHACKERSTONE RLWY)   01827 880754

Shackerstone Station, Shackerstone, nr Nuneaton, Warks CV13 6NW

1998	1	2	3	4	5	6	7	8	9	10	11	12	13	14	15	16	17	18	19	20	21	22	23	24	25	26	27	28	29	30	31
Mar							X	X						B	B						B	B						B	B		
Apr				B	A						B	A	A					B	A						B	A					
May		B	A	A		C			B	A			C			B	A			C			B	A	A		C			B	A
June			X			X	X			X			B	A			X			B	A			X			B	A			
July	C			B	A			C			B	A			C			B	A			C			B	A			C		
Aug	B	A			C			B	A			C			B	A			C			B	A			C			B	A	A
Sept		C			B	A			C			B	A			C			B	A			C			B	A				
Oct			B	A						B	A						B	A						B	A						B
Nov	A						X	X							B							B									
Dec	← SANTA SPECIALS →																														

X denotes special service, see local announcements.

No service in January and February.

Service A

Shackerstone	dep	11.15	12.30	13.45	15.00	16.15
Mkt Bosworth	dep	11.27	12.42	13.57	15.12	16.27
Shenton	arr	11.35	12.50	14.05	15.20	16.35
Shenton	dep	11.50	13.05	14.20	15.35	16.50
Mkt Bosworth	dep	11.58	13.13	14.28	15.43	16.58
Shackerstone	arr	12.10	13.25	14.40	15.55	17.10

Service B

12.30	13.45	15.00	16.15
12.42	13.57	15.12	16.27
12.50	14.05	15.20	16.35
13.05	14.20	15.35	16.50
13.13	14.28	15.43	16.58
13.25	14.40	15.55	17.10

Service C

13.00	14.00	15.00	16.00
13.12	14.12	15.12	16.12
13.20	14.20	15.20	16.20
13.30	14.30	15.30	16.30
13.38	14.38	15.38	16.38
13.50	14.50	15.50	16.50

BLUEBELL RAILWAY

Sheffield Park Station, Uckfield, East Sussex TN22 3QL   01825 723777

Trains run between

SHEFFIELD PARK - HORSTED KEYNES - KINGSCOTE

Bus service 473 operates between Kingscote and East Grinstead, connecting with Connex South Central services from London Victoria and East Croydon.

TRAINS RUN EVERY WEEKEND.
DAILY FROM MAY TO SEPTEMBER AND DURING SCHOOL HOLIDAYS

Please phone for details.

Talking timetable 01825 722370 **General Enquiries** 01825 723777

BODMIN & WENFORD RAILWAY

Lostwithiel Road, Bodmin, Cornwall PL31 1AQ **01208 73666**

1998	1	2	3	4	5	6	7	8	9	10	11	12	13	14	15	16	17	18	19	20	21	22	23	24	25	26	27	28	29	30	31
Apr					A	A	A	A	A	X	X	X	X	A	A	A	A	A	A			A				A			A		
May			A	A	A	A				A			A				A			A			X	X	A	A	A	A	A	A	A
June	A	A	A	A	A	A	A	A	A	A	A	A	A	A	A	A	A	A	A	A	A	A	A	A	A	A	A	A	A	A	
July	A	A	A	A	A	B	B	B	B	B	A	A	B	B	B	B	B	A	A	B	B	B	B	B	A	A	B	B	B	B	B
Aug	A	A	B	B	B	B	X	X	X	X	B	B	B	B	A	A	B	B	B	B	B	A	A	B	B	B	B	B	A	B	B
Sept	B	B	B	B	X	X	A	A	A	A	A	A	A	A	A	A	X	X	A	A	A	A	A	A	A	A	A			A	
Oct				A			A				A			A			X	X			A				A	A	A	A	A	A	
Dec					X	X						X	X						X	X	X	X	X	X		X	X				X

X denotes special service, see local announcements

No service in January, February, March and November.

Service A

		★				
Bodmin General	dep	10.25	11.20	12.25	14.05	15.10
Bodmin Parkway	arr	10.38	–	12.42	–	15.27
Boscarne Junction	arr	–	11.35	–	14.20	–
Boscarne Junction	dep	–	11.45	–	14.30	–
Bodmin Parkway	dep	10.40	–	12.53	–	15.38
Bodmin General	arr	10.55	12.02	13.15	14.47	16.00

★ Only runs Mondays to Fridays 25th May to 3rd July (Diesel Train).

† Diesel Train.

‡ Pasty Special Runs TUESDAYS ONLY, 21st July to 1st September.

¶ Murder Mystery Special Runs, FRIDAYS ONLY, 24th July to 28th August.

Service B

		†							‡	¶	¶
Bodmin General	dep	10.15	11.00	12.10	13.10	14.20	15.20	16.30	19.00	19.00	20.10
Bodmin Parkway	arr	–	11.17	–	13.27	–	15.37	–	19.15	–	20.27
Boscarne Junction	arr	10.25	–	12.25	–	14.35	–	16.45	–	19.20	–
Bodcame Junction	dep	10.30	–	12.35	–	14.45	–	16.55	–	19.30	–
Bodmin Parkway	dep	–	11.28	–	13.38	–	15.48	–	19.25	–	20.38
Bodmin G	arr	10.42	11.50	12.52	14.00	15.02	16.10	17.12	20.05	19.47	21.10

BO'NESS & KINNEIL RAILWAY

Union Street, Bo'ness, West Lothian EH51 9AQ **01506 822298**

1998	1	2	3	4	5	6	7	8	9	10	11	12	13	14	15	16	17	18	19	20	21	22	23	24	25	26	27	28	29	30	31
Apr				A	A					A	A	A	A					A	A						A	A					
May		A	A	A					A	A						X	X						A	A	A					A	A
June			X	X		A	A			X	X		A	A			X	X		A	A						A	A			
July				B	B		B	B	B	B	B	B		B	B	B	B	B	B		B	B	B	B	B	B		B	B	B	B
Aug	B	B		B	B	B	B	X	X		B	B	B	B	B	B		B	B	B	B	B	B		B	B	B	B	B	B	B
Sept					X	X						A	A						A	A						A	A				
Oct			A	A						A	A						A	A													
Nov																												S	S		
Dec					S	S						S	S						S	S											

X denotes special service. S denotes Santa specials, see local announcements.

No service in January, February and March.

Service A

Bo'ness	dep	11.20	12.30	14.00	15.15	16.30

Service B

10.30	11.20	12.30	14.00	15.15	16.30

BRECON MOUNTAIN RAILWAY

Pant Station, Merthyr Tydfil CF48 2UP **01685 722988**

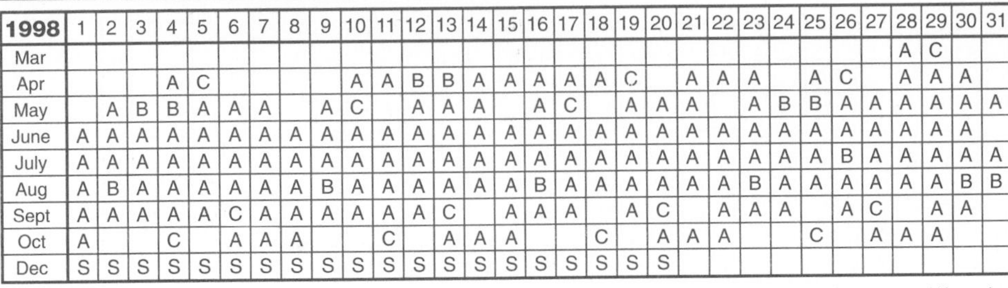

1998	1	2	3	4	5	6	7	8	9	10	11	12	13	14	15	16	17	18	19	20	21	22	23	24	25	26	27	28	29	30	31
Mar																												A	C		
Apr				A	C					A	A	B	B	A	A	A	A	A	C		A	A	A		A	C		A	A	A	
May		A	B	B	A	A	A		A	C		A	A	A		A	C		A	A	A		A	B	B	A	A	A	A	A	A
June	A	A	A	A	A	A	A	A	A	A	A	A	A	A	A	A	A	A	A	A	A	A	A	A	A	A	A	A	A	A	
July	A	A	A	A	A	A	A	A	A	A	A	A	A	A	A	A	A	A	A	A	A	A	A	A	A	B	A	A	A	A	A
Aug	A	B	A	A	A	A	A	A	B	A	A	A	A	A	A	B	A	A	A	A	A	A	B	A	A	A	A	A	A	B	B
Sept	A	A	A	A	A	C	A	A	A	A	A	A	C		A	A	A		A	C		A	A	A		A	C		A	A	
Oct	A			C		A	A	A			C		A	A	A			C		A	A	A			C		A	A	A		
Dec	S	S	S	S	S	S	S	S	S	S	S	S	S	S	S	S	S	S	S	S											

S denotes Santa specials, see local announcements.

No service in January, February and November.

Service A

Pant	dep	10.45	12.00	13.15	14.30	15.45

Service B

10.45	12.00	13.15	14.30	15.45	17.00

Service C

Pant	dep	12.00	13.15	14.30	15.45

Return journey takes 65 minutes. There is no other access to Pontsticill station though break of journey is permitted.

BURE VALLEY RAILWAY

Aylsham Station, Norwich Road, Aylsham, Norfolk NR11 6BW **01263 733858**

1998	1	2	3	4	5	6	7	8	9	10	11	12	13	14	15	16	17	18	19	20	21	22	23	24	25	26	27	28	29	30	31
Apr				B	B	B	B	B	B	B	A	A	A	B	B	B			B							B					
May			B	A	B	B	B			B	B	B	B	B			B	B	B	B	B			X	X	A	A	A	A	A	A
June	A	A	A	A			A	A	A	A	A			A	A	A	A	A			A	A	A	A	A			A	A	A	
July	A	A	A	A	A	A	A	A	A	A	A	A	A	A	A	A	A	A	A	A	A	A	A	A	A	A	A	A	A	A	A
Aug	A	A	A	A	A	A	A	A	A	A	A	A	A	A	A	A	A	A	A	A	A	A	A	A	A	A	A	A	A	A	A
Sept	A	A	A	A	B	B	B	B	B	B			B	B	B	B	B			B	B	B	B	B		X	X	B	B	B	
Oct	B																							B	B	B	B	B	B	B	
Nov																												X	X		
Dec					X	X			X	X		X	X			X	X		X	X	X	X	X	X							

X denotes special services, see local announcements.

No services in January, February and March.

Service A

Aylsham	dep	10.15	11.30	12.45	14.00	15.15	16.30
Wroxham	arr	11 00	12.15	13.30	14.45	16.00	17.15
Wroxham	dep	10.15	11.30	12.45	14.00	15.15	16.30
Aylsham	arr	11.00	12.15	13.30	14.45	16.00	17.15

Service B

10.15	12.45	15.15
11.00	13.30	16.00
11.30	14.00	16.30
12.15	14.45	17.15

All trains call at intermediate stations: Brampton (12), Buxton (17) and Coltishall (30) minutes after leaving Aylsham and at Coltishall (15), Buxton (28) and Brampton (33) minutes after leaving Wroxham.

CLEETHORPES COAST LIGHT RAILWAY

Lakeside Station, Kings Road, Cleethorpes, Lincs DN35 0AG **01427 604657**

1998	1	2	3	4	5	6	7	8	9	10	11	12	13	14	15	16	17	18	19	20	21	22	23	24	25	26	27	28	29	30	31
Jan			A	B						A	B						A	B						A	B						B
Feb	B						B	B						B	B	A	A	A	A	A	B	B						B			
Mar	C						B	C						B	C						B	C						B	C		
Apr				B	C	B	B	B	B	C	C	D	D	B	B	B	B	B	C	B	B	B	B	B	B	C	B	B	B	B	
May	B	C	D	D	B	B	B	B	C	C	B	B	B	B	B	E	E	B	B	B	B	B	C	D	D	C	C	C	C	X	X
June	B	B	B	B	B	C	C	B	B	B	B	B	X	X	B	B	B	B	B	C	C	B	B	B	B	B	C	C	B	B	
July	B	B	B	E	E	B	B	B	B	B	C	D	B	B	B	B	X	X	X	B	B	B	B	B	C	D	C	C	C	C	C
Aug	C	D	C	C	C	C	C	C	D	C	C	C	C	C	C	D	C	C	C	C	C	C	D	C	C	C	C	C	C	D	D
Sept	C	C	C	C	X	X	B	B	B	B	B	C	C	A	A	A	A	A	C	C	A	A	A	A	A	X	X	A	A	A	
Oct	A	A	B	C	A	A	A	A	A	B	C	A	A	A	A	A	B	C	A	A	A	A	A	B	C	B	B	B	B	B	B
Nov	B						B	B						B	B						B	B						B	B		
Dec					B	B						B	B						X	X						B	B				

X denotes Santa Specials.

Service A

Lakeside	dep	11.00	11.45	12.30	then every 45 minutes until	15.30	16.15#
Kingsway	dep	11.15	12.00	12.45		15.45	16.30#

Service B

10.20*	11.00	11.40	then every 40 minutes until	17.00	17.40#
10.35*	11.25	11.55		17.15	17.55#

Service C

Lakeside	dep	10.00*	10.30	11.00	then every 30 minutes until	17.00	17.30#	18.00#
Kingsway	dep	10.15*	10.45	11.15		17.15	17.45#	18.15#

Does not run in January, February, March or in November and December.
* Runs only 1st May to 30th September inclusive.
† Runs in July and August only.

Service D

Lakeside	dep	10.00	10.30	11.00	11.05	11.20	then every 20 minutes until	17.20	–	17.45	18.15	18.45†
Kingsway	dep	10.15	10.45	11.10	11.30	11.50		17.30	17.35	18.00	18.30	19.00†

Service X special event timetables and fares apply.

COLNE VALLEY RAILWAY

Castle Hedingham, Halstead, Essex CO9 3DZ **01787 461174**

1998	1	2	3	4	5	6	7	8	9	10	11	12	13	14	15	16	17	18	19	20	21	22	23	24	25	26	27	28	29	30	31
Mar	D							D							D							A							A		
Apr					A					A	A	B	B		A	D		D	A						D	A					
May		A	B	B					D	A						D	A						A	B	B		A	D		D	A
June						D	A						D	A	L	L	L	L	L	T	T	L	L	L	L	L	T	T			
July				D	A						D	A						D	G						D	A		D	A	A	D
Aug	D	A		D	A	A	D	D	A		D	A	A	D	D	A		D	A	A	D	D	A		D	A	A	D	A	B	B
Sept	D	A	A			A							A							A							A				
Oct				A	V	V	V	V	V		A							A							A		D	A	D		
Nov																															
Dec						S						S	S				S		S	S			S								

No service in January, February and November.

Service A – Steam 12.00–16.00
Service B – Steam 11.00–16.00
Service D – Diesel 11.00–16.00
Service G – Gala Day 11.00–16.15

Pre-booking only
Service L – Learning with Thomas (Educational Event)
Service S – Santa Special
Service T – Friends of Thomas
Service V – Victorian (Educational Event)

DEAN FOREST RAILWAY

Norchard Centre, Lydney, Gloucestershire GL15 4ER — 01594 843423

1998	1	2	3	4	5	6	7	8	9	10	11	12	13	14	15	16	17	18	19	20	21	22	23	24	25	26	27	28	29	30	31
Apr					A					A	A	A	A						A							A					
May		A	A	A						A							A						A	A	A	A	A	A	A	A	A
June			A				A			A				A			A				A			A				A			
July	A			A	A			A			A	A			A			A	A			A			A	A			A		
Aug	A	A		A	A	A		A	A		A	A	A		A	A		A	A	A		A	A		A	A	A		A	A	A
Sept				A	A	A							A							A						A	A				
Oct				A							A							X													
Dec						X						X	X						X	X	X	X	X	X			Y	Y			

X denotes Santa and other specials.
Y denotes mince pie specials (including 1st January 1999).

No service in January, February, March and November.

Service A

							Z
Norchard	dep	11.00	12.00	13.30	14.30	15.30	16.30
Lydney Junction	arr	11.15	12.15	13.45	14.45	15.45	16.45
Lydney Junction	dep	11.25	12.25	13.55	14.55	15.55	16.55
Norchard	arr	11.40	12.40	14.10	15.10	16.10	17.10

Trains call at St Mary's Halt in both directions ten minutes after leaving Norchard and three minutes after leaving Lydney Junction.

Z: Sundays and Bank Holidays only

DIDCOT RAILWAY CENTRE

Didcot, Oxon OX11 7NJ — 01235 817200

1998	1	2	3	4	5	6	7	8	9	10	11	12	13	14	15	16	17	18	19	20	21	22	23	24	25	26	27	28	29	30	31
Jan	S	W	W	W						W	W						W	W						W	W						W
Feb	W						W	W						W	W	W	W	W	W	W	W	W						W			
Mar	S						O	O					T	T	T						O	O						O	S		
Apr				O	S	O	O	O	O	S	S	S	S	O	O	O	O	O	O	O	O	O	O	O	O	S	O	O	O	O	
May	O	O	S	S	O	O	O	O	O	O	O	O	O	O	O	O	O	O	O	O	O	O	O	S	S	O	O	O	O	O	S
June	O	O	O	O	O	O	S	O	O	O	O	O	O	S	O	O	O	O	O	O	S	O	O	O	O	O	O	S	O	O	
July	S	O	O	O	S	O	O	S	O	O	O	S	O	O	S	O	O	O	S	O	O	S	O	O	O	S	O	O	S	O	O
Aug	S	S	O	O	S	O	O	S	S	O	O	S	O	O	S	S	O	O	S	O	O	S	S	O	O	S	O	O	S	S	S
Sept	O	O	O	O	O	S	O	O	O	O	O	O	O	O	O	O	O	O	O	O	O	O	O	O	O	S	S				
Oct		T	T	T						O	O						O	O						O	S	O	O	O	O	S	S
Nov	S						W	W						W	W						W	W						W	S		
Dec					W	S					X	X	X						X	X							W	W	W	W	W

O Open 10.00-17.00
S Steamday – trains run continuously
T Friends of Thomas Steamday
W Winter opening 11.00 – 16.00
X Santa Steaming

EAST SOMERSET RAILWAY

Cranmore Station, Shepton Mallet, Somerset — 01749 880417

This two mile railway operates a limited service throughout the year based on departures from Cranmore Station near Shepton Mallett. Please phone for timetable details.

EAST LANCASHIRE RAILWAY

Bolton Street Station, Bury, Lancs PR4 3RS **0161-764 7790**

1998	1	2	3	4	5	6	7	8	9	10	11	12	13	14	15	16	17	18	19	20	21	22	23	24	25	26	27	28	29	30	31
Jan			A	A						A	A						A	A						A	A						A
Feb	A						A	A						A	A						A	A						A			
Mar	A						A	A						A	A						A	A						A	A		
Apr				A	A						A	A						A	A						A	A					
May		A	A						A	A						A	A						A	A						A	A
June						A	A						A	A						A	A						A	A			
July				X	X	X	X	X	X	X	X						X	A	A					X	A	A					X
Aug	A	A					X	A	A	X	X	X	X	X	X	X					X	A	A						A	A	X
Sept					A	A				X	X	A	A	X					A	A						A	A				
Oct			A	A						A	A						A	A						A	A						A
Nov	A						A	A						A	A						A	A						X	X		
Dec					X	X						X	X						X	X						X	X				

X denotes special service, see local announcements.

		W	Z	X	Z	X	Z	X	Z	Y
Bury	dep	09.00	10.00	11.00	12.00	13.00	14.00	15.00	16.00	17.00
Rawtenstall	arr	09.41	10.41	11.41	12.41	13.41	14.41	15.41	16.41	17.41
Rawtenstall	dep	10.00	11.00	12.00	13.00	14.00	15.00	16.00	17.00	18.00
Bury	arr	10.38	11.38	12.38	13.38	14.38	15.38	16.38	17.38	18.38

W Saturdays only (diesel).
X Saturdays (diesel), Sundays and Bank Holidays (steam).
Y Saturdays (diesel), Sundays and Bank Holidays (steam).
Z Steam train.

All trains call at intermediate stations: Summerseat (11), Ramsbottom (16) and Irwell Vale (32) minutes after leaving Bury and at Irwell Vale (8), Ramsbottom (15) and Summerseat (26) minutes after leaving Rawtenstall.

EMBSAY & BOLTON ABBEY RAILWAY

Embsay Station, Embsay, Skipton, Yorks BD23 6AX **01756 795189**

1998	1	2	3	4	5	6	7	8	9	10	11	12	13	14	15	16	17	18	19	20	21	22	23	24	25	26	27	28	29	30	31
Jan	A			A							A							A							A						
Feb	A							A							A							A									
Mar	A							A							A							A							A		
Apr					A							A							A							A					
May		O	A	O						A							A							A							A
June		A				A	A		A				A	A		A				A	A		A				A	A		A	
July				A	A		A				A	A		A				A	A		A	A	A		A	A		A	A	A	
Aug	A	A		A	A	A		A	A		A	A	A		A	A		A	A	A		A	A		A	A	A		A	A	
Sept	A				A	A		A				A	A		A				A	A		A				A	A		A		
Oct				A							A							A							A						
Nov	A							A							A							A							A		
Dec							A						A							A							A				

O: Official opening celebrations of Bolton Abbey Station.

Service A

Trains run on the details marked 'A' in the grid between Embsay and Bolton Abbey. No timetable is yet available and intending customers are advised to phone 01756 794727 for details.

FFESTINIOG RAILWAY

Harbour Station, Porthmadog, Gwynedd, LL49 9NF **01766 512340**

1998	1	2	3	4	5	6	7	8	9	10	11	12	13	14	15	16	17	18	19	20	21	22	23	24	25	26	27	28	29	30	31
Jan	1																														
Feb														10	10	10	10	10	10	10	10	10						1			
Mar	1						1	1						1	1						2	2	3	3	3	3	3	2	2	3	3
Apr	3	3	3	2	2	3	3	3	3	3	4	4	4	4	4	3	3	2	2	3	3	3	3	3	2	2	3	3	3	3	
May	3	4	4	4	3	3	3	3	2	2	3	3	3	3	3	2	2	3	3	3	3	3	2	5	6	6	6	6	5	2	2
June	7	7	7	7	3	2	2	7	7	7	7	3	2	2	7	7	7	7	3	2	2	7	7	7	7	3	2	2	8	8	
July	8	8	3	2	2	8	8	8	8	3	2	2	8	8	8	8	3	2	2	8	8	8	8	3	5	5	6	6	6	6	5
Aug	5	5	6	6	6	6	5	5	5	6	6	6	6	5	5	5	6	6	6	6	5	5	5	6	6	6	6	5	5	5	6
Sept	6	6	6	5	5	2	8	8	8	8	3	2	2	8	8	8	8	3	2	2	3	3	3	3	3	2	9	3	3	3	
Oct	3	3	3	9	3	3	3	3	3	3	9	3	3	3	3	3	3	9	3	3	3	3	3	3	9	3	3	3	3	3	3
Nov	9	10	10	10	10	10	9	9																							
Dec																															

X denotes special service, see local announcements.

Service 1

Porthmadog	dep	10.35	13.45
Blaenau	arr	11.40	14.50
Blaenau	dep	11.55	15.10
Porthmadog	arr	13.10	16.20

Service 2

10.30	12.45	13.45	16.00
11.40	13.50	14.55	17.05
11.55	14.00	15.10	17.25
13.10	15.05	16.20	18.35

Service 3

	D		D
10.30	12.45	13.45	16.00
11.40	13.50	14.55	17.05
11.55	14.00	15.10	17.25
13.10	15.05	16.20	18.35

Service 4

		D					D
Porthmadog	dep	09.30	10.30	12.15	13.30	15.05	16.15
Blaenau	arr	10.30	11.40	13.25	14.35	16.15	17.20
Blaenau	dep	10.40	12.00	13.45	14.50	16.30	17.30
Porthmadog	arr	11.45	13.05	14.50	15.55	17.35	18.35

Service 5

D							D
09.30	10.30	11.35	12.45	13.45	14.55	16.00	17.05
10.35	11.40	12.50	13.50	14.55	16.05	17.05	18.20
10.45	11.55	13.00	14.00	15.10	16.15	17.25	18.55
12.05	13.10	14.10	15.15	16.20	17.30	18.35	20.00

Service 6

		D	D							D	D
Porthmadog	dep	08.25	09.30	10.30	11.35	12.45	13.45	14.55	16.00	17.05	18.10
Blaenau	arr	09.30	10.35	11.40	12.50	13.50	14.55	16.05	17.05	18.20	19.20
Blaenau	dep	09.40	10.45	11.55	13.00	14.00	15.10	16.15	17.25	18.30	19.30
Porthmadog	arr	10.55	12.05	13.10	14.10	15.15	16.20	17.30	18.35	19.35	20.35

Service 7

		D				
Porthmadog	dep	09.30	10.30	12.45	13.45	16.00
Blaenau	arr	10.35	11.40	13.50	14.55	17.05
Blaenau	dep	10.45	11.55	14.00	15.10	17.25
Porthmadog	arr	12.05	13.10	15.05	16.20	18.35

Service 8

D			D			D
09.30	10.30	11.35	12.45	13.45	14.55	16.00
10.35	11.40	12.50	13.50	14.55	16.05	17.05
10.45	11.55	13.00	14.00	15.10	16.15	17.25
12.05	13.10	14.10	15.15	16.20	17.25	18.35

Service 9

Porthmadog	dep	10.30	13.45
Blaenau	arr	11.40	14.50
Blaenau	dep	11.55	15.10
Porthmadog	arr	13.10	16.20

Service 10

D	D
10.30	13.45
11.40	14.50
11.55	15.10
13.10	16.20

All trains call at intermediate stations: Minffordd (10), Penrhyn (15) and Tan-y-Bwlch (35) minutes after leaving Porthmadog and at Tan-y-Bwlch (25), Penrhyn (40) and Minffordd (55) minutes after leaving Blaenau.

D denotes diesel hauled service.

Please telephone for winter services beyond November 8th.

FAIRBOURNE & BARMOUTH RAILWAY

Beach Road, Fairbourne, Gwynedd **01341 250362**

1998	1	2	3	4	5	6	7	8	9	10	11	12	13	14	15	16	17	18	19	20	21	22	23	24	25	26	27	28	29	30	31
Apr				A	A	A	A	A	A	A	B	B	B	B	A	A	A	A	A						A	A					
May		B	B	B	B	A	A	A	B	B	A	A	A	A	A	B	B	A	A	A	A	A	B	B	B	B	B	B	B	B	B
June	A	A	A	A	A	B	B	A	A	A	A	A	B	B	A	A	A	A	A	B	B	A	A	A	A	A	B	B	A	A	
July	A	A	A	B	B	A	A	A	A	A	B	B	B	B	B	B	B	B	B	B	B	B	B	B	B	B	B	B	B	B	B
Aug	B	B	B	B	B	B	B	B	B	B	B	B	B	B	B	B	B	B	B	B	B	B	B	B	B	B	B	B	B	B	B
Sept	B	B	B	B	B	B	B	B	A	A	A	A	A	A	A	A	A	A	B	B	A	A	A	A	A	B	B				
Oct																	A	A	A	A	A	A	A	A	A	A	A	A	A	A	A
Dec												X	X																		

X denotes Santa specials.

No service in January, February, March and November.

Service A

Fairbourne	dep	10.40	12.00	13.40	15.00	16.20*
Porth Penrhyn	dep	11.20	12.40	14.20	15.40	17.00*

**Does not run October 17th to 31st*

Service B

10.40	11.20	12.00	12.40	13.40	14.20	15.00	15.40	16.20
11.20	12.00	12.40	13.40	14.20	15.00	15.40	16.20	17.00

GOLDEN VALLEY LIGHT RAILWAY

Butterley Station, Ripley, Derbyshire DE5 3QZ **01773 570140**

1998	1	2	3	4	5	6	7	8	9	10	11	12	13	14	15	16	17	18	19	20	21	22	23	24	25	26	27	28	29	30	31
Mar							X	X																							
Apr	A			A	A			A			B	B	B		B			B	B			B			B	B			B		
May		B	B	B		B			B	B			B			B	B			B			X	X	X	X	X	X	X	X	X
June			B			B	B						B	B			B			B	B			B			B	B			
July	B			B	B			B			B	B			B			B	B			B			B	B	B	B	B	B	B
Aug	X	X	X	X	X	X	X	X	X	B	B	B	B	B	X	X	B	B	B	B	B	B	B	B	B	B	B	B	B	B	B
Sept	B	B	B	B	B	B	B		B			B	B			B			B	B			B			B	B			B	
Oct			B	B			B			B	B			B			B	B			B			B	B			B			X
Nov	B						X																								

X denotes special service, see local announcements.

No services in January, February and December.

Service A

Frequent service from Butterley Park to Brands Siding from 13.00 to 16.30, also calling at Brands Crossing.

All trains from Newlands Inn call at Brands Crossing (5 minutes).

Service B

Butterley Park	dep	13.00	13.45	14.30	15.15	16.00
Newlands Inn	arr	13.10	13.55	14.40	15.25	16.10
Newlands Inn	dep	13.20	14.05	14.50	15.35	16.20
Butterley Park	arr	13.30	14.15	15.00	15.45	16.30

GLOUCESTERSHIRE WARWICKSHIRE RAILWAY

The Railway Station, Toddington, Gloucs GL54 5DT **01242 621405**

1998	1	2	3	4	5	6	7	8	9	10	11	12	13	14	15	16	17	18	19	20	21	22	23	24	25	26	27	28	29	30	31
Jan	X	X	X	X							C							C							C						
Feb	C							C							C							C									
Mar	E						B	D						X	X						B	D						X	X		
Apr				D	D					D	D	A	A	E	E	E	E	D	A						D	A					
May		A	A	A					D	D						A	A						A	A	A	E	E	E	E	D	D
June						D	D						D	D						X	X						D	D			
July				A	A						A	A						A	A	A	A	A	A	A	A	A		E	E	E	
Aug	A	A	E	E	E	E	D	A	A	E	E	E	E		X	X		E	E	E	D	A	A		E	E	E		A	A	A
Sept	E	E	E	E	D	D						D	D						D	D						D	D				
Oct			A	D						D	D						X	X						D	D			C			D
Nov						X	X	X						D	C						D	C						D	C		
Dec					X	X						X	X						X	X			X	X		X	X	X			

X denotes special service, see local announcements or send SAE to the railway for full details.

Service A

Toddington	dep	10.45	11.32	12.19	13.50	14.37	15.24	16.11
Winchcombe	dep	10.59	11.46	12.33	14.04	14.51	15.38	16.25
Winchcombe	dep	11.49	12.35	13.17	14.53	15.40	16.27	17.09
Toddington	arr	12.00	12.47	13.29	15.05	15.52	16.39	17.21

All trains proceed on to and return from Gotherington which is beyond Winchcombe but at which there is no passenger access or egress.

Not all trains are steam hauled.

Service B

Toddington	dep	11.00	12.15	13.45	15.00	16.15
Winchcombe	dep	11.12	12.27	13.57	15.12	16.27
Winchcombe	dep	11.43	12.58	14.28	15.43	16.58
Toddington	arr	11.53	13.08	14.38	15.53	17.08

Service C

11.00	12.15	14.00	15.15
11.12	12.27	14.12	15.27
11.43	12.58	14.43	15.58
11.53	13.08	14.53	16.08

Service D

Toddington	dep	10.30	11.55	13.20	14.45	16.10
Winchcombe	dep	10.44	12.09	13.34	14.59	16.24
Winchcombe	dep	11.28	12.53	14.18	15.43	17.08
Toddington	arr	11.40	13.05	14.30	15.55	17.20

Service E

10.45	12.15	14.15	15.45
10.59	12.29	14.29	15.59
11.43	13.13	15.13	16.43
11.55	13.25	15.25	16.55

GWILI RAILWAY

Bronwydd Arms Station, Carmarthen, Dyfed SA33 6HT **01267 230666**

1998	1	2	3	4	5	6	7	8	9	10	11	12	13	14	15	16	17	18	19	20	21	22	23	24	25	26	27	28	29	30	31
Apr										A	A	A	X			X	X	X	X												
May			A	A		A				A			A				A			A			A	A	X	A	A	A	A		A
June			A				A			A				A			A				A			A				A			
July	A			A	A			A			A	A			A			A	A			A			A	A	A	A	A	A	A
Aug	A	A	A	A	A	A	A	A	A	A	A	A	A	A	A	A	A	A	A	A	A	A	A	A	A	A	A	A	A	A	X
Sept	A					A							A							A							A				
Oct																									A			A	A		
Dec												X	X						X	X	X	X	X	X							

X denotes special service, see local announcements. *No service in January, February, March and November.*

Service A

Bronwydd Arms	dep	11.30	12.30	14.00	15.00	16.00
Llwyfan	dep	12.00	13.00	14.30	15.30	16.30

GREAT CENTRAL RAILWAY

Mere Way, Ruddington, Nottingham NG11 6NX **01509 230726**

1998	1	2	3	4	5	6	7	8	9	10	11	12	13	14	15	16	17	18	19	20	21	22	23	24	25	26	27	28	29	30	31
Jan	X	X	X							B	B						B	B						B	B						B
Feb	B						B	B						B	B						B	B						B			
Mar	B						B	B						B	B						B	B						B	B		
Apr				B	B					B	B	B	B	A	A	A	A	B	B						B	B					
May		B	B	B					B	B						B	B	A	A	A	A	A	B	B	B	A	A	A	A	B	B
June	A	A	A	A	A	B	B	A	A	A	A	A	B	B	A	A	A	A	A	B	B	A	A	A	A	A	B	B	A	A	
July	A	A	A	B	B	A	A	A	A	A	B	B	A	A	A	A	A	B	B	A	A	A	A	A	B	B	A	A	A	A	A
Aug	B	B	A	A	A	A	A	B	B	A	A	A	A	A	B	B	A	A	A	A	A	B	B	A	A	A	A	A	B	B	B
Sept	A	A	A	A	B	B	A	A	A	A	A	B	B	A	A	A	A	A	B	B	A	A	A	A	A	B	B				
Oct			B	B						B	B						B	B						B	B						B
Nov	B						B	B						B	B						B	B						X	X	X	

X denotes special service, see local announcements

No service in December.

Service A

Loughborough Central	dep	11.00	13.15	15.30
Leicester North	arr	11.29	13.55	15.39
Leicester North	dep	11.50	14.10	16.20
Loughborough Central	arr	12.20	14.20	16.50

Service B

09.30	10.15	11.45	13.15	14.05	15.30	17.00	19.30
09.59	10.44	12.14	13.55	14.34	15.59	17.29	20.25
10.20	11.05	12.35	14.10	14.50	16.20	17.50	20.45
10.50	11.35	13.05	14.40	15.20	16.50	18.20	22.15

Additional trains run during "Gala" days and Bank Holiday Mondays and also from 28th November 1998 until 3rd January 1999 when a special timetable will be in operation; please telephone 01509 230726 for information. Most trains have catering facilities and a dining special runs on Wednesday evenings, 20th May to 23rd September.

All trains call at intermediate stations: Quorn (8) and Rothley (17) minutes after leaving Loughborough and at Rothley (9) and Quorn (22) minutes after leaving Leicester North.

ISLE OF MAN STEAM RAILWAY

Strathallan Crescent, Douglas, Isle of Man IM2 4NR **01624 663366**

1998	A	2	3	4	5	6	7	8	9	10	11	12	13	14	15	16	17	18	19	20	21	22	23	24	25	26	27	28	29	30	31
Apr										A	A	A	A	A	A	A	A	A	A	A	A	A	A	A	A	A	A	A	A	A	
May	A	A	A	A	A	A	A	A	A	A	A	A	A	A	A	A	A	A	A	A	A	A	A	A	A	A	A	A	A	A	A
June	A	A	A	A	A	A	A	A	A	A	A	A	A	A	A	A	A	A	A	A	A	A	A	A	A	A	A	A	A	A	
July	A	A	A	A	A	A	A	A	A	A	A	A	B	B	B	B	A	A	A	B	B	B	B	A	A	A	B	B	B	B	A
Aug	A	A	B	B	B	B	A	A	A	B	B	B	B	A	A	A	B	B	B	B	A	A	A	B	B	B	B	A	A	A	B
Sept	A	A	A	A	A	A	A	A	A	A	A	A	A	A	A	A	A	A	A	A	A	A	A	A	A	A	A				
Oct																								A	A	A	A	A	A	A	A
Nov	A																														

No services in January, February, March and December.

Service A

Douglas	dep	10.10	11.45	14.10	16.10
Port Erin	arr	11.15	12.50	15.15	17.15
Port Erin	dep	10.15	12.05	14.15	16.15
Douglas	arr	11.20	13.10	15.20	17.20

Service B

10.10	10.50	11.45	14.10	15.55	16.55
11.15	12.00	12.50	15.15	17.00	18.00
10.15	12.05	14.15	15.15	16.15	17.15
11.20	13.10	15.20	16.20	17.20	18.20

All trains call at intermediate stations: Port Soderick (13), Ballasalla (35), Castletown (42), Colby (53) and Port St Mary (62) minutes after leaving Douglas and at Port St Mary (4), Colby (12), Castletown (23), Ballasalla (30) and Port Soderick (52) minutes after leaving Port Erin.

May be subject to alteration due to "Steam 125" events. Please phone to confirm.

ISLE OF WIGHT STEAM RAILWAY

The Station, Havenstreet Village, Ryde, IOW PO3 4DS **01983 882204**

1998	1	2	3	4	5	6	7	8	9	10	11	12	13	14	15	16	17	18	19	20	21	22	23	24	25	26	27	28	29	30	31
Mar																										A			A		
Apr		A			A				B	B	B	B	B	B	B	B	B	B	A				B			A				B	
May			B	B		B	B			A			B	B			A			B	B		A	B	B	B	B	B	A	A	A
June	A	B	B	B	A	A	B	A	B	B	B	A	A	B	A	B	B	B	A	A	B	A	B	B	B	A	A	B	A	B	
July	B	B	A	A	B	A	B	B	B	A	A	B	A	B	B	B	A	A	B	A	B	B	B	A	A	B	B	C	C	C	B
Aug	B	B	B	C	C	C	B	B	B	B	C	C	C	B	B	B	B	C	C	C	B	B	B	B	C	C	C	C	C	C	C
Sept	B	B	B	A	A	B	A	B	B	B	A	A	B	A	B	B	B	A	A	B	A	A	A	A	A	A	B				
Oct	B			A				B			A				B			A				A			B		B	B	B		
Dec																			X	X	X	X	X	X		X	X				

X denotes special service, see local announcements.

No service in January, February and November.

Service A

Smallbrook Jct	dep	–	11.00	12.15	–	14.00	15.35
Havenstreet	arr	–	11.13	12.28	–	14.13	15.48
Havenstreet	dep	–	11.17	12.32	–	14.17	15.52
Wootton	arr	–	11.23	12.38	–	14.23	15.58
Wootton	dep	–	11.30	12.45	–	14.30	16.05
Havenstreet	arr	–	11.36	12.51	–	14.36	16.11
Havenstreet	dep	10.36	11.52	–	13.36	15.11	–
Smallbrook Jct	arr	10.49	12.05	–	13.49	15.24	–

Service B

										†	†	†
Smallbrook Jct	dep	–	10.53	11.53	12.53	–	14.32	15.32	16.32	–	18.55	19.55
Havenstreet	arr	–	11.04	12.04	13.04	–	14.43	15.43	16.43	–	19.07	20.05
Havenstreet	dep	–	11.07	12.07	13.07	–	14.46	15.46	16.46*	18.05	19.09	–
Wootton	arr	–	11.12	12.12	13.12	–	14.51	15.51	16.51*	18.11	19.15	–
Wootton	dep	–	11.18	12.18	13.18	–	14.57	15.57	16.57*	18.20	19.20	–
Havenstreet	arr	–	11.23	12.23	13.23	–	15.02	16.02	17.02*	18.26	19.26	–
Havenstreet	dep	10.36	11.36	12.36	–	14.15	15.15	16.15	–	18.35	19.35	–
Smallbrook Jct	arr	10.47	11.47	12.47	–	14.26	15.26	16.26	–	18.45	19.45	–

Service C

																	†	†	†
Smallbrook Jct	dep	–	–	10.53	11.23	11.53	12.23	12.53	–	–	14.02	14.32	15.02	15.32	16.02	16.32	–	18.55	19.55
Havenstreet	arr	–	–	11.04	11.34	12.04	12.34	13.04	–	–	14.13	14.43	15.13	15.43	16.13	16.43	–	19.07	20.05
Havenstreet	dep	–	–	11.07	11.37	12.07	12.37	13.07	–	–	14.16	14.46	15.16	15.46	–	16.46	18.05	19.09	–
Wootton	arr	–	–	11.12	11.42	12.12	12.42	13.12	–	–	14.21	14.51	15.21	15.51	–	16.51	18.11	19.15	–
Wootton	dep	–	–	11.18	11.48	12.18	12.48	13.18	–	–	14.27	14.57	15.27	15.57	–	16.57	18.20	19.20	–
Havenstreet	arr	–	–	11.23	11.53	12.23	12.53	13.23	–	–	14.32	15.02	15.32	16.02	–	17.02	18.26	19.26	–
Havenstreet	dep	10.36	11.06	11.36	12.06	12.36	–	–	13.45	14.15	14.45	15.15	15.45	16.15	–	–	18.35	19.35	–
Smallbrook Jct	arr	10.47	11.17	11.47	12.17	12.47	–	–	13.56	14.26	14.56	15.26	15.56	16.26	–	–	18.45	19.45	–

* Does not operate after 24th October.
† Thursday evenings in July and August only.

KEIGHLEY & WORTH VALLEY RAILWAY

Haworth Station, Keighley, West Yorkshire BD22 8NJ **01535 647777**

1998	1	2	3	4	5	6	7	8	9	10	11	12	13	14	15	16	17	18	19	20	21	22	23	24	25	26	27	28	29	30	31
Jan	C		A	C						A	C						A	C						A	C						A
Feb	C						A	C						A	C						A	C						A			
Mar	A						A	A						A	A						A	A						A	A		
Apr				A	A					A	A	B	B	A	E	E	E	A	X						A	X					
May		X	X	B					A	X						A	X						A	B	B	E	E	E	E	X	X
June						X	X						A	B						A	B	E	E	E	E	E	A	B	E	E	
July	E	E	E	A	B	E	E	E	E	E	A	B	E	E	E	E	E	A	B	E	E	E	E	E	A	B	E	E	E	E	E
Aug	X	B	E	E	E	E	E	A	B	E	E	E	E	E	A	B	E	E	E	E	E	A	B	E	E	E	E	E	A	B	B
Sept	E	E	E	E	A	B						A	B						X	X						A	B				
Oct			A	A						A	A						A	A	X	X	X	X	X	A	A						A
Nov	C						A	C						A	C						A	C						D	D		
Dec					D	D						D	D						D	D						C	C	C	C	C	C

X denotes special service, see local announcements.

Service A

Oxenhope	dep	09.20	10.35	11.10	12.30	13.50	15.20	16.45
Keighley	arr	09.45	10.55	11.35	12.55	14.15	15.45	17.10
Keighley	dep	10.05	11.15	11.50	13.10	14.35	16.05	17.25
Oxenhope	arr	10.26	11.36	12.15	13.35	15.00	16.30	17.50

Service C

11.35	13.00	14.25	15.50
12.00	13.25	14.50	16.15
12.20	13.45	15.10	16.35
12.45	14.10	15.35	17.00

Service B

Oxenhope	dep	09.05	10.05	10.45	11.25	12.10	13.00	13.45	14.30	15.15	1600	16.45	17.30
Keighley	arr	09.25	10.25	11.10	11.50	12.35	13.25	14.10	14.55	15.40	16.25	17.10	17.55
Keighley	dep	09.35	10.45	11.25	12.10	13.00	13.45	14.30	15.15	16.00	16.45	17.30	18.15
Oxenhope	arr	09.57	11.12	11.57	12.37	13.27	14.12	14.57	15.42	16.27	17.12	17.57	18.42

Service D

Oxenhope	dep	09.00	09.55	11.15	12.25	13.35	14.45	15.55
Keighley	arr	09.25	10.15	11.40	12.50	14.00	15.10	16.20
Keighley	dep	09.30	10.48	11.58	13.08	14.18	15.28	17.03
Oxenhope	arr	09.50	11.10	12.17	13.27	14.37	15.47	17.20

Service E

11.25	13.00	14.35	1610
11.50	13.25	15.00	16.35
12.10	13.45	15.20	16.55
12.35	14.10	15.45	17.20

All trains call at intermediate stations: Haworth (6), Oakworth (9), Damems (14) and Ingrow West (18) minutes after leaving Oxenhope and at Ingrow West (4), Damems (6), Oakworth (10) and Haworth (15) minutes after leaving Keighley.

KENT & EAST SUSSEX RAILWAY

Tenterden Town Station, Tenterden, Kent TN30 6HE **01580 765155**

1998	1	2	3	4	5	6	7	8	9	10	11	12	13	14	15	16	17	18	19	20	21	22	23	24	25	26	27	28	29	30	31
Jan	X	X	X	X																											
Feb														D	D	D	D	D	D	D	D	D									
Mar	A							A							A							X							A		
Apr				A	A			D	D	X	X	X	X	A	A	A	A	A	A						A	A					
May		X	X	X					A	A						A	A						A	X	X	A	A	A	A	A	C
June		B	A	B		A	C		B	A	B		X	X		B	A	B		A	X		B	A	B		A	C		B	
July	A	B	B	A	C	B	B	A	B	B	A	C	B	B	A	B	B	A	C	B	B	A	B	B	X	X	A	A	A	A	A
Aug	A	C	A	A	A	A	A	A	C	A	A	A	A	A	A	C	A	A	A	A	A	A	C	A	A	A	A	A	A	X	X
Sept	A	A	A	A	A	C	B	B	B	B		A	A		B	B	B		X	X		D	D	D		A	A		D	D	
Oct			A	A						X	X						A	A						X	X	D	D	D	D	D	A
Nov	A																												X		
Dec					X	X						X	X						X	X	X	X	X	X			X	X			

X denotes special service, see local announcements.

Service A

		P	V	Q	V	Q	V
Tenterden Town	dep	10.30	11.40	12.50	14.00	15.10	16.20
Northiam	arr	11.02	12.12	13.22	14.32	15.42	16.52
Northiam	dep	11.25	12.35	13.45	14.55	16.05	17.00
Tenterden Town	arr	12.02	13.12	14.22	15.32	16.42	17.31

Service B

P	D	P	D	P	D
10.30	11.40	12.50	14.00	15.10	16.20
11.02	12.12	13.22	14.32	15.42	16.52
11.25	12.35	13.45	14.55	16.05	17.00
12.02	13.12	14.22	15.32	16.42	17.31

Service C

		M	P	V	R	V	P	R	V	P
Tenterden Town	dep	10.30	11.35	12.15	12.45	13.45	14.45	15.25	15.55	16.30
Northiam	arr	11.01	12.07	12.46	13.25	14.13	15.15	15.57	16.31	17.05
Northiam	dep	11.20	12.25	13.00	13.50	14.30	15.35	16.10	16.45	17.15
Tenterden Town	arr	11.56	13.06	13.29	14.25	15.05	16.15	16.50	17.15	17.45

Service D

P	P	P
11.00	13.20	15.20
11.32	13.52	15.52
11.50	14.10	16.05
12.24	14.44	16.39

All trains call at Rolvenden Station and most serve Wittersham Road in each direction.

Table A: two engines in steam. Table B: one locomotive in steam and heritage diesel observation train running. Table C: three locomotives in steam. Table D: one locomotive in steam.

D Heritage Diesel Observation Train – affords excellent driver's eye views of the line.
M Old-time mixed train – passenger coaches and goods wagons!
P Steam train of 1930s and 50s carriages including First Class accommodation, on-board refreshment service and facilities for passengers with disabilities. Morning coffee, Ploughman's lunches and Kentish Cream Tea available if booked in advance.
Q as P above, except on Sundays when service operates as Wealden Belle luxury dining train serving luncheon or tea – diners are advised to book in advance.
R Wealden Belle luxury dining train serving luncheon or tea – diners are advised to book in advance.
V Victorian steam train including First Class saloons and limited accommodation for passengers with disabilities.

LAKESIDE & HAVERTHWAITE RAILWAY

Haverthwaite Station, Nr Ulverston, Cumbria LA12 8AL **015395 31594**

1998	1	2	3	4	5	6	7	8	9	10	11	12	13	14	15	16	17	18	19	20	21	22	23	24	25	26	27	28	29	30	31
Apr				A	A	A	A	A	A	A	A	A	A	A	A	A	A	A	A						A	A					
May		A	A	A	A	A	A	A	A	A	A	A	A	A	A	A	A	A	A	A	A	A	A	A	A	A	A	A	A	A	A
June	A	A	A	A	A	A	A	A	A	A	A	A	A	A	A	A	A	A	A	A	A	A	A	A	A	A	A	A	A	A	
July	A	A	A	A	A	A	A	A	A	A	A	A	A	A	A	A	A	A	A	A	A	A	A	A	A	A	A	A	A	A	A
Aug	A	A	A	A	A	A	A	A	A	A	A	A	A	A	A	A	A	A	A	A	A	A	A	A	A	A	A	A	A	A	A
Sept	A	A	A	A	A	A	A	A	A	A	A	A	A	A	A	A	A	A	A	A	A	A	A	A	A	A	A	A	A	A	
Oct	A	A	A	A	A	A	A	A	A	A	A	A	A	A	A	A	A	A	A	A	A	A	A	A	A	A	A	A	A	A	A
Nov	A																														

No service in January, February, March, November (except 1st) and December.

Service A

Haverthwaite	dep	10.35	11.45	13.00	14.05	15.10	16.15†	17.20*
Lakeside	arr	10.53	12.03	13.18	14.23	15.28	16.33†	17.38*
Lakeside	dep	11.15	12.30	13.35	14.40	15.45	16.50†	17.48*
Heverthwaite	arr	11.33	12.48	13.53	14.58	16.03	17.08†	18.06*

* operates 24th May to 31st May and 19th July to 6th September.
† operates until 24th October.

All trains call at Newby Bridge (12) minutes after leaving Haverthwaite and (6) minutes after leaving Lakeside.

LEIGHTON BUZZARD RAILWAY

Pages Park Station, Billington Road, Leighton Buzzard LU7 8TN 01525 373888

1998	1	2	3	4	5	6	7	8	9	10	11	12	13	14	15	16	17	18	19	20	21	22	23	24	25	26	27	28	29	30	31
Mar															A							A							B		
Apr					A					A	A	B	B						A							A					
May		A	B	B						A							A						A	B	B		A				A
June			C				A			C				A			C				A			C			B	B			
July	C				A			C				B			C				B			A				B			A		
Aug	D	★		A	A	A		D	B		A	A	A		D	B		A	A	A		D	B		A	A	A		D	B	B
Sept					B	★							A							A							B				
Oct				A							A																				
Dec					X	X						X	X						X	X						X	X	X			

X denotes Christmas trains, telephone for details from September onwards.
★ Special intensive service will operate on 2nd August and 6th September.

No service in January, February and November.

Service A / D (Service D is diesel hauled)

Page's Park	dep	11.15	12.45	14.15	15.45
Stonehenge Wks	arr	11.40	13.10	14.40	16.10
Stonehenge Wks	dep	11.55	13.25	14.55	16.25
Page's Park	arr	12.20	13.50	15.20	16.50

Service C

10.30	12.00	13.30
10.55	12.25	13.55
11.10	12.40	14.10
11.35	13.05	14.35

Service B

Page's Park	dep	11.15	12.00	12.45	13.30	14.15	15.00	15.45	16.30
Stonehenge Wks	arr	11.40	12.25	13.10	13.55	14.40	15.25	16.10	16.55
Stonehenge Wks	dep	11.55	12.40	13.25	14.10	14.55	15.40	16.25	17.10
Page's Park	arr	12.20	13.05	13.50	14.35	15.20	16.05	16.50	17.35

LLANBERIS LAKE RAILWAY

Gilfach Ddu, Llanberis, Gwynedd LL55 4TY — **01286 870549**

1998	1	2	3	4	5	6	7	8	9	10	11	12	13	14	15	16	17	18	19	20	21	22	23	24	25	26	27	28	29	30	31
Mar																							A	A	A	A				A	A
Apr	A	A				B	B	B	B	B	B	B	B	B	B	B	B	B	B	B	B	B	B	B			B	B	B	B	
May	B		B	B	B	B	B	B		B	B	B	B	B	B		B	B	B	B	B	B	B	B	D	D	D	D	B		B
June	B	B	B	B	B		B	B	B	B	B	B		B	B	B	B	B	B		B	B	B	B	B	B		B	B	B	
July	B	B	B		B	D	D	D	D	B	B	C	D	D	D	D	B	B	C	D	D	D	D	B	B	C	D	D	D	D	B
Aug	B	C	D	D	D	D	B	B	C	D	D	D	D	B	B	C	D	D	D	D	B	B	C	D	D	D	D	B	B	C	D
Sept	D	D	D	B		B	B	B	B	B	B		B	B	B	B	B	B		B	B	B	B	B	B		B	B	B	B	
Oct	B	B			A	A	A	A				A	A	A	A				A	A	A	A				A	A	A	A	A	

No service in January, February, November and December.

Service A

Llanberis	dep	11.30	13.00	14.00	15.00

Service B

11.00*	11.45*	13.00	14.00	15.00	16.00†

Service C

Llanberis	dep	13.00	14.00	14.45	15.30	16.30

* Not Saturdays or Sundays except Bank Holiday weekends.
† Not Fridays in April and May.

Service D

Llanberis	dep	11.00	11.45	12.30	13.00	13.30	14.00	14.30	15.00	15.30	16.00	16.30

LLANGOLLEN RAILWAY

The Station, Abbey Road, Llangollen, Denbighshire LL20 8SN — **01978 860979**

1998	1	2	3	4	5	6	7	8	9	10	11	12	13	14	15	16	17	18	19	20	21	22	23	24	25	26	27	28	29	30	31
Jan	A	A	A	A																				A	A						X
Feb	X						A	A						X	X	B	B	B	B	B	X	X	A	A	A	A	A	A			
Mar	A						A	A						A	A						A	A						A	A		
Apr				A	A					B	C	C	C	B	B	B	B	X	X						B	C					
May		B	C	C	A	A	A	A	B	C	A	A	A	A	A	B	C	A	A	A	A	A	X	X	X	A	A	A	A	B	C
June	A	A	A	A	A	C	C	A	A	A	A	A	B	C	B	B	B	B	B	B	C	B	B	B	B	B	B	C	B	B	
July	B	B	B	B	C	B	B	B	B	B	C	C	B	B	B	B	B	B	C	B	B	B	B	B	B	C	B	B	B	B	B
Aug	X	X	B	B	B	B	B	C	C	B	B	B	B	B	C	C	B	B	B	B	B	C	C	B	B	B	B	B	C	C	C
Sept	B	B	B	B	B	C	B	B	B	B	B	B	B	A	A	A	A	A	X	X	A	A	A	A	A	A	B	A	A	A	
Oct	A	A	C	B	A	A	A	A	A	A	A	A	A	A	A	A	X	X	A	A	A	A	A	X	X	B	B	B	B	B	X
Nov	X						A	A						A	A																
Dec					X	X						X	X						X	X	X	X	X	X		A	A	A	A	A	A

X denotes special service, see local announcements.

Service A

Llangollen	dep	11.00	13.00	15.00
Carrog	dep	11.50	13.50	15.50

Service B

11.00	12.45	14.30	16.15
11.45	13.30	15.15	17.00

Service C

								★
Llangollen	dep	11.00	12.00	13.00	14.00	15.00	16.00	17.00
Carrog	dep	12.00	13.00	14.00	15.00	16.00	17.00	18.00

★ 26th July – 31st August only

All trains call at intermediate stations: Berwyn (7) and Glyndyfrdwy (25) minutes after leaving Llangollen and at Glyndyfrdwy (9) and Berwyn (18) minutes after leaving Carrog.

MANX ELECTRIC RAILWAY

Strathallan Crescent, Douglas, Isle of Man IM2 4NR **01624 663366**

1998	1	2	3	4	5	6	7	8	9	10	11	12	13	14	15	16	17	18	19	20	21	22	23	24	25	26	27	28	29	30	31
Jan					E	E	E	E	E			E	E	E	E	E			E	E	E	E	E			E	E	E	E	E	
Feb		E	E	E	E	E			E	E	E	E	E			E	E	E	E	E			E	E	E	E	E				
Mar		E	E	E	E	E			E	E	E	E	E			E	E	E	E	E			E	E	E	E	E			E	E
Apr	E	E	E			A	A	A	A	A	A	A	A	A	A	A	A	A	A	A	A	A	A	A	A	A	A	A	A	A	
May	A	A	A	A	A	A	A	A	A	A	A	A	A	A	A	A	A	A	A	A	A	A	A	B	B	B	B	B	B	B	B
June	B	B	B	B	B	B	B	B	B	B	B	B	B	B	B	B	B	B	B	B	B	B	B	B	B	B	B	B	B	B	
July	B	B	B	B	B	B	B	B	B	B	B	B	C	C	C	C	D	D	B	C	C	C	C	D	D	B	C	C	C	C	D
Aug	D	B	C	C	C	C	D	D	B	C	C	C	C	D	D	B	C	C	C	C	D	D	B	C	C	C	C	D	D	B	C
Sept	B	B	B	B	B	B	A	A	A	A	A	A	A	A	A	A	A	A	A	A	A	A	A	A	A	A	A	A	A	A	
Oct	A	A	A	A	A	A	A	A	A	A	A	A	A	A	A	A	A	A	A	A	A	A	A	A	A	A	A	A	A	A	A
Nov	A	★																													

★ Limited service Monday to Friday only from 2nd November.

No service in December.

Service A

Douglas Derby Castle	dep	10.00	12.00	14.00	15.00	17.00
Laxey	dep	10.30	12.30	14.30	15.30	17.30
Ramsey	arr	11.15	13.15	15.15	16.15	18.15
Ramsey	dep	10.00	12.00	13.30	15.30	16.30
Laxey	dep	10.45	12.45	14.15	16.15	17.15
Douglas Derby Castle	arr	11.15	13.15	14.45	16.45	17.45

Service E

09.40	13.40	–
10.10	14.10	–
10.55	14.55	–
–	12.10	15.30
8.55	12.55	16.15
9.25	13.25	–

Subject to amendment.
Please phone to confirm.

Service B

Douglas Derby Castle	dep	10.00	10.30	11.00	12.00	13.00	–	14.00	14.30	15.00	16.00	17.00	17.45
Laxey	dep	10.30	11.00	11.30	12.30	13.30	–	14.30	15.00	15.30	16.30	17.30	18.15
Ramsey	arr	11.15	11.45	12.15	13.15	14.15	–	15.15	15.45	16.15	17.15	18.15	–
Ramsey	dep	–	10.00	11.30	12.00	12.30	13.30	14.30	–	15.30	16.00	16.30	17.30
Laxey	dep	09.45	10.45	12.15	12.45	13.15	14.15	15.15	–	16.15	16.45	17.15	18.15
Douglas Derby Castle	arr	10.15	11.15	12.45	13.15	13.45	14.45	15.45	–	16.45	17.15	17.45	18.45

Service C

Douglas Derby Castle	dep	10.00	10.30	11.00	12.00	13.00	13.30	14.00	14.30	15.00	16.00	17.00	17.45	18.00	19.30
Laxey	dep	10.30	11.00	11.30	12.30	13.30	14.00	14.30	15.00	15.30	16.30	17.30	18.15	18.30	20.00
Ramsey	arr	11.15	11.45	12.15	13.15	14.15	14.45	15.15	15.45	16.15	17.15	18.15	–	19.15	20.45
Ramsey	dep	–	10.00	11.30	12.00	12.30	13.30	14.30	15.00	15.30	16.00	16.30	17.30	18.30	21.15
Laxey	dep	09.45	10.45	12.15	12.45	13.15	14.15	15.15	15.45	16.15	16.45	17.15	18.15	19.15	22.00
Douglas Derby Castle	arr	10.15	11.15	12.45	13.15	13.45	14.45	15.45	16.15	16.45	17.15	17.45	18.45	19.45	22.30

Service D

Douglas Derby Castle	dep	10.00	10.30	11.00	12.00	13.00	–	14.00	14.30	15.00	16.00	17.00	17.45	18.00	19.30
Laxey	dep	10.30	11.00	11.30	12.30	13.30	–	14.30	15.00	15.30	16.30	17.30	18.15	18.30	20.00
Ramsey	arr	11.15	11.45	12.15	13.15	14.15	–	15.15	15.45	16.15	17.15	18.15	–	19.15	20.45
Ramsey	dep	–	10.00	11.30	12.00	12.30	13.30	14.30	–	15.30	16.00	16.30	17.30	18.30	21.15
Laxey	dep	09.45	10.45	12.15	12.45	13.15	14.15	15.15	–	16.15	16.45	17.15	18.15	19.15	22.00
Douglas Derby Castle	arr	10.15	11.15	12.45	13.15	13.45	14.45	15.45	–	16.45	17.15	17.45	18.45	19.45	22.30

MIDDLETON RAILWAY

Middleton Station, Moor Road, Leeds, Yorks LS11 0SS **0113-271 0320**

This two mile railway operates a limited service throughout the year based on departures from Middleton. Please phone for timetable details.

MID-HANTS RAILWAY

Alresford, Hants SO24 9JG

01962 733810

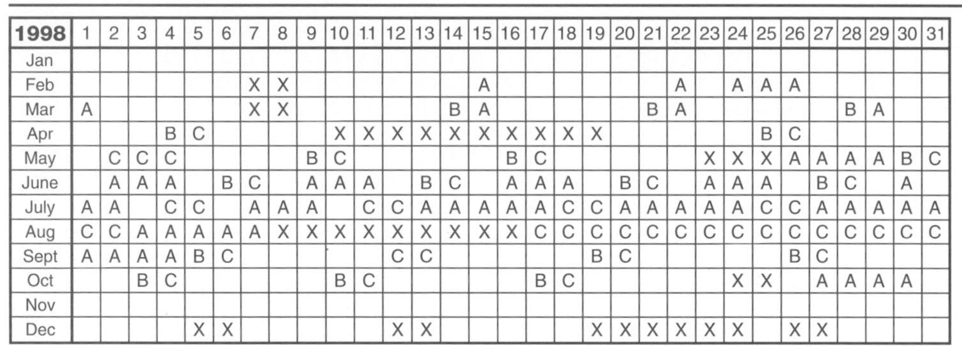

1998	1	2	3	4	5	6	7	8	9	10	11	12	13	14	15	16	17	18	19	20	21	22	23	24	25	26	27	28	29	30	31
Jan																															
Feb							X	X							A							A		A	A	A					
Mar	A						X	X						B	A						B	A						B	A		
Apr				B	C					X	X	X	X	X	X	X	X	X	X						B	C					
May		C	C	C					B	C						B	C						X	X	X	A	A	A	A	B	C
June		A	A	A		B	C		A	A	A		B	C		A	A	A		B	C		A	A	A		B	C		A	
July	A	A		C	C		A	A	A		C	C	A	A	A	A	A	C	C	A	A	A	A	A	C	C	A	A	A	A	A
Aug	C	C	A	A	A	A	A	X	X	X	X	X	X	X	X	X	C	C	C	C	C	C	C	C	C	C	C	C	C	C	C
Sept	A	A	A	A	B	C						C	C						B	C						B	C				
Oct			B	C						B	C						B	C						X	X		A	A	A	A	
Nov																															
Dec					X	X						X	X						X	X	X	X	X	X		X	X				

X denotes special service, see local announcements.

No service in January and November.

Service A

Alresford	dep	10.40	12.25	14.25	16.05*
Alton	arr	11.15	13.00	15.00	16.38*
Alton	dep	11.30	13.30	15.20	16.50*
Alresford	arr	12.04	14.04	15.53	17.19*

Service B

–	11.30	13.15	15.00	16.36
–	12.05	13.56	15.32	17.08
10.45	12.25	14.20	15.43	–
11.17	12.57	14.49	16.12	–

* Does NOT operate on mid-week days in February, June and October.

Service C

Alresford	dep	–	10.30	11.30	12.30	13.38	14.45	15.32	16.30	17.10
Alton	arr	–	11.08	12.08	13.08	14.19	15.26	16.08	17.06	17.48
Alton	dep	10.41	11.41	12.41	13.52	14.42	15.41	16.20	17.22	–
Alresford	arr	11.13	12.13	13.13	14.27	15.12	16.12	16.51	17.51	–

All trains call at intermediate stations: Ropley (7) and Medstead (21) minutes after leaving Alresford and at Medstead (12) and Ropley (22) minutes after leaving Alton.

MIDLAND RAILWAY CENTRE

Butterley Station, Ripley, Derbys DE5 3QZ

01773 570140

1998	1	2	3	4	5	6	7	8	9	10	11	12	13	14	15	16	17	18	19	20	21	22	23	24	25	26	27	28	29	30	31
Jan	X																A	A						A	A						A
Feb	A						A	A						A	A						A	B	A	A	A	A	A	A			
Mar	B						X	X						B	B						B	C						X	X		
Apr	B			B	B		B	B	B	B	B	C	C	B	B	B	B	B	C			B			B	C			B		
May		X	X	X		B			B	C			B			B	C			B			X	X	X	X	X	X	X	X	X
June			B			B	C						B	C			B			B	C	B	B	B	B		X	X		B	
July	B	B		B	C		B	B	B		B	C		B	B	B	B	B	C		B	B	B	B	B	C	B	B	B	B	B
Aug	X	X	X	X	X	X	X	X	X	B	B	B	B	B	C	C	B	B	B	B	B	B	C	B	B	B	B	B	X	X	X
Sept	B	B	B	B	B	C	B		B			X	X			B			B	C			B			B	C			B	
Oct			B	C			B			B	C			B			X	X			B			B	A	A	A	A	A	A	X
Nov	A						X	A							A							A						X	X		
Dec					X	X						X	X				X		X	X	X	X	X	X		X	X	X	X	X	X

X denotes special service, see local announcements.

Service A

Butterley	dep	11.15	12.30	14.00	15.05
Hammersmith	arr	11.55	13.10	14.40	15.45
Hammersmith	dep	12.05	13.20	14.50	15.55
Butterley	arr	12.07	13.22	14.52	15.57

Service B

11.15	12.30	14.00	15.00	16.15
11.55	13.10	14.40	15.40	17.05
12.05	13.20	14.50	15.50	17.15
12.07	13.22	14.52	15.52	17.17

All trains call at intermediate stations: Riddings Junction (14) and Swanwick Junction (32) minutes after leaving Butterley.

Service C

Butterley	dep	10.45	11.20	11.55	12.30	13.05	14.00	14.35	15.10	15.45	16.15
Hammersmith	arr	11.30	12.05	12.40	13.15	13.50	14.45	15.20	15.55	16.30	17.10
Hammersmith	dep	11.40	12.15	12.50	13.25	14.00	14.55	15.30	16.05	17.40	17.20
Butterley	arr	11.42	12.17	12.52	13.27	14.02	14.57	15.32	16.07	17.42	17.22

MULLRAIL

Old Pier Station, Craignure, Isle of Mull PA65 6AY 01680 812494

1998	1	2	3	4	5	6	7	8	9	10	11	12	13	14	15	16	17	18	19	20	21	22	23	24	25	26	27	28	29	30	31
Apr									A	A	A	A	A	A	A	A	A	A	A	A	A	A	A	A	A	A	A	A	A	A	
May	A	A	A	A	A	A	A	A	A	A	A	A	A	A	A	A	A	A	A	A	A	A	A	A	C	C	C	C	B	B	B
June	C	C	C	C	B	B	B	C	C	C	C	B	B	B	C	C	C	C	B	B	B	C	C	C	C	B	B	B	C	C	
July	C	C	C	B	B	C	C	C	C	C	B	B	C	C	C	C	C	B	B	C	C	C	C	C	B	B	C	C	C	C	C
Aug	B	B	C	C	C	C	C	B	B	C	C	C	C	C	B	B	C	C	C	C	C	B	B	C	C	C	C	C	B	B	C
Sept	C	C	C	C	A	A	A	A	A	A	A	A	A	A	A	A	A	A	A	A	A	A	A	A	A	A	A	A	A	A	
Oct	A	A	A	A	A	A	A	A	A	A	A	A	A	A	A	A	A														

No services in January, February, March, November and December.

Service A

Craignure	dep	11.15	13.15	14.30‡	15.10	16.45
Torosay	dep	10.40	12.10	14.10	14.50‡	16.10

Service B

11.15	13.15	14.30	15.15	16.45	–
10.45	12.10	14.10	14.50	16.10	17.30#

Service C

Craignure	dep	11.10	11.20	11.50*	12.30	13.10	13.30	14.20	15.10	15.25	15.55	16.35	17.00†
Torosay	dep	10.45	11.35*	11.50	12.15	12.55	14.00	14.15	15.05	15.40	16.10	16.20†	17.30†¶

‡ Commences on 11h May and ceases on 13th September.
# Commences on 4th July.
* Commences on 6th July.
† Does not run on Fridays.
¶ Runs 25th May – 28th May and then from 6th July.

NENE VALLEY RAILWAY

Wansford Station, Stibbington, Peterborough PE8 6LR 01780 784444

1998	1	2	3	4	5	6	7	8	9	10	11	12	13	14	15	16	17	18	19	20	21	22	23	24	25	26	27	28	29	30	31
Jan				W							W							W							W						
Feb	W							W							A			A			A	A									
Mar	A							A						B	B							A						D	D		
Apr				B	B					A	B	D	D	A	A	A	A	B	B						B	B					
May		D	D	D		A							A							A			D	D	D	A	A	A	A	B	B
June			A			D	D			A	A		C	C			A	A		C	C			A		A	D	D			
July	A			C	C			A			D	D			A			C	C		A	A	A	A	C	C		A	A	A	A
Aug	D	D		A	A	A	A	C	C		A	A	A	A	C	C		A	A	A	A	C	C		A	A	A	A	D	D	D
Sept	A	A	A		B	B						B	B			A			B	B						B	B				
Oct			A	A			A			A	A						A	A			A			A	A			A			A
Nov	A							W							W							W							S		
Dec		S			S	S			S			S	S			S			S	S			S	S			A	A			

W denotes Winter service (11.30-4.30), S denotes Santa specials (various times). Booking essential.

Service A

Wansford #	dep	11.00	12.45	14.30
Yarwell #	arr	11.05	12.50	14.35
Wansford	dep	11.20	13.05	14.50
Peterborough NV	arr	11.45	13.30	15.15
Peterborough NV	dep	12.00	13.45	15.30
Wansford	arr	12.25	14.10	15.55

Service B

11.00	12.45	14.30	16.30
11.05	12.50	14.35	16.35
11.20	13.05	14.50	16.45
11.45	13.30	15.15	17.10
12.00	13.45	15.30	17.20
12.25	14.10	15.55	17.44

Service C

10.30	12.00	13.30	15.00	16.30
10.35	12.05	13.35	15.05	16.35
10.45	12.15	13.45	15.15	16.45
11.10	12.40	14.10	15.40	17.10
11.20	12.50	14.20	15.50	17.20
11.44	13.14	14.44	16.14	17.44

Service D

Wansford	dep	10.30	11.30	12.30	13.30	14.30	15.30	16.30
Yarwell	arr	10.35	11.35	12.35	13.35	14.35	15.35	16.35
Wansford	dep	10.45	–	–	–	–	–	16.45
Peterborough NV	arr	11.10	12.10	13.10	14.10	15.10	16.10	17.10
Peterborough NV	dep	11.20	12.20	13.20	14.20	15.20	16.20	17.20
Wansford	arr	11.44	12.44	13.44	14.44	15.44	16.44	17.44

Services may not operate to Yarwell Junction during February, October and November. PASSENGERS CANNOT ALIGHT AT YARWELL JUNCTION.

All trains call at intermediate stations: Ferry Meadows (13) and Orton Mere (34) minutes after leaving Wansford and at Orton Mere (7) and Ferry Meadows (12) minutes after leaving Peterborough NV.

NORTH NORFOLK RAILWAY

Sheringham Station, Sheringham, Norfolk NR26 8RA **01263 822045**

This railway operates a service between Sherringham and Holt along the North Norfolk coast. Please phone or write for timetable details.

NORTH YORKSHIRE MOORS RAILWAY

Pickering Station, Pickering, North Yorks **01751 472508**

1998	1	2	3	4	5	6	7	8	9	10	11	12	13	14	15	16	17	18	19	20	21	22	23	24	25	26	27	28	29	30	31
Mar																					B	A	B	B	B	B	B	B	A	B	B
Apr	B	B	B	B	A	B	B	B	B	B	A	C	C	B	B	B	B	B	A	B	B	B	B	B	B	A	B	B	B	B	
May	B	A	C	C	B	B	B	B	B	A	B	B	B	B	B	B	A	B	B	B	B	B	B	C	C	C	C	C	B	B	A
June	A	A	A	A	B	B	A	A	A	A	A	B	C	C	A	A	A	A	B	B	A	A	A	A	A	B	B	A	A	A	
July	A	A	B	B	A	A	A	A	A	B	B	A	A	A	A	A	B	C	C	C	C	C	C	A	B	C	C	C	C	C	A
Aug	B	C	C	C	C	C	A	B	C	C	C	C	C	A	B	C	C	C	C	C	A	B	C	C	C	C	C	A	B	C	C
Sept	A	A	A	B	B	A	A	A	A	A	B	C	C	A	A	A	A	B	B	A	B	B	B	B	B	B	A	B	B	B	
Oct	B	B	C	C	B	B	B	B	B	B	A	B	B	B	B	B	B	A	B	B	B	B	B	C	C	A	A	A	A	B	B
Nov	A																														

No service in February and November (except the 1st). For January and December services, please phone for details.

Service A

Grosmont	dep		09.50	10.50	11.50	12.50*	13.50	14.50	16.50
Pickering	arr		11.00	12.00	13.00	14.00*	15.00	16.00	18.00
Pickering	dep	10.20	11.20	12.20	13.20	14.20*	15.20	16.20	
Grosmont	arr	11.25	12.25	13.25	14.25	15.25*	16.25	17.25	

Service B

Grosmont	dep		09.50	11.50	12.50	14.50	16.50
Pickering	arr		11.00	13.00	14.00	16.00	18.00
Pickering	dep	10.20	11.20	13.20	14.20	16.20	
Grosmont	arr	11.25	12.25	14.25	15.25	17.25	

Service C

Grosmont	dep		09.50	10.50	11.50	12.50*	13.50	14.50	15.50	16.50
Pickering	arr		11.00	12.00	13.00	14.00*	15.00	16.00	17.00	18.00
Pickering	dep	10.20	11.20	12.20	13.20	14.20*	15.20	16.20	17.20	
Grosmont	arr	11.25	12.25	13.25	14.25	15.25*	16.25	17.25	18.25	

* On Sunday includes 'The Moorland Lunch Train'.

All trains call at intermediate stations: Goathland (15), Newtondale (35) and Levisham (50) minutes after leaving Grosmont and at Levisham (20), Newtondale (31) and Goathland (50) minutes after leaving Pickering.

PAIGNTON & DARTMOUTH RAILWAY

Queens Park Station, Torbay Road, Paignton TQ4 6AF — 01803 555872

1998	1	2	3	4	5	6	7	8	9	10	11	12	13	14	15	16	17	18	19	20	21	22	23	24	25	26	27	28	29	30	31
Apr						A	A	A	A	A	A	A	A	A	A	A	A		A		A		A			A		A		A	
May			A	A	A	A	A			A		A	A	A			A	A	A	A	A	A	C	C	A	A	A	A	A	A	A
June	A	A	A	A	A	A	A	A	A	A	A	A	A	A	B	B	B	B	B	A	A	B	B	B	B	B	A	A	B	B	
July	B	B	B	A	A	B	B	B	B	B	A	A	B	B	B	B	B	A	A	C	C	C	C	C	A	A	C	C	C	C	C
Aug	A	A	C	C	C	C	C	A	A	C	C	C	C	C	B	B	C	C	C	C	C	A	A	C	C	C	C	C	A	A	B
Sept	B	B	B	B	A	A	A	A	A	A	A	A	A	A	A	A	A	A	A	A	A	A	A	A	A	A	A	A	A	A	
Oct	A			A		A		A			A		A		A			A		A		A			A	A	A	A	A	A	
Dec						X						X	X						X	X		X	X	X							

X denotes special service, see local announcements. *No service in January, February, March and November.*

Service A

Paignton	dep	10.30	12.15	14.15	16.15
Kingswear	arr	11.00	12.45	14.45	16.45
Kingswear	dep	11.15	12.55	15.15	17.00
Paignton	arr	11.45	13.25	15.45	17.30

Service B

10.15	11.35	13.30	14.50	16.15
10.45	12.05	14.00	15.20	16.45
10.55	12.15	14.10	15.30	17.00
11.25	12.45	14.40	16.00	17.30

Service C

Paignton	dep		10.15	11.00	11.45	12.30	14.00	14.45	15.30	16.15	17.00
Kingswear	arr		10.50	11.35	12.20	13.05	14.35	15.20	16.05	16.50	17.30
Kingswear	dep	10.15	11.00	11.45	12.30	14.00	14.45	15.30	16.15	17.00	17.45
Paignton	arr	10.50	11.35	12.20	13.05	14.35	15.20	16.05	16.50	17.30	18.15

All trains call at intermediate stations: Goodrington (5) and Churston (15) minutes after leaving Paignton and at Churston (15) and Goodrington (25) minutes after leaving Kingswear.
Pullman Observers Car (supplement) runs on all trains in Services A and B and in alternate trains in Service C.

PEAK RAIL

Matlock Station, Matlock, Derbys DE4 3NA — 01629 580381

1998	1	2	3	4	5	6	7	8	9	10	11	12	13	14	15	16	17	18	19	20	21	22	23	24	25	26	27	28	29	30	31
Jan				A							A							A							A						
Feb	A							A							A							A									
Mar	A							A							A							A						S	A		
Apr				A	A						A	A	A	A	A			A	A						A	A					
May		S	S	S					A	A						A	A						S	S	S	A	A			A	A
June			A			A	A			A			A	A			A			A	A			A			A	A			
July	A			A	A			A			A	A	S	S	A			S	S			A			A	A		A	A	A	
Aug	A	A		A	A	A		A	A		A	A	A		A	A		A	A	A		A	A		A	A	A		S	S	S
Sept	A	A	A		A	A						A	A						A	A						A	A				
Oct			A	A						A	A						S	A						A	A			A	A		S
Nov	A							A							A							A							A		
Dec					S	S			S			S	S			S			S	S				S			S				

S denotes Special Services, see local announcements.

Service A

Matlock	dep		11.55	13.05	14.15	15.25	16.35 †
Darley Dale	arr		12.05	13.15	14.25	15.35	16.40
Darley Dale	dep	11.00	12.10	13.20	14.30	15.40	16.45
Rowsley	arr	11.05	12.15	13.25	14.35	15.45	16.55
Rowsley	dep	11.25	12.35	13.45	14.55	16.05	17.15
Darley Dale	arr	11.30	12.40	13.50	15.00	16.10	17.20
Darley Dale	dep	11.35	12.45	13.55	15.05	16.15	
Matlock	arr	11.45	12.55	14.05	15.15	16.25	

† This service does not operate on dates in January, February, November and on the 27th December. 16.05 from Rowsley terminates at Darley Dale at 16.10 in January, February, November and on the 27th December.

ROMNEY, HYTHE & DYMCHURCH RAILWAY

New Romney Station, New Romney, Kent TN28 8PL **01797 362353**

1998	1	2	3	4	5	6	7	8	9	10	11	12	13	14	15	16	17	18	19	20	21	22	23	24	25	26	27	28	29	30	31
Mar							A	A						A	A						A	A						A	A		
Apr				C	C	C	C	C	C	D	E	D	D	C	C	C	C	C	C	B	B	B	B	B	A	A	B	B	B	B	
May	B	E	D	D	B	B	B	B	A	X	B	B	B	B	B	A	A	B	B	B	B	B	E	D	D	D	D	D	D	E	C
June	C	C	C	C	C	C	C	C	C	C	C	C	C	C	C	C	C	C	C	C	C	C	C	C	C	C	C	C	C	C	
July	C	C	C	C	X	C	C	C	C	C	C	C	C	C	C	C	C	C	C	C	C	C	C	C	E	D	D	D	D	D	D
Aug	E	D	D	D	D	D	D	E	D	D	D	D	D	D	E	D	D	D	D	D	D	E	D	D	D	D	D	D	E	D	D
Sept	D	D	D	D	X	X	C	C	C	C	C	C	C	C	C	C	C	C	C	C	A	A	A	A	A	A	A				
Oct			A	A						A	A						A	A						A	A	A	A	A	A	A	A

X denotes special service, see local announcements.

No service in January, February, November and December.

Service A – (Early and late season) Saturdays and Sundays

Hythe	dep	10.30	12.00	14.00	15.20	16.45*	18.00*
Dungeness	arr	11.35	13.05	15.05	16.25		
Dungeness	dep	12.05	13.35	15.25	16.50		
Hythe	arr	13.10	14.40	16.30	17.55		

Service B

11.15	14.20	17.10*
12.20	15.25	
12.50	15.55	
13.55	17.00	

Service C

Hythe	dep	10.30*	10.30	11.30	12.30	13.30	14.30	15.30	16.30*	17.30†	18.15*
Dungeness	arr	10.57	11.35	12.35	13.35	14.35	15.35	16.35			
Dungeness	dep	11.05	12.05	13.05	14.05	15.05	16.05	17.05			
Hythe	arr	12.10	13.10	14.10	15.10	16.10	17.10	18.10			

Service D – (High Season) Sunday to Friday

Hythe	dep	10.20	11.05	11.50	12.35	13.20	14.05	14.50	15.35	16.20	16.55*	17.30†	18.15*
Dungeness	arr	11.25	12.10	12.55	13.40	14.25	15.10	15.55	16.40	17.25			
Dungeness	dep	11.40	12.25	13.10	13.55	14.40	15.25	16.10	16.55	17.40			
Hythe	arr	12.45	13.30	14.15	15.00	15.45	16.30	17.15	18.00	18.45			

Service E – (High Season) Saturdays

Hythe	dep	10.20	11.05	11.50	12.35	13.20	14.05‡	14.20	15.20	16.20	16.40*	17.30#	18.15
Dungeness	arr	11.25	12.10	12.55	13.40	14.25	14.50‡	15.25	16.25	17.25		18.35#	
Dungeness	dep	11.40	12.25	13.10	13.55	14.55	15.35‡	15.55	16.55	17.40			
Hythe	arr	12.45	13.30	14.15	15.00	16.00	16.20‡	17.00	18.00	18.45			

* Terminates or starts at New Romney.
† Runs beyond New Romney to Romney Sands for holders of return tickets purchased at Romney Sands.
‡ Non-Stop Kent Coast Express does not stop at intermediate stations between Hythe and Dungeness.
# Runs beyond New Romney to Dungeness for holders of return tickets purchased at Dungeness or Romney Sands.

Trains call at Romney Sands (15), New Romney (28), Jefferstone Lane (38) and Dymchurch (45) minutes after leaving Dungeness. Trains call at Dymchurch (18), Jefferstone Lane (23), New Romney (35) and Romney Sands (50) minutes after leaving Hythe.

RAVENGLASS & ESKDALE RAILWAY

Ravenglass, Cumbria CA18 1SW **01229 717171**

1998	1	2	3	4	5	6	7	8	9	10	11	12	13	14	15	16	17	18	19	20	21	22	23	24	25	26	27	28	29	30	31
Jan	B	B	B	B																											
Feb														B	B	B	B	B	B	B	B	B	A	A	A	A	A	B			
Mar	B	A	A	A	A	A	B	B	A	A	A	A	A	B	B	A	A	A	A	A	B	B	A	A	A	A	A	C	C	C	C
Apr	C	C	C	C	C	C	C	C	C	D	D	D	D	D	D	D	D	D	D	C	C	C	C	C	C	C	C	C	C	C	
May	C	D	D	D	C	C	C	C	C	C	C	C	C	C	C	D	D	D	D	D	D	D	E	E	E	E	E	E	D	D	D
June	D	D	D	D	D	D	D	D	D	D	D	D	D	D	D	D	D	D	D	D	D	D	D	D	D	D	D	D	D	D	
July	D	D	D	D	D	D	D	D	D	D	D	D	D	D	D	D	D	D	D	D	D	D	D	D	D	E	E	E	E	E	D
Aug	D	E	E	E	E	E	D	D	E	E	E	E	E	D	D	E	E	E	E	E	D	D	E	E	E	E	E	D	D	E	E
Sept	E	E	E	D	D	D	D	D	D	D	D	D	D	D	D	D	D	D	D	D	D	D	D	D	D	D	D	C	C	C	
Oct	C	C	C	C	C	C	C	C	C	C	C	C	C	C	C	C	C	C	C	C	C	C	C	C	C	C	C	C	C	C	C
Nov	C	A	A	A	A	A	B	B	A	A	A	A	A	B	B	A	A	A	A	A	B	B	A	A	A	A	A	B	B	A	
Dec																										B	B	B	B	B	B

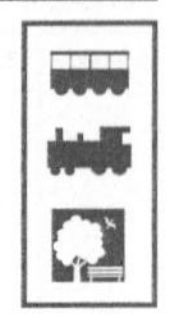

Service A

Ravenglass	dep	16.20
Eskdale (Dalegarth)	arr	16.55
Eskdale (Dalegarth)	dep	07.30
Ravenglass	arr	08.05

Service B

11.30	13.50
12.10	14.30
12.50	14.50
13.25	15.25

Service C

–	–	10.30	11.30	12.50	13.50	14.50	16.20
–	–	11.10	12.10	13.30	14.30	15.30	16.55
†	x						
07.30	10.10	11.30	12.50	13.50	14.50	16.00	–
08.05	10.50	12.10	13.30	14.30	15.30	16.40	–

Service D

Ravenglass	dep	–	09.10	10.30	11.30	12.10	12.50	13.50	14.50	15.50	17.00
Eskdale (Dalegarth)	arr	–	09.45	11.10	12.10	12.50	13.30	14.30	15.30	16.30	17.35
		†									
Eskdale (Dalegarth)	dep	07.30	10.10	11.30	12.30	13.30	13.50	14.50	15.50	17.00	–
Ravenglass	arr	08.05	10.50	12.10	13.10	14.10	14.30	15.30	16.30	17.40	–

† not Saturdays and Sundays
* not Fridays, Saturdays or Sundays
¶ not Fridays and Saturdays
‡ not Sundays
x Saturdays and Sundays only

Service E

		†		*				†			¶		¶			¶		*		
Ravenglass	dep	–	09.10	10.10	10.30	11.10	11.30	11.50	12.10	12.50	13.10	13.50	14.10	14.30	14.50	15.10	15.50	16.10	17.00	18.20
Eskdale	arr	–	09.45	10.50	11.10	11.50	12.10	12.30	12.50	13.30	13.50	14.30	14.50	15.10	15.30	15.50	16.30	16.50	17.35	18.55
		†		*				†			¶		¶			¶		*		
Eskdale	dep	07.30	10.10	11.10	11.30	12.10	12.30	13.10	13.30	13.50	14.10	14.50	15.10	15.30	15.50	16.10	17.00	17.20	18.00	–
Ravenglass	arr	08.05	10.50	11.50	12.10	12.50	13.10	13.50	14.10	14.30	14.50	15.30	15.50	16.10	16.30	16.50	17.40	18.00	18.40	–

All trains call at intermediate stations: Muncaster Mill (5), Irton Road (20), The Green (24), Fisherground (28) and Beckfoot – to set down only (33) minutes after leaving Ravenglass and at Beckfoot – to pick up only (2), Fisherground (6), The Green (10), Irton Road (14) and Muncaster Mill (28) minutes after leaving Eskdale.

SITTINGBOURNE & KEMSLEY LIGHT RAILWAY

Kemsley Down, Sittingbourne, Kent ME10 2SG **01622 755313**

1998	1	2	3	4	5	6	7	8	9	10	11	12	13	14	15	16	17	18	19	20	21	22	23	24	25	26	27	28	29	30	31
Apr										A	A	B	B						A							A					
May			B	B						A							A							X	B						A
June							A							A							X							A			
July				X	X							A							A							A					
Aug	A	A			A			A	A			A			A	A			A			A	A			A			A	B	B
Sept						A			X	X	X	X	A			X	X	X	X	A							A				
Dec												X	X						X	X											

No service in January, February, March, October and November.

Service 'A' – Sittingbourne departures at 13.30, 14.30, 15.30 and 16.30.

Service 'B' – Sittingbourne departures at 11.30, 12.30, 13.30, 14.30, 15.30 and 16.30.

Service 'X' – Special service, see local announcements. 24th May – Gala Day, 21st June – Friends of Thomas Day.

Trains depart from Sittingbourne Viaduct Station (5 minutes walk from BR) at the following times and call at Milton Regis Halt 5 minutes later. 60 minutes should be allowed for the round trip from Sittingbourne to Kemsley Down and return.
TALKING TIMETABLE: 01795 424899. For special trains, party bookings, son et lumiere and Christmas telephone 01622 755313.

SEVERN VALLEY RAILWAY

The Railway Station, Bewdley, Worcs DY12 1BG **01299 403816**

1998	1	2	3	4	5	6	7	8	9	10	11	12	13	14	15	16	17	18	19	20	21	22	23	24	25	26	27	28	29	30	31
Jan	A	A	A	A						A	A						A	A						A	A						A
Feb	A						A	A						A	A						A	A	A	A	A	A	A	A			
Mar	A						A	A						A	A						B	B						B	B		
Apr				B	B					B	B	D	D	B	B	B	B	B	B						X	X					
May		B	D	D					B	B						B	B						C	D	D	B	B	B	B	X	X
June	A	A	A	A	A	X	X	A	A	A	A	A	C	B	B	B	B	B	B	C	B	B	B	B	B	B	C	B	B	B	
July	B	B	B	D	D	B	B	B	B	B	C	B	B	B	B	B	B	C	B	B	B	B	B	B	C	D	B	B	B	B	B
Aug	C	D	B	B	B	B	B	C	D	B	B	B	B	B	C	D	B	B	B	B	B	C	D	B	B	B	B	B	C	D	D
Sept	B	B	B	B	X	X	B	B	B	B	B	C	B	B	B	B	B	X	X	X	A	A	A	A	A	C	B	A	A	A	
Oct	A	A	C	B	A	A	A	A	X	X	D						B	B						B	B	B	B	B	B	B	B
Nov	B						A	A						A	A						A	A						A	X		
Dec					X	X						X	X						X	X	X	X	X	X		A	A	A	A	A	A

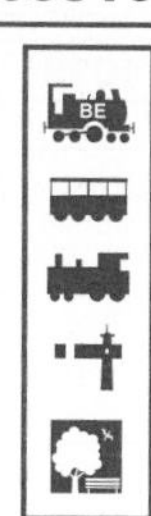

X denotes special service, see local announcements.

Service A

				★		
Kidderminster	dep	10.30	12.10	12.30	14.00	15.50
Bridgnorth	arr	11.34	13.14	13.46	15.04	16.56
					★	
Bridgnorth	dep	10.20	12.00	13.50	15.10	15.40
Kidderminster	arr	11.25	13.05	16.55	16.16	16.45

Service B

		★				
10.30	11.45	12.15	13.00	14.15	15.30	16.45
11.39	12.54	13.26	14.09	15.24	16.39	18.03
				★		
11.00	12.15	13.30	14.15	14.45	16.00	17.25
12.11	13.27	14.42	15.25	15.57	17.07	18.32

Service C

										†
Kidderminster	dep	09.45	10.30	11.15	12.45	13.30	14.15	15.00	16.30	19.00
Bridgnorth	arr	11.00	11.45	12.30	13.59	14.44	15.29	16.14	17.44	19.50
										†
Bridgnorth	dep	11.05	11.50	12.35	13.20	14.50	15.35	16.20	17.05	21.15
Kidderminster	arr	12.22	13.07	13.52	14.37	16.07	16.52	17.37	18.18	22.05

† Does not call at intermediate stations between Bewdley and Bridgnorth.
★ Sundays only. Restaurant car service.

Service D

Kidderminster	dep	10.30	11.15	12.00	12.45	13.30	14.15	15.00	15.45	16.30	17.15
Bridgnorth	arr	11.45	12.30	13.14	13.59	14.44	15.29	16.14	16.59	17.44	18.25
Bridgnorth	dep	11.05	11.50	12.35	13.20	14.05	14.50	15.35	16.20	17.05	17.50
Kidderminster	arr	12.22	13.07	13.52	14.37	15.22	16.07	16.52	17.37	18.18	18.56

All trains call at intermediate stations: Bewdley (20), Arley (38), Highley (47) and Hampton Loade (58) minutes after leaving Kidderminster and at Hampton Loade (22), Highley (34), Arley (47) and Bewdley (66) minutes after leaving Bridgnorth.

SNAEFELL MOUNTAIN RAILWAY

Strathallan Crescent, Douglas, Isle of Man IM2 4NR **01624 663366**

1998	1	2	3	4	5	6	7	8	9	10	11	12	13	14	15	16	17	18	19	20	21	22	23	24	25	26	27	28	29	30	31
Apr																											A	A	A	A	
May	A	A	A	A	A	A	A	A	A	A	A	A	A	A	A	A	A	A	A	A	A	A	A	A	A	A	A	A	A	A	A
June	A	A	A	A	A	A	A	A	A	A	A	A	A	A	A	A	A	A	A	A	A	A	A	A	A	A	A	A	A	A	
July	A	A	A	A	A	A	A	A	A	A	A	A	A	A	A	A	A	A	A	A	A	A	A	A	A	A	A	A	A	A	A
Aug	A	A	A	A	A	A	A	A	A	A	A	A	A	A	A	A	A	A	A	A	A	A	A	A	A	A	A	A	A	A	A
Sept	A	A	A	A	A	A	A	A	A	A	A	A	A	A	A	A	A	A	A	A	A	A	A	A	A	A	A				

No service in January, February, March, October, November and December.

All services subject to the weather. Journey time 30 minutes, but allow 90 minues for Laxey to Summit round trip.
Regular departures from Laxey from 10.30am. Last guaranteed departure to summit 3.30pm.

SEATON TRAMWAY

Riverside Depot, Harbour Road, Seaton, Devon EX12 2NQ **01297 20375**

1998	1	2	3	4	5	6	7	8	9	10	11	12	13	14	15	16	17	18	19	20	21	22	23	24	25	26	27	28	29	30	31
Apr				A	A	A	A	A	A	A	A	A	A	A	A	A	A	A	A	A	A	A	A	A	A	A	A	A	A	A	
May	A	A	A	A	A	A	A	A	A	A	A	A	A	A	A	A	A	A	A	A	A	A	A	A	A	A	A	A	A	A	A
June	A	A	A	A	A	A	A	A	A	A	A	A	B	B	B	B	B	B	B	B	B	B	B	B	B	B	B	B	B	B	
July	B	B	B	B	B	B	B	B	B	B	B	B	B	B	B	B	B	B	B	B	B	B	B	B	B	B	B	B	B	B	B
Aug	B	B	B	B	B	B	B	B	B	B	B	B	B	B	B	B	B	B	B	B	B	B	B	B	B	B	B	B	B	B	B
Sept	B	B	B	B	B	A	A	A	A	A	A	A	A	A	A	A	A	A	A	A	A	A	A	A	A	A	A	A	A	A	
Oct	A	A	A	A	A	A	A	A	A	A	A	A	A	A	A	A	A	A	A	A	A	A	A	A	C	C	C	C	C	C	C
Nov	C						C	C						C	C						C	C						C	C		
Dec						S							S							S											

S denotes Santa specials, please enquire for details.

No service in January, February and March.

Service A

Seaton	dep	09.40	then at these minutes past each hour	00	20	40	until	17.20
Colyford	dep	09.53		13	33	53		17.33
Colyton	arr	10.03		23	43	03		17.43
Colyton	dep	10.10	then at these minutes past each hour	30	50	10	until	17.50
Colyford	dep	10.20		40	00	20		18.00
Seaton	arr	10.34		54	14	34		18.33

Service B

09.40	then at these minutes past each hour	00	20	40	until	20.40
09.53		13	33	53		20.53
10.03		23	43	03		21.03
10.10	then at these minutes past each hour	30	50	10	until	21.10
10.20		40	00	20		21.20
10.34		54	14	34		21.34

Service C

Seaton	dep	10.40	then at these minutes past each hour	00	20	40	until	15.20
Colyford	dep	10.53		13	33	53		15.33
Colyton	arr	11.03		23	43	03		15.43
Colyton	dep	11.10	then at these minutes past each hour	30	50	10	until	15.50
Colyford	dep	11.20		40	00	20		16.00
Seaton	arr	11.34		54	14	34		16.14

Pre-booked groups welcomed all year round.

SNOWDON MOUNTAIN RAILWAY

Llanberis, Gwynedd LL55 4TY **01286 870223**

DAYS OF OPERATION

Passenger trains run every day from **15th March** to **1st November inclusive, weather permitting.**

TIMES OF TRAINS

Trains do not run to a strict timetable. Weather permitting, and if there are at least 25 passengers, the **first train** of the day is scheduled to depart from Llanberis at **09.00** (**08.30** in August). Thereafter trains run at frequent intervals until mid-late afternoon.

At **Peak Periods (Bank Holidays** and from **Mid July to early September**) trains are scheduled to depart from Llanberis at **half hourly intervals** until **17.00** (15.30 on Saturdays).

At periods of lesser demand the frequency is reduced and the time of last departure brought forward.

Each train can carry a maximum of 59 passengers and trains will not normally run with less than 25 passengers (but see also paragraph below).

The company uses its **best endeavours** to run **at least** three trains every day that the railway is open to the public, subject to considerations of safety and with the proviso that there are at least ten passengers on each of these trains.

JOURNEY TIMES

The train journey from Llanberis to the Summit takes approximately one hour. Each train waits empty at the Summit for ½ hour before leaving again for the descent to Llanberis. The downhill journey also lasts one hour making a total of 2½ hours for the round trip.

Passengers with return tickets are entitled to a seat from the Summit on the same train by which they travelled to the Summit. Seats on later trains cannot be guaranteed.

In early (prior to mid/late May) and late (after mid October) season the upper section of the line and summit facilities are normally closed. Train services **then terminate at Clogwyn Station or Rocky Valley Halt.** Clogwyn is approximately ¾ of the way to the Summit. The round trip to Clogwyn and back lasts just under two hours including ½ hour stay at Clogwyn. If the destination is Rocky Valley, the round trip lasts just over 1½ hrs including 15 minutes at Rocky Valley.

SOUTH DEVON RAILWAY

Buckfastleigh Station, Buckfastleigh, Devon TQ11 0DZ 01364 642338

1998	1	2	3	4	5	6	7	8	9	10	11	12	13	14	15	16	17	18	19	20	21	22	23	24	25	26	27	28	29	30	31
Mar														A	A						A	A						A	A		
Apr	A			A	A	A	A	A	A	A	A	B	B	A	A	A	A	A	A		A	A			A	A		A	A		
May		A	X	X	A	A			A	A						A	A	A	A	A	A	A	A	A	B	B	A	A	A	A	A
June	A	A	A	A	A	A	A	A	A	A	A	A	A	A	A	A	A	A	A	A	A	A	A	A	A	A	A	A	A	A	
July	A	A	A	A	A	A	A	A	A	A	A	A	A	A	A	A	A	A	A	B	B	B	B	A	A	A	B	B	B	B	A
Aug	A	A	B	B	B	B	A	A	A	B	B	B	B	A	A	A	B	B	B	B	A	A	A	B	B	B	B	A	A	B	B
Sept	A	A	A	A	A	A	A	A	A	A	A	A	A	A	A	A	A	A	A	A	A	A	A	A	A	A	B	A	A	A	
Oct	A	A	A	A			A			A	A			A			A	A			A			X	X	A	A	A	A	A	A
Nov	A																														
Dec						X						X	X						X	X	X	X	X					A			A

X denotes special service, see local announcements. Open 1st January 1999. *No services in January and February.*

Service A

Buckfastleigh	dep	10.45	12.15	14.10	15.30
Totnes	arr	11.10	12.40	14.35	15.55
Totnes	dep	11.25	12.55	14.50	16.10
Buckfastleigh	arr	11.50	13.20	15.15	16.35

Service B

10.45	12.00	13.45	15.00	16.15
11.10	12.25	14.10	15.25	16.40
11.20	12.35	14.20	15.35	16.50
11.45	13.00	14.45	16.00	17.15

All trains call at intermediate station: Staverton (10) minutes after leaving Buckfastleigh and Totnes.

SOUTH TYNEDALE RAILWAY

Alston Station, Cumbria CA9 3JB 01434 382828

1998	1	2	3	4	5	6	7	8	9	10	11	12	13	14	15	16	17	18	19	20	21	22	23	24	25	26	27	28	29	30	31
Apr				B	B					A	A	A	A	B	B	B	B	B	B						B	B					
May		A	A	A					B	B						B	B						A	A	A	B	B	B	B	A	A
June				B		A	A				B		A	A				B		A	A				B		A	A			
July	B	B	B	A	A	B	B	B	B	B	A	A	B	B	B	B	B	A	A	B	B	B	B	B	A	A	B	B	B	B	B
Aug	A	A	B	B	B	B	B	A	A	B	B	B	B	B	A	A	B	B	B	B	B	A	A	B	B	B	B	B	A	A	A
Sept	B	B	B	B	A	A		B	B	B		A	A				C		X	X				C		A	A				
Oct			C	C						C	C						C	C						B	B	C	C	C	C	C	B
Nov	B																														
Dec						X						X	X						X	X							X				

X denotes special service, see local announcements. *No service in January, February and March.*

Service A

Alston	dep	11.00	12.00	13.30	14.30	15.30	16.30
Kirkhaugh	arr	11.15	12.15	13.45	14.45	15.45	16.45
Kirkhaugh	dep	11.30	12.30	14.00	15.00	16.00	17.00
Alston	arr	11.45	12.45	14.15	15.15	16.15	17.15

Service B

11.00	12.00	14.00	15.00	16.00
11.15	12.15	14.15	15.15	16.15
11.30	12.30	14.30	15.30	16.30
11.45	12.45	14.45	15.45	16.45

Service C

12.00	14.00	15.00
12.15	14.15	15.15
12.30	14.30	15.30
12.45	14.45	15.45

EXTENSION OF LINE TO KIRKHAUGH: *This is expected to open during 1998.*
Until the extension opens, trains departing from Alston at the times shown will run only to Gilderdale (10 minutes journey) and departures from Gilderdale will be 25 minutes after departures from Alston.

STRATHSPEY RAILWAY

Aviemore Station, Dalfaber Road, Aviemore PH22 1PY   01479 810725

1998	1	2	3	4	5	6	7	8	9	10	11	12	13	14	15	16	17	18	19	20	21	22	23	24	25	26	27	28	29	30	31
Jan	A	A																													
Mar																													A		
Apr	A	A		A	A	A	A	A	A	A	A	A	A		A	A		A	A			A	A		A	A			A	A	
May		X	X	X		A	A		A	A			A	A		A	A			A	A		X	A	A		A	A		A	A
June	A	A	A	A	A	A	A	A	A	A	A	A	A	A	A	A	A	A	A	A	A	A	A	A	A	A	A	A	A	A	
July	A	A	A	A	A	A	A	A	A	A	A	A	A	A	A	A	A	A	A	A	A	A	A	A	A	A	A	A	A	A	A
Aug	A	A	A	A	A	A	A	A	A	A	A	A	A	A	A	A	A	A	A	A	A	A	A	A	A	A	A	A	A	A	A
Sept	A	A	A	A	X	X	A	A	A	A	A	A	A	A	A	A	A	A	A	A	A	A	A	A	A	A	A	A	A	A	
Oct	A		A	A	A		A	A		A	A	A	A	A	A	A	A	A	A	A	A	A	A	A	A			A	A		A
Dec													A						A	A						A	A				A

X denotes special services, see local announcements.

No service in February and November.

Service A

Boat of Garten	dep	10.10	11.20	12.40	14.30	15.50
Aviemore	arr	10.30	11.40	13.00	14.50	16.10
Aviemore	dep	10.40	12.00	13.30	15.10	16.20
Boat of Garten	arr	11.00	12.20	13.50	15.30	16.40

Special Note: During 1998 the Strathspey Railway expects to operate its services from Aviemore Station, Aviemore (Speyside) will then be closed. The proposed opening date of Aviemore Station is 29th March 1998 but this is subject to completion of arrangements with Railtrack.

SWANAGE RAILWAY

Station House, Railway Station, Swanage, Dorset BH19 1HB   01929 425800

1998	1	2	3	4	5	6	7	8	9	10	11	12	13	14	15	16	17	18	19	20	21	22	23	24	25	26	27	28	29	30	31
Jan	D		D	D						D	D						D	D						D	D						D
Feb	D						D	D						E	E	E	E	E	E	E	E	E						D			
Mar	D						D	D						D	D						D	D						D	D		
Apr				A	A			B	B	B	B	C	C	B	B	B	B	B	B	A	A	A	A	A	B	B	A	A	A	A	
May	A	X	X	X	B	B	B	B	B	B	B	B	B	B	B	B	B	B	B	B	B	B	C	C	C	B	B	B	B	B	B
June	B	B	B	B	B	B	B	B	B	B	B	B	B	B	B	B	B	B	B	B	B	B	B	B	B	B	B	B	B	B	
July	B	B	B	B	B	B	B	B	B	B	C	C	C	C	C	C	C	C	C	C	C	C	C	C	C	C	C	C	C	C	C
Aug	C	C	C	C	C	C	C	C	C	C	C	C	C	C	C	C	C	C	C	C	C	C	C	C	C	C	C	C	C	C	C
Sept	C	C	B	B	B	B	B	B	B	B	B	X	X	B	B	B	B	B	B	B	A	A	A	A	A	A	A	A	A	A	
Oct	A	A	A	A	A	A	A	A	A	A	A	A	A	A	A	A	A	A	A	A	A	A	A	X	X	A	A	A	A	A	A
Nov	A						A	A						A	A						A	A						A	X		
Dec					X	X						X	X						X	X	X	X	X	X		A	A	A	A	A	A

X denotes special timetable oeprates on these days. Phone for details.

Service A

Swanage	dep	10.30	11.40	12.50	14.00	15.10
Norden	arr	10.55	12.05	13.15	14.25	15.35
Norden	dep	11.05	12.15	13.25	14.35	15.45
Swanage	arr	11.28	12.38	13.48	14.58	16.08

Service B

10.30	11.40	12.50	14.00	15.10	16.20	17.30
10.55	12.05	13.15	14.25	15.35	16.45	17.55
11.05	12.15	13.25	14.35	15.45	16.55	18.05
11.28	12.38	13.48	14.58	16.08	17.18	18.28

Service C

																	★	★	★	★
Swanage	dep	–	10.30	11.05	11.40	12.15	12.50	13.25	14.00	14.35	15.10	15.45	16.20	16.55	17.30	18.05	19.10	20.20	22.00	23.00
Norden	arr	–	10.55	11.30	12.05	12.40	13.15	13.50	14.25	15.00	15.35	16.10	16.45	17.20	17.55	18.30	19.30	20.40	22.20	23.18
																	★	★	★	★
Norden	dep	10.30	11.05	11.40	12.15	12.50	13.25	14.00	14.35	15.10	15.45	16.20	16.55	17.30	18.05	18.35	19.45	21.10	22.30	23.25
Swanage	arr	10.53	11.28	12.03	12.38	13.13	13.48	14.23	14.58	15.33	16.08	16.43	17.18	17.53	18.28	18.57	20.03	21.28	22.48	23.42

Service D

Swanage	dep	11.10	12.30	13.50	15.10
Norden	arr	11.36	12.56	14.16	15.36
Norden	dep	11.50	13.10	14.30	15.50
Swanage	arr	12.16	13.36	14.56	16.16

Service E

10.30	11.50	13.10	14.30	15.50	17.10
10.56	12.16	13.36	14.56	16.16	17.36
11.10	12.30	13.50	15.10	16.30	17.50
11.36	12.56	14.16	15.36	16.56	16.16

★: To and from Corfe Castle only.

All trains call at Corfe Castle 5 minutes before arriving at Norden and Swanage.

TAL-Y-LLYN RAILWAY

Wharf Station, Tywyn, Gwynedd LL36 9EY — 01654 710472

1998	1	2	3	4	5	6	7	8	9	10	11	12	13	14	15	16	17	18	19	20	21	22	23	24	25	26	27	28	29	30	31
Feb																						A									
Mar	A							A							A							A							A	A	A
Apr	A	A	A	A	A	A	A	A	A	B	B	B	B	B	B	B	B	A	A	A	A	A	A	A	A	A	A	A	A	A	
May	A	A	A	A	A	A	A	A	A	A	A	A	A	A	A	A	A	A	A	A	A	A	C	X	D	D	D	D	D	B	B
June	B	B	B	B	B	B	B	B	B	B	B	B	B	B	B	B	B	B	B	B	B	B	B	B	B	B	B	B	B	B	
July	B	B	B	B	B	B	B	B	B	B	B	B	B	B	B	B	B	B	B	D	D	D	D	D	C	C	D	D	D	D	D
Aug	C	C	D	D	D	D	D	C	C	D	D	D	D	D	X	C	D	D	D	D	D	C	C	D	D	D	D	D	C	X	D
Sept	B	B	B	B	B	B	B	B	B	B	B	B	B	B	B	B	B	B	B	B	B	B	B	B	B	A	A	A	A	A	
Oct	A	A	A	A	A	A	A	A	A	A	A	A	A	A	A	A	A	A	A	A	A	E	E	E	E	E	E	E	E	E	E
Dec												X	X						X	X				X		A	A	A	A	A	A

X denotes special service, see local announcements. *No service in January and November.*

Service A

Tywyn (Wharf)	dep	11.40	14.30
Nant Gwernol	arr	12.32	15.22
Nant Gwernol	dep	12.45	15.35
Tywyn (Wharf)	arr	14.05	16.55

Service B

10.00	11.40	12.50	14.30	15.40
10.55	12.32	13.42	15.22	16.47
11.05	12.45	13.55	15.35	16.57
12.20	14.05	15.10	16.55	17.50

Service C

10.00	11.40	12.40*	14.30	16.10	19.00*
10.55	12.32	13.32*	15.22	17.17	19.52*
11.05	12.50	13.50*	15.35	17.27	20.00*
12.21	14.11	15.11*	16.51	18.20	21.55*

Service D

Tywyn (Wharf)	dep	10.00	10.50	11.40	12.40	13.30	14.30	15.20	16.10
Nant Gwernol	arr	10.55	11.42	12.32	13.32	14.22	15.22	16.12	17.17
Nant Gwernol	dep	11.05	12.00	12.50	13.50	14.40	15.35	16.25	17.27
Tywyn (Wharf)	arr	12.21	13.21	14.11	15.11	16.01	16.51	17.45	18.20

Service E

10.35	11.40	13.25	14.30
11.30	12.32	14.17	15.22
11.40	12.45	14.30	15.35
12.55	14.05	15.45	16.55

* Sundays only.

All trains call at intermediate stations: Rhydyronen (12), Dolgoch Falls (31) and Abagynolwyn (45) minutes after leaving Tywyn and depart from Abergynolwyn (35), Dolgoch Falls (49) and Rhydyronen (64) minutes after leaving Nant Gwernol.

TANFIELD RAILWAY

Old Marley Hill, Gateshead, Tyne & Wear — 0191-388 7545/0191-274 2002

1998	1	2	3	4	5	6	7	8	9	10	11	12	13	14	15	16	17	18	19	20	21	22	23	24	25	26	27	28	29	30	31
Jan				X							X							X							X						
Feb	X							X							X							X									
Mar	X							X							X							X							X		
Apr					X					X	X	X	X						X							X					
May			X	X						X							X							X	X						X
June						X	X							X							X							X			
July					X							X							X			X	X			X			X	X	
Aug		X			X	X		X	X			X	X			X			X	X			X			X	X			X	X
Sept						X						X	X							X							X				
Oct				X							X							X							X						
Nov	X							X							X							X							X		
Dec					X	X						X	X						X	X			X	X		X	X				

X denotes steam trains running. Please enquire locally for special events programme and train times.

VALE OF RHEIDOL RAILWAY

Park Avenue, Aberystwyth SY23 1PG **01970 625819**

1998	1	2	3	4	5	6	7	8	9	10	11	12	13	14	15	16	17	18	19	20	21	22	23	24	25	26	27	28	29	30	31
Apr										A	A	A	A	A	A	A		A	A		A	A	A		A	A		A	A	A	
May		A	A	A	A	A	A		A	A	A	A	A	A		A	A	A	A	A	A		A	A	B	B	B	B	A	A	A
June	A	A	A	A	A	A	A	A	A	A	A	A	A	A	A	A	A	A	A	A	A	A	A	A	A	A	A	A	A	A	
July	A	A	A	A	A	A	A	A	A	A	A	A	A	A	A	A	A	A	A	B	B	B	B	A	A	A	B	B	B	B	A
Aug	A	A	B	B	B	B	A	A	A	B	B	B	B	A	A	A	B	B	B	B	A	A	A	B	B	B	B	A	A	A	B
Sept	B	B	B	A	A	A	A	A	A	A		A	A	A	A	A	A		A	A	A	A	A	A		A	A	A	A	A	
Oct	A		A	A		A	A	A		A	A		A	A	A		A	A		A	A	A		A	A		A	A	A		

No service in January, February, March, November and December.

Service A

Aberystwyth	dep	11.00	14.30
Devil's Bridge	arr	12.00	15.30
Devil's Bridge	dep	13.00	16.30
Aberystwyth	arr	14.00	17.30

Service B

10.45	12.15	14.00	15.45
11.45	13.15	15.00	16.45
12.30	14.15	16.00	17.30
13.30	15.15	17.00	18.30

All trains call at intermediate stations on request.

WELLS & WALSINGHAM RAILWAY

Wells-next-the-Sea, Norfolk NR23 1QB **01328 710631**

1998	1	2	3	4	5	6	7	8	9	10	11	12	13	14	15	16	17	18	19	20	21	22	23	24	25	26	27	28	29	30	31
Apr										A	A	A	A	A	A	A	A	A	A	A	A	A	A	A	A	A	A	A	A	A	
May	A	A	A	A	A	A	A	A	A	A	A	A	A	A	A	A	A	A	A	A	A	A	A	A	A	A	A	A	A	A	A
June	A	A	A	A	A	A	A	A	A	A	A	A	A	A	A	A	A	A	A	A	A	A	A	A	A	A	A	A	A	A	
July	B	B	B	B	B	B	B	B	B	B	B	B	B	B	B	B	B	B	B	B	B	B	B	B	B	B	B	B	B	B	B
Aug	B	B	B	B	B	B	B	B	B	B	B	B	B	B	B	B	B	B	B	B	B	B	B	B	B	B	B	B	B	B	B
Sept	A	A	A	A	A	A	A	A	A	A	A	A	A	A	A	A	A	A	A	A	A	A	A	A	A	A	A	A	A	A	
Oct																								A	A	A	A	A	A	A	A

No service in January, February, March, November and December.

Service A
Comprises four trains per day in each direction.

Service B
Comprises five trains per day in each direction.

Please phone for timetable details.

WELSHPOOL & LLANFAIR LIGHT RAILWAY

The Station, Llanfair Caereinion SY21 0SF **01938 810441**

1998	1	2	3	4	5	6	7	8	9	10	11	12	13	14	15	16	17	18	19	20	21	22	23	24	25	26	27	28	29	30	31
Apr				A	A	A	A	A	A	A	A	B	B	A	A	A	A	A	A						A	A					
May		A	A	A					A	A						A	A						A	B	B	A	A	A	A	A	A
June						A	A						A	A		A	A	A		A	A		A	A	A		A	A		A	
July	A	A		A	A		A	A	A		A	A		A	A	A		A	A	A	A	A	A	A	A	A	A	A	A	A	A
Aug	A	A	A	A	A	A	A	A	A	A	A	A	A	A	A	A	A	A	A	A	A	A	A	A	A	A	A	A	A	B	B
Sept	A	A	A	A	X	X						A	A						A	A						A	A				
Oct																								A	A	A	A				
Nov																															
Dec												X	X						X	X											

X denotes special service, see local announcements. *No service in January, February, March and November.*

Service A

Llanfair	dep	10.30	13.30	16.15
Welshpool	arr	11.20	14.20	17.05
Welshpool	dep	11.45	14.45	17.15
Llanfair	arr	12.35	15.35	18.05

Service B

09.30	10.30	12.05	13.30	15.05	16.30
10.20	11.20	12.55	14.20	15.55	17.20
10.45	11.45	13.10	14.45	16.10	17.30
11.35	12.35	14.00	15.35	17.00	18.20

Please note: For one weekend in early May or early June, services between Castle Caereinion and Llanfair may be replaced by a Vintage Bus to allow bridge work to take place.

WEST SOMERSET RAILWAY

Minehead, Somerset TA24 5BG **01643 704996**

1998	1	2	3	4	5	6	7	8	9	10	11	12	13	14	15	16	17	18	19	20	21	22	23	24	25	26	27	28	29	30	31
Mar								A							A							A						X	X		
Apr	A			A	A			A	A	A	B	B	B	A	A	A	A	A	A		A	A	A		A	A		A	A	A	
May		A	B	B	A	A	A	X	X	X		A	A	A		A	A		A	A	A		B	B	B	B	B	B	B	A	A
June	A	A	A	A	A	A	A	A	A	A	A	A	A	A	A	A	A	A	A	A	A	A	A	A	A	A	A	A	A	A	
July	A	A	A	X	X	B	B	B	B	B	B	B	B	B	B	B	B	B	B	B	B	B	B	B	B	B	B	B	B	B	B
Aug	B	B	B	B	B	B	B	B	B	B	B	B	B	B	B	B	B	B	B	B	B	B	B	B	B	B	B	B	B	B	B
Sept	B	B	B	B	B	B	B	B	B	B	X	X	X	A	A	A	A	A	A	A	A	A	A	A	A	A	A		A	A	
Oct	A		A	A		A	A	A		A	A		A	A	A		A	A	A	A	A	A		A	A		A	A	A		A
Nov																															
Dec					X	X						X	X						X	X				X		A	A	A			A

X denotes special service, see local announcements. *No service in January, February. and November.*

Service A

Minehead	dep	10.15	12.10	14.25	16.00
Bishops Lydeard	arr	11.29	13.24	15.35	17.06
Bishops Lydeard	dep	10.25	12.20	14.35	16.05
Minehead	arr	11.32	13.27	15.40	17.13

§ = Diesel service to and from Williton only.

* = Runs 26th July to 30th August only.

Service B

Minehead	dep	–	10.15	11.10	12.10	14.00	14.55	15.30	16.45	17.45*
Bishops Lydeard	arr	–	11.33	§	13.26	15.20	§	17.09	17.51	18.59
Bishops Lydeard	dep	09.40	10.25	§	12.20	14.10	§	16.05	17.55*	–
Minehead	arr	10.44	11.39	12.31	13.34	15.27	16.19	17.17	19.01	–

All trains call at intermediate stations: Dunster (6), Blue Anchor (14), Washford (23), Watchet (31), Williton (48), Stogumber (54) and Crowcombe (64), minutes after leaving Minehead and at Crowcombe (14), Stogumber (22), Williton (32), Watchet (38), Washford (47), Blue Anchor (54) and Dunster (61) minutes after leaving Bishops Lydeard.

"WE'RE TRAVELLING THE GREAT CENTRAL WAY"

PASSENGER TIMETABLE 1998

TRAINS BETWEEN LOUGHBOROUGH CENTRAL AND LEICESTER NORTH FROM 10TH JANUARY 1998 UNTIL 22ND NOVEMBER 1998

Please refer to General Notes for explanation of symbols and operating days.

			Summer Weekday Service					Saturdays, Sundays and Bank Holiday Mondays throughout the year							
			W	W	W	B		■	■	■D	■A	■	■	■	C
Miles			☕	⊘	☕	✗		☕	⊘	⊘	✗	⊘	⊘	☕	✗
0	LOUGHBOROUGH CENTRAL	dep.	11 00	1 15	3 30	7 30	...	09 30	10 15	11 45	1 15	2 05	3 30	5 00	7 30
$2^1/_4$	Quorn & Woodhouse	dep.	11 08	1 23	3 38	7 38		09 38	10 23	11 53	1 23	2 13	3 38	5 08	7 38
$5^1/_2$	Rothley	arr.	11 17	1 42	3 47	8 04	.	09 47	10 32	12 02	1 42	2 22	3 47	5 17	8 04
	Rothley	dep.	11 20	1 46	3 50	8 15		09 50	10 35	12 05	1 46	2 25	3 50	5 20	8 15
8	LEICESTER NORTH	arr.	11 29	1 55	3 59	8 25	...	09 59	10 44	12 14	1 55	2 34	3 59	5 29	8 25

Light refreshments are usually available at Loughborough Central Station every day and at other stations at weekends.

			W	W	W	B		■	■	■D	■A	■	■	■	C
Miles			☕	⊘	☕	✗		☕	⊘	⊘	✗	⊘	⊘	☕	✗
0	LEICESTER NORTH	dep.	11 50	2 10	4 20	8 45	...	10 20	11 05	12 35	2 10	2 50	4 20	5 50	8 45
$2^1/_2$	Rothley	arr.	11 59	2 19	4 29	8 55		10 29	11 14	12 44	2 19	2 59	4 29	5 59	8 55
	Rothley	dep.	12 03	2 23	4 35	9 10	.	10 33	11 18	12 48	2 23	3 03	4 35	6 03	9 10
$5^3/_4$	Quorn & Woodhouse	dep.	12 12	2 32	4 42	n/s		10 42	11 27	12 57	2 32	3 12	4 42	6 12	n/s
8	LOUGHBOROUGH CENTRAL	arr.	12 20	2 40	4 50	10 15	...	10 50	11 35	1 05	2 40	3 20	4 50	6 20	10 15

GENERAL NOTES TO TIMETABLES

■ **Trains run on Saturdays, Sundays and Bank Holiday Mondays throughout the year.**

W **Trains run on Weekdays only from: 14th to 17th April 1998 and from 18th May 1998 to 25th September 1998.**

☕ **Buffet-Car** provided for the sale of snacks, hot and cold drinks etc.

⊘ **Griddle-Car** provided for the sale of hot food including "all-day" breakfast, afternoon teas, snacks, hot and cold drinks etc.

✗ **Restaurant-Car** available from Loughborough Central for First Class ticket holders who have booked seats in advance.

A **The "SILVER JUBILEE"** runs on Saturdays, Sundays and Bank Holiday Mondays, to provide a First Class traditional luncheon service for which advance booking is obligatory; please telephone 01509 230726 for details.

B **The "MASTER CUTLER*"** runs on Wednesday evenings, from 20th May 1998 until 23rd September 1998 to provide a First Class traditional dining service for which advance booking is obligatory; please telephone 01509 230726 for details.

C **The "CHARNWOOD FORESTER"** runs on most Saturday evenings, as advertised, to provide a First Class prestigious dining service for which advance booking is obligatory; please telephone 01509 230726 for details.

Seats for non-dining passengers are available on all Restaurant-Car trains.

D This train will be hauled by a classic diesel locomotive during the months of March to November inclusive.

n/s No scheduled stop at this station.

First Class accommodation is normally available on all trains.

Additional trains run during "Gala" days and Bank Holiday Mondays and also from 28th November 1998 until 3rd January 1998 when a special timetable will be in operation; please telephone 01509 230726 for information. Passengers are conveyed by the Company's trains in accordance with the Company's Conditions of Carriage of Passengers and their Luggage (copies of which are available for inspection in the Company's booking offices) and subject to the special condition that the Company reserves the right to cancel or amend any advertised train services. *Use of the title The "MASTER CUTLER" is by arrangement with the British Railways Board.

GREAT CENTRAL RAILWAY

LOUGHBOROUGH, LEICESTERSHIRE

FOR MORE INFORMATION RING 01509 230726